Electrical Interference

Electrical Interference

ROCCO F. FICCHI

Engineer, Member of the Professional
Technical Group on Electromagnetic
Compatibility of the IEE

HAYDEN BOOK COMPANY, INC., NEW YORK
a division of HAYDEN PUBLISHING COMPANY, INC.

TO GRACE

Copyright © *1964*

HAYDEN BOOK COMPANY, INC.

Library of Congress Catalog Card Number 63-22511

Printed in the United States of America

PREFACE

The purpose of this book is to provide the tools and techniques to enable the engineer to minimize interference in electronic equipment and systems.

Particular effort has been made to provide necessary information on all levels—project, design, field engineering, and engineering management. Survey course material for engineers who may require additional background in solving interference problems and for technical schools that may want to present a practical course is also provided. Any practitioner in the electronics industry will find the book useful because of its integrated approach to the problem of controlling electrical interference.

An extensive bibliography enables the reader to pursue particular topics in depth. However, the reader does not have to be at a library to answer most of his questions because essential information is contained in the book.

This book is organized in such a manner that the electrical interference problem is considered in its historical perspective, its present state, and then the fundamental approach to the solution of the problem is described. Major topics are covered in detail—shielding, filtering, bonding, etc. Particular attention is given to the grounding problem as related to electronic equipment.

There are, of course, many topics that have not been covered. This was necessary to give the book a broad, integrated approach, enabling the reader to see the whole area of the electrical interference problem. The topics that are included give the most useful information in dealing with commonly occurring problems.

The book originated from my work in providing guidelines for the design engineer concerned with the electrical interference problem, and developed because of the interest of the Professional Technical Group on

Electromagnet Compatability of the IEEE. The most important contribution was made by Mr. Rexford Daniels, president, Interference Consultants, Boston, Mass., who, with his encouragement and advice, was the guiding star for this venture. Acknowledgement is also due to Dr. Ralph Showers, professor of Electrical Engineering at the University of Pennsylvania and to others who assisted in various ways. Thanks are also due to the Armour Research Foundation, McGraw-Hill Book Company, Edison Electric Institute, the IEEE, Electronics Industries, The General Electric Company and Westinghouse Corporation for permission to reprint various items.

Rocco F. Ficchi

Haddonfield, New Jersey,
December 1963

CONTENTS

1 – INTRODUCTION

Electrical interference, its reduction and control, has always been a problem to the communication engineer. As long as equipment was uncomplicated and few in number the problem did not come into focus. But, with the tremendous growth of the communication industry during World War II, and afterwards, the full impact of the interference problem became apparent. As communication systems expanded, and large extended systems were developed with increased receiver sensitivity, more powerful transmitters, relays, motors, switching circuits and pulse circuits, the problem did come into focus and became glaring in intensity.

During the war, failure and malfunctions frequently occurred in various navigation and communication devices in airplanes, and on ship and land installations. After the war, steps were taken to combat the future possibility of these failures and more rigid specifications were developed. The frequency spectrum, due to the constant expansion of the electronics industry, is now accommodating literally millions of different signals and accommodation of these signals in the limited frequency spectrum presents a major problem.

The key to the problem of electrical interference is that equipment must operate satisfactorily not only independently but in conjunction with other equipment as well. Equipment should not be adversely affected by interfering sources of energy which reach it externally; conversely, equipment should not be a source of interference which might adversely affect the operation of other equipment. It is exactly this point—the operation of equipment in conjunction with other equipment—that causes the interference problem to grow as systems grow.

1

1.1. Early History

Electrical interference became a problem when the first telegraph key was pressed to complete a communication circuit. Fortunately for the communication industry, interference, in its various ramifications, developed rather slowly, because of the limited use of electrical communication. The telegraph developed about 1830, and the network of telegraph and telephone lines, which became extensive about 1885, were not interfered with by other communication systems. As the systems increased in number, coupling transformers or capacitors compensated for the mutual interference developed between the lines.

When power transmission came into more extensive use around 1890, no interference was expected because the power lines were generally short (power generation being usually close to the point of use) and power systems were ungrounded. Actually, the first interference problem arose when power systems with grounded neutrals, d-c electric railways, and long high-voltage transmission lines were introduced. The grounding parameter was, therefore, introduced into the interference problem at a very early stage.

About 1900, with the introduction of two-wire circuits for telephone systems, it appeared that telephone, telegraph and power lines could be strung in close proximity. However, interfering noise and high voltage considerations did not permit such construction. And, as the transmission of electrical power at high voltages became an overriding consideration the growing interference problem required corrective measures. In Europe these corrective measures included the use of separate transmission poles for the individual lines. In the United States, where rural electrification became important, corrective measures permitted the joint use of transmission poles, but only with the proper use of conductors, and good installation practices.

After World War I, telephone and telegraph systems became much more complicated: two-wire circuits were used to transmit microphone currents, dialing pulses, and other special circuits, in addition to intelligence and ringing signals. This reduced the symmetry of the metallic circuits in relation to ground and the circuits again became subject to interference. Also, newly developed component parts of sophisticated power systems, as well as electrical machinery that generated harmonics, added to the growing interference problem.

From these difficulties arose the first attempts to minimize the problem by coordination. These remedies, technically and economically sound, vary widely, depending on the installation and the particular locale. Each country has its individual problems that are solved by cooperation between power and communication companies. Interference problems in systems maintained by different countries are often resolved by international bodies such as Comite Consultatif International Telephonique (CCIF).

1.2. Later History

Radio communication developed in the early 20th century. Since that time it has developed into a number of rather sophisticated communication systems that includes broadcast radio and TV, as well as military applications. Like the telegraph, electrical interference, here too, started when the first key was closed to transmit a CW pulse.

In the early days of radio communication, the typical operator (there was no unattended equipment) could easily detect interference and take corrective measures because of the relative simplicity of the equipment. As radio developed, equipment became automatic, eliminating the "self correction" provided by the human operator. For example, a pulse is transmitted which activates a receiver which in turn initiates a control function. However, if a noise pulse is received in place of the signal pulse, the receiver cannot distinguish the signals and the results could be tragic— airplane landings are facilitated by the use of radio signals as navigation aids, and a noise pulse can possibly convey incorrect information to the pilot.

At the present time, radio communication interference is complicated by the use of broad transmission lines, multiplex systems, and television. Also, transmitters are radiating more power than ever before, resulting in an increasing number of difficult harmonics to suppress. Overcrowding of the communication spectrum, which has fixed limits, adds to the interference problem because of the higher frequencies that must be used, resulting in higher order harmonics.

Because of the increased interference developed within the communication industry, the federal government established the Federal Communications Commission in 1934 to regulate the use of radio and wire communications. Though the authority of the Commission is limited to the *user* of the communication device, it is continually seeking the cooperation of manufacturers to eliminate much of the interference developed by a device.

At present the FCC is concerned with a number of interference problems. Part 15 of the FCC regulations covers control of interference from the many devices which generate r-f energy either intentionally or unintentionally. FM and television broadcast receivers are serious sources of interference. TV broadcast bands, particularly, interfere with communication and navigational bands allocated to airplanes. Carrier-current systems used by power companies on frequencies below 200 kc, present interference by radiation. This form of interference *was* eliminated by shifting frequencies, but such a procedure is now impossible because the new available frequencies are limited.

Part 18 of the FCC regulations covers the operation of industrial, scientific, and medical devices. Frequencies, known as ISM (Industrial, Scientific, Medical) frequencies, are specified on which unlimited radiation is permitted; however, on other frequencies, the radiation limits are specified. The equipment covered by the ISM frequencies must fall into the following groupings:

1. Medical diathermy equipment.
2. Industrial heating equipment.
3. Ultrasonic equipment.
4. Miscellaneous equipment.

1.3. Military History

Electrical interference has been a problem to the military for many years because of the unique requirements of the military. From a civilian viewpoint, electrical interference, at its worst, can cause problems that may perhaps endanger the safety of an airplane but, from the military viewpoint, it can create problems, which, in the case of guided missile installations, may jeopardize the national defense of a nation. And, most importantly, it should be noted that the possibility of electrical interference causing a guided missile to be launched inadvertently is a real threat.

In addition to the "misguided" missile, there is the possibility that the vast network of new military equipment might not be able to operate simultaneously. To combat this possible degradation of electronic systems, the Department of Defense has established an "Electromagnetic Compatibility Program" with the following objectives:

1. Designing maximum practical compatibility in components, equipments, and systems.
2. Attaining the maximum effective use of the frequency in planning the ambient electronic environment for specific equipments and systems.

The various armed forces became concerned with interference control at different times and because of differing reasons.

The Army. In the early thirties the Army increased their mobility by adding more vehicles, which were equipped with high-frequency mobile radios. The ignition and electrical systems of the vehicles generated interference that prevented the operation of the radios at maximum efficiency.

As part of an Electromagnetic Compatability Program, the Army issued their first interference specification entitled *Manufacturing Requirement SCL-49—Radio Set Operation in Vehicles.* With the advent of World War II, the number of mobile radios increased, coupled with their operation at higher frequencies and with greater sensitivity. This resulted in U. S. Army Tentative Specification 71-1303, *Vehicular Noise Suppression,* which made interference control over a range between 0.5 to 30 mc mandatory. Components (filters and capacitors) were specified to control interference by U. S. Army Specification 71-1305.

Besides the increased mobility, the Army introduced sophisticated weapon systems which required interference control. To cover this and interference in *all* kinds of equipment, the Army issued Regulation AR-105-68, *Communication, Radio Interference Reduction.*

The Navy. The interference problem became a crisis with the Navy Bureau of Ships at the start of World War II. The use of transmitters, receivers, radars, and marine mobile equipment created an expanding interference problem. Overall planning of interference control began with the Electronics Division of the Bureau of Ships. After studying the problem, a technical group developed the following basic guideline in the construction of new ships: all electronic equipment installed in its operational environment must be free from interference from any installed source which might cause an undesired response from any source on the ship more than 3 db above the to-be-expected background level of unwanted signals. At the present time the program of interference reduction includes the following:

1. Establishing standards and definitions.
2. Developing methods and techniques of interference measurements.
3. Recommending acceptable interference levels in specific environments.
4. Establishing criteria for interference reduction in the design and procurement of equipment.

With the Navy Department, the Bureau of Aeronautics' Interference Control Program concerns itself with the control and elimination of interference in Navy aircraft. The efforts of this agency were coordinated with similar programs of the other branches of the military, and led to the development of the well known military specification MIL-I-6181, a coordinated interservice specification. Basic specifications MIL-I-6181B and MIL-I-6051 relate to electronics equipment and systems, and were also developed from this same coordinated interservice effort.

The Air Force. They felt the need to modify earlier specifications so that special requirements could be satisfied, and developed Exhibit RADC-2313A, entitled *Radio Interference Limits and Methods of Measurement (150 kc to 1000 mc) Ground Electrical and Electronic Equipment.* When an interference specification separate from those of the other services was required, Exhibit ENG-1208 was issued. Necessary measuring devices to test devices for compliance to the specification meant that test devices acceptable by the other services had to be used. Later, measuring instruments for specific Air Force needs were developed as Radio Interference Measuring Set AN/URM-28. As Exhibit ENG-1208 became obsolete, due to unrealistic limits, BuShips MIL-I-16910, suitable for ground electronic equipment, was used as a replacement in conjunction with Air Force Specification MIL-I-6181, which was concerned primarily with aircraft equipment. Finally, Exhibit RADC-2313A was written as the Air Force version of MIL-I-16910. Presently the Air Force's effort is joined with the other services in the Department of Defense Electromagnetic Compatibility Program.

1.4. Recent Developments

With the development of the Department of Defense Electromagnetic Compatibility Program, the idea of compatibility of equipment was put into proper perspective, since it is the key to solving the electrical interference problem. Compatibility and the accommodation of a particular signal within a frequency spectrum, are the only considerations in using communication equipment. From a practical engineering viewpoint, compatibility should be a key factor in mechanical, acoustical, and optical interference considerations, as well.

Great progress has been made in recent years in the resolution of the interference problem. The accumulation of experience and information has caused this problem to change to such an extent that it has become amenable to solution when realistic control has been exercised early enough in the design of equipment or in system planning. A factor that should be considered first in the stages of design is the assurance of system compatibility; then, a thorough study of each subsystem in the complete system should be carried out. Fourier analysis for all major waveforms, approximation of switching transients, carrier-wave and broadband radiations should be considered. Pedestrian items, such as intercomponent wiring, must be studied carefully. Everything that can generate interference, either conducted or radiated, must be reviewed thoroughly. This detailed attention is tedious and time consuming, but it is the only way that desired results can be obtained with a minimum expenditure of engineering time so that production schedules can be met, for the least suppression cost and, in the case of aircraft applications, for the least weight penalty.

Basic steps to be taken in a typical interference reduction program are:

1. A thorough study of all interference sources contained within the system, as well as interference coupling betwen system parts, should be accomplished.
2. Reduction of radiated interference by determining the shielding effectiveness required to reduce the expected radiation to less than the specification limits should be accomplished to insure adequate, permanent, and dependable interference insulation.
3. Constant and continual monitoring of the design in progress to insure that necessary design changes will not compromise the achieved interference controlled status of the equipment.
4. Continued monitoring and control of the equipment when it is installed, checked out and finally goes "on the air" so that no field repairs will abort the interference control program.

Interference is categorized into two groups: radiated and conducted, see Fig. 1-1. Radiated interference is that which is transmitted by electromagnetic fields and picked up by the antenna effect of other equipment.

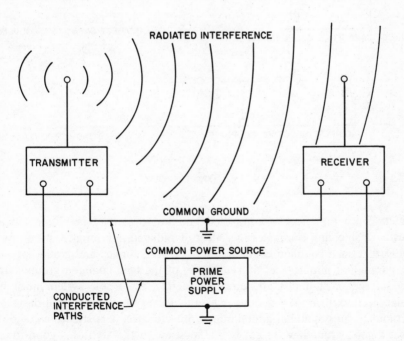

RADIATED INTERFERENCE

TRANSMITTER

RECEIVER

COMMON GROUND

COMMON POWER SOURCE

PRIME POWER SUPPLY

CONDUCTED INTERFERENCE PATHS

Fig. 1-1. Two methods of interference propagation.

Reducing the antenna effect, and adding shielding, controls this type of interference.

Conducted interference is that which is introduced into a circuit by either direct or indirect coupling. Both direct and indirect coupling is classified into three specific types:

1. Resistive
2. Capacitive
3. Inductive

Examples of these types of coupling are shown in Fig. 1-2. It should be noted that circuits such as those shown in Fig. 1-2B, D and F occur most frequently where common return circuits — power supplies and grounds —

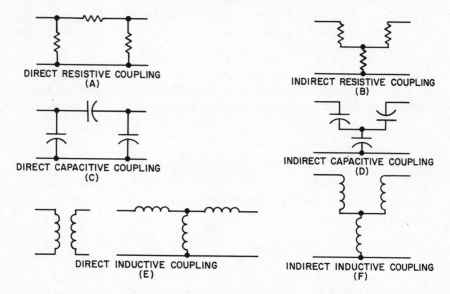

Fig. 1-2. Types of coupling.

exist. Since the effect of conducted interference cannot be eliminated as easily as shielding eliminates the effect of radiated interference, it becomes clear that such common connections as power supplies and grounding are of paramount importance. Furthermore, of the two, common grounds are by far the most important, since, ultimately, the whole system must be referenced to them. It is for this reason that the system with a well-designed grounding subsystem has a minimum of interference. Experience has shown that a good grounding system is the keystone in the arch of a good interference-controlled system.

2 – INTERFERENCE REDUCTION AS A SYSTEM PROBLEM

2.1. Introduction

The electronics industry has had to solve a vast and bewildering array of seemingly insoluble problems during its evolution to its present state of complexity. One of these problems, which in the early days was resolved with almost no difficulty, but which has grown to a point where it requires a great deal of attention, is interference reduction as a system problem. As was pointed out in Chapter 1, the only way the system problem can be resolved is to have a completely formalized program to "watch dog" the problem through to its solution. However, before such a program can be instituted, basic terms should be defined:

1. Interference is an electrical disturbance created by equipment in one part of a system which is carried into equipment in another part of the system, causing malfunctioning of the latter part.
2. The system approach considers the system as a whole rather than to specific parts. The first consideration is examination of the compatibility of one part of the system with another, followed by examination of the individual parts of the system, see Fig. 2-1.

Once the system approach has been taken, we can be sure that the solution to the interference problem will be adequate, since the system approach enables one to obtain comprehensive information of the compatibility consideration. If one views an electronic system from a parts, or subsystem approach, not only is erroneous information sometimes obtained, but, oftentimes, the system itself will be inoperable because of extreme interference.

The ideal way to resolve the system interference problem is to require an operating system from design and systems groups which is entirely compatible within itself and with its external environment. The classical approach is for the design and systems groups to follow the interference specifications, but such specifications are broad in their coverage so that they do not solve the interference problem in every system. This often

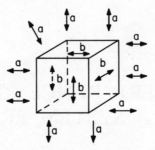

a = RELATIONSHIP OF SYSTEM TO OTHER SYSTEMS AND ENVIRONMENT
b = RELATIONSHIP OF PARTS OF SYSTEM TO THE SYSTEM

Fig. 2-1.   The system viewpoint.

leads to the "crisis" approach, which is the suppression of interference after the equipment has been constructed—an expensive, time consuming approach that limits overall system performance to a point below the original requirements.

2.2.   The System Approach

When applying the system approach to the interference reduction problem, a well integrated effort covering the original planning, design, "breadboard" stages, production, and system installation should be established and maintained. In this way, not only will interference be reduced, but the optimum system performance will be obtained at an economical cost and with the minimum of effort. An appointed systems group should have a two-fold responsibility—making sure that the systems approach is applied, and monitoring the interference problems for which the design engineers require a solution. This group should also make certain that any design changes do not compromise the overall system performance.

Application of the systems approach can be divided into a well defined four-stage program:

1. System planning
2. Subsystem planning

3. Design stage
4. Fabrication and installation

Concurrent with these four stages, the new discipline of "value engineering" must be introduced so that cost trading can be made for any modification deemed necessary. Value engineering has been defined by Armed Services Procurement Regulations   as: "An intensive apprisal of all of the elements of the design, manufacture and construction, procurement, inspection, installation and maintenance of an item and its components, including the applicable specifications and operational requirements, in order to achieve the necessary *performance* . . . of the item at minimum cost."

Value engineering, which ascertains that every element of cost contributes proportionately to the functioning of an item, enables one to determine whether or not the implementation of the interference program is an economical contribution to the functioning of equipment. A flow chart of the application of an interference control program to a large electronic system is shown in Fig. 2-2.

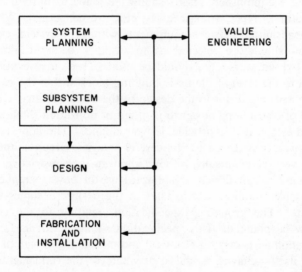

Fig. 2-2. Application of interference program to a large electronic system.

In the system planing stage, the first task is to investigate the compatibility of the system to its electronic environment; it must not be susceptible to external disturbances. It is very important, at this stage, to have information of the radiating fields existing near the system and of any indicated sources of interference. Obviously, the more detailed the information available about ambient noise level, for example, the more useful it would be in solving the problem. Specific disturbing characteristics of the individual pieces of equipment should be examined and their relation to the overall system put in perspective. The noise-generating, or interfering, potentialities, and the noise-receiving, or interfering, susceptibilities of each piece of equipment should be thoroughly investigated. These studies should provide the basis for development of a specification covering design parameters to be used as interference limits for each piece of subsystem equipment, as well as a general interference specification for the overall system. Also at this stage, basic grounding considerations should be established so that the more troublesome parts of conducted interference, especially as pertains to the system, as a whole, may be controlled.

The next phase involves the subsystem or "individual equipment" planning. The major effort should be directed toward preparing a detailed specification for the signal transmission circuits. All the various signals, their voltages and general characteristics should be tabulated and, while this is being accomplished, efforts should be made to introduce standardization insofar as types, voltage levels, etc., are concerned. When signals are being transmitted between equipments within the system, a method of transmission should be selected as to whether balanced lines, coaxial cables, or twisted pairs, etc., should be used. These investigations should be pursued to the level of the basic building block within the equipment—module, chassis, etc. Prior to the design of the basic circuitry, a fundamental method of distributing power to its point of utilization should be studied and criteria established to provide design guidance. The importance of this cannot be overstressed, because by careful analysis, circuit coupling can be minimized very economically without imposing any restrictive limitations on consequent circuit design. Haphazard use of power supplies tends to cause excessive coupling, which, later in the design, becomes very costly to eliminate. The grounding specification, relating to the equipments, should now be planned. This specification should particularly emphasize the information necessary for electrical and mechanical design of the equipment rack itself—chassis, modules, or whatever the fundamental building block is within the equipment—and for connections that have to be made to the equipotential ground plane where, possibly, the prime power system ground, the building (that houses the equipment) ground, and any direct earth connections all come together, electrically. This is also the ideal point at which a more thorough investigation relating to the compatibility of the various components in the equipment should be made. Such an investigation would greatly enhance integration of the components into the equipment and of the equipment into a system. By studying equipment compatibility at this time, various interference problems could be brought to the attention of the design engineers, and detailed information of the requirements of signal levels at both the input and output sides of a transmission circuit could be gathered. Problems, such as mismatch due to improper cable termination, disparity of signal levels, and improper use of wiring between building blocks or chassis could be minimized. We are now ready for the next stage.

While the system and the subsystem "equipment planning" stage is being carried out, the design of the various parts of the system has started. Generally, design engineers utilize the specifications written by the systems groups. Compliance with applicable specifications goes a long way toward the resolution of interference problems. However, to assure that specifications are adhered to, properly interpreted, and that compliance with them does not negate their purposes, all equipment should be subjected to a critical design review with respect to the noise-generating and noise-susceptibility characteristics of the particular equipment. In this way problems will be brought into focus and recommendations made for solution. This design review procedure was developed several years ago and has been carried out successfully by equipment designers. All interequipment cabling and intra-equipment wiring should be reviewed at this time. The effects of the power distribution system on the signal transmission system can now be examined. The grounding problem will become very important in this phase. As these various aspects are examined, many filtering and shielding problems will become apparent and should easily be handled. Also, ideas relating to qualification testing of the equipment should become apparent. Tests should be designed to assure that the system will perform properly under all operating conditions and will be minimally affected by its ambient electronic environment. These tests, properly associated with the overall system operation, must assure that the basic building blocks are operable. Finally, plans should be made to correlate test data with the originally planned system concepts to give assurance that the system will satisfy all basic interference-free operational requirements.

While the design is in progress, fabrication of the system equipment should also be in progress. Fabrication and production can easily become the most sensitive part of the whole program and, if not adequately considered, can compromise the entire program.

A new group is now introduced to the program—the factory production group—and they should be aware of the interference problems so that changes are not made solely to satisfy the needs of production meanwhile losing control of the interference reduction program.

The installation group, aware of the interference problem, should not make modifications to accommodate installation. Though the necessity for field installation modifications occur—because of the growth of electronics technology, ever expanding communication requirements, and installation without a pre-installation site survey—they should only be implemented with the approval of the systems group and made by personnel familiar with the latest techniques of interference control.

Sound engineering practices in all four stages of the program will result in a system that requires few, if any, necessary changes.

The advantages of the four-stage program should now be apparent— minimized interference, elimination of "crisis" changes, reduced equipment cost, increased customer satisfaction, and increased profits because of reduced overall costs.

2.3. *Interference Prediction*

The parts of the program that enables the reduction of interference with a minimum of modifications are the system and subsystem planning stages. In the design, and fabrication and installation stages, the system approach consists mainly of monitoring the equipment for interference with implementation of modifications, if necessary. In the subsystem stage, interference reduction is possible because of written specifications. And, in the system planning stage, positive steps are also possible because this stage involves the collection of interference data, reduction of interference, and the prediction of interference levels in an operable system. To attain the latter of the three steps, a vast amount of experimental data coupled with the use of relatively sophisticated mathematics is required. However, there are some conservative methods that can be used to determine interference levels with reasonable accuracy. All predictions, however, require a suitable method for collection and correlation of data in terms of interfering and interfered with frequencies. Since every device is either a transmitter or receiver, the possible data can be categorized as shown in Fig. 2-3.

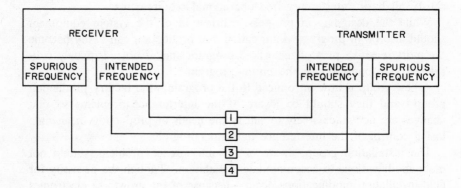

Fig. 2-3. Paths between transmitter and receiver.

Path 1 indicates normal operation; the receiver is operating at its intended frequency and responding to the intended frequency of the transmitter. Path 2 indicates that the receiver is operating at its normal frequency, but the transmitter is interfering because of spurious frequency transmission. Path 3 indicates that the receiver is operating at a spurious frequency and, consequently, picking up an intended frequency as though it were interference. Path 4 indicates spurious operation from both receiver and the transmitter and, while this type of operation is common, it becomes important under certain topographical conditions and equipment combinations. It is the identification of these frequencies and their interaction that constitutes the first step in the data accumulation for prediction.

To correlate these frequencies, we must first examine all the equipment used in the system that contributes to the interference problem. In present day communications, this examination would include every piece of equipment. The equipment is classified in the following manner, see Fig. 2-4. Each item, with its identifying number, identifying name, manufacturer's

ITEM NO.	PHYS-ICAL LOCA-TION	NOMEN-CLATURE	MODEL NO.	OPERA-TIONAL USE	OPERA-TIONAL FRE-QUENCY	ELECTRONIC	OPTICAL	INFRARED	RADIATE	RECEIVE	NON-ELECTRONIC	STRUCTURE	PERMANENT	TRANSISTORY	PLANNED	REMARKS

Fig. 2-4. Chart for surveying equipment.

name, model number, operational use and physical location is listed. Also, the operating frequency is listed and overall function identified.

The next step is to prepare a frequency-index chart, see Fig. 2-5. Operating frequencies for the particular equipment are plotted on the chart. With this is prepared a transparent overlay for the transmitters that are to be considered in the analysis, which has three parallel lines, placed logarithmically at 1, 2 and 10, inscribed on it. The center line of this overlay is placed on the line indicating the operating frequency on the frequency chart which has been prepared for a receiver. Transmitters that fall between the two extremes are considered further; the others are eliminated as interfering with the specific receiver. The harmonics of the transmitters must also be considered when they occur within 10 bandwidths of the receiver's fundamental frequency.

For any remaining items data cards are prepared containing all the information available about a particular item: specification requirements, manufacturer's data, measurements, etc. After the cards have been prepared the final sorting can be made. Cards for transmitters specify the operating frequency, second and third harmonic, item number, expected or measured bandwidth, model number and physical installation location. Cards for receivers specify fundamental and image frequency. From these

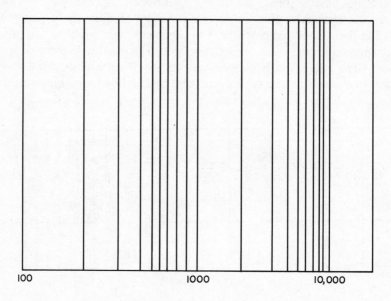

Fig. 2-5.   Frequency-index chart.

cards can be determined the frequencies to be considered and those which can be dropped. Only harmonic responses at, or near the fundamental or image of the receiver, are considered unless the fundamental frequency has already been dropped out as nonpertinent. Any spurious responses of the receiver's operating frequencies must be kept for further consideration.

The magnitude of the suspected interfering signal must now be calculated as well as the magnitude of the various signals following paths 2, 3 and 4 (Fig. 2-3). From these calculations, can be determined those signals worth further consideration, as well as those signals to be dropped. The equations necessary to determine this magnitude are as follows:

For spurious receiver response at intended transmitter operating frequency

$$\Psi_1 = 10 \log P_T + 30 + S'_R + 10 \log B_R - 10 \log B_T$$

$$(2\text{-}1)$$

where Ψ_1 is the interference assuming direct coupling and is in db related to 1 mw,

P_T is the transmitter's total power output at its operating frequency,

S'_R is the receiver's rejection in db at transmitters operating frequency,

B_R is the receiver's bandwith,

B_T is the transmitter's signal bandwidth.

$$I_1 = \Psi_1 + G_{TS} + G'_{RS} - 20 \log R - 20 \log f_T + 38.0$$

$$(2\text{-}2)$$

where I_1 is the effective, interference power in dbm at receiver input,

G_{TS} is the transmitting antenna gain in db at the transmitter frequency at an angle θ off the main beam axis of the antenna,

G'_{RS} is the receiving antenna gain in db at the transmitter frequency at an angle θ off the main beam axis of the antenna,

R is the distance between antennas in feet,

f_T is the transmitter frequency in megacycles per second.

For spurious transmitter output at receiver's intended operating frequency

$$\Psi_2 = 10 \log P_T + 30 + S'_T + 10 \log B_R - 10 \log B_T$$

$$(2\text{-}3)$$

where Ψ_2 is the interference assuming direct coupling and is in db related to 1 mw,

S'_T is the spurious transmitter output at the receiver's intended frequency in db with respect to the transmitters total power output.

B_R and B_T are as in Eq. 2-1.

$$I_2 = \Psi_2 + G'_{TS} + G_{RS} - 20 \log R - 20 \log f_R + 68.0$$

$$(2\text{-}4)$$

where I_2 is the effective interference power in dbm at receiver input,

G'_{TS} is transmitter's antenna gain in db at operating frequency,

G_{RS} is the receiver's antenna gain in db at operating frequency,

f_R is the receiver's operating frequency in megacycles per second,

R is the distance between antennas in feet.

For spurious transmissions at a harmonic or at the receiver image frequency (f_s)

$$\Psi_3 = 10 \log P_T + 30 + S'_T + S'_R + 10 \log B_R - 10 \log B_T$$

$$(2\text{-}5)$$

where Ψ_3 is the interference assuming direct coupling and is in db related to 1 mw,

      S'_R is the spurious transmitter output at f_s in db to the total transmitter power output,

      S'_T is the receiver rejection at f_s,

      B_R and B_T are as in Eq. 2-1.

$$I_3 = \Psi_3 + G'_{TS} + G'_{RS} - 20 \log R - 20 \log f_s$$

$$(2\text{-}6)$$

where I^3 is the effective interference power in dbm at the receiver input,

      G'_{TS} is the transmitting antenna gain in db at spurious frequency f_s,

      G'_{RS} is the receiving antenna gain in db at spurious frequency f_s,

      f_s is the spurious frequency in megacycles per second,

      R is the distance between antennas in feet.

For the interference pairs still remaining after it has been determined that there is sufficient power to affect receivers (Eqs. 2-1 to 2-6), geographical sorting is then done. It is first assumed, using a worst-case analysis technique, that the mean beam of the receiver and transmitter antenna are in direct line of sight. Using the values of power calculated previously, corrections are made for range and antenna gains. If the interference source is beyond the line of sight, correction for scatter is added to the losses. These procedures will eliminate a number of interfering pairs still remaining. Equipment still remaining after these eliminations should be handled on a specialized, detailed basis to achieve the best results obtainable under the circumstances so that predictions can be made about their operation.

Tabulated lists are then developed which provide the following data for the remaining interfering equipments.

1. Magnitude of interfering power due to spurious response of the receiver.
2. Magnitude of interfering power due to spurious transmission from the transmitter.
3. Magnitude of interfering power due to spurious response of the receiver to spurious transmission of the transmitter.
4. Total magnitude of interfering power.
5. General category of the interference, with time prediction for each category.
6. Any other appropriate data.

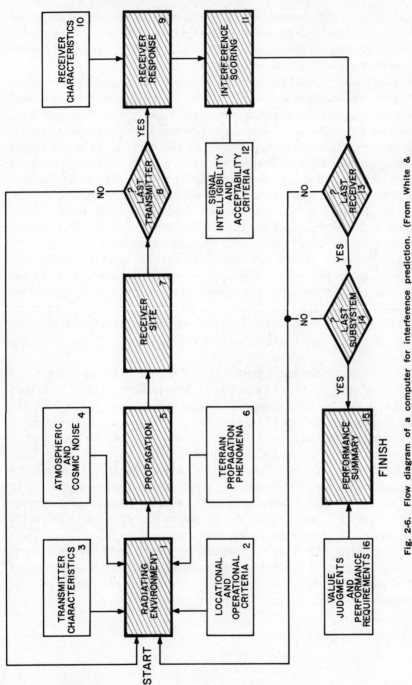

Fig. 2-6. Flow diagram of a computer for interference prediction. (From White & Marcus—Fifth Conf. on Radio Interference Reduction October, 1959 — Armour Research Foundation)

Finally, with all data tabulated, a last prediction can be made as to exactly what can be expected to happen to the system as a whole when it is operated based on the detailed information that has been obtained about the operating mode of each subsystem or "piece of equipment."

Even a casual perusal of the manual method for interference prediction described, would reveal that as the number of equipments increases, and, as systems must operate in juxtaposition with many other systems, the mass of manual data collection and manipulation would render the task formidable and sometimes almost impossible. As systems grow, there are simply too many parameters to be considered, too many operational and trade-off factors for an accurate interference prediction. In addition, poorly defined conditions and varying needs and application changes compound the problem. Because of the large number of parameters, the mass of data, and the repetitive nature of the calculations, high-speed digital computers have been employed for interference prediction calculations.

Fig. 2-6 shows a general flow diagram of a typical computer model used for interference prediction. The main flow line is represented by the shadowed blocks. Nonshadowed blocks represent memory storage in the computer. Diamonds signify computer decisions based on data made available to it. Each of the blocks represents one or more submodels, but are so developed that interfaces permit the substitution of one block for another.

When the computer run is started (Fig. 2-6), the radiating environment (1) is developed by (2), (3) and (4). Propagation criteria (5) is then introduced and by using stored data relating to terrain effects (6), the signal density at a receiver (7) is established. This process is then repeated for all the radiating items and the total signal at the receiver compared to the receiver characteristics (9). Resultant receiver output, including signal and interference (10), is checked with assistance from stored intelligibility or acceptability criteria (11 and 12). It may be necessary to repeat (1) to (13) when considering other subsystems. Finally, receiver performances are elevated (15) and compared with judgments representing the user's needs (16). This completes the computer run.

The computer, in making this run, can answer the basic questions necescary for interference prediction. With the growing and more advanced use of computers, more elaborate and sophisticated procedures may be employed.

3 – ATTACKING THE FUNDAMENTAL EQUIPMENT PROBLEM

3.1. Introduction

The use of prediction techniques described in Chapter 2, enabled one to obtain the data necessary to determine sources of interference, eliminate or reduce some of the sources, and determine which interference sources remain. To reduce the remaining interference sources, our principal concern will be with the third and fourth stages of the interference control program—design, and fabrication and installation. We will examine a specific piece of equipment as to what can be done to reduce interference. The principal area to be examined is unwanted energy—what can be done to prevent it from developing, or, once it has developed, to prevent it from interfering with the particular equipment.

3.2. Basic Considerations

In Fig. 1-1, a simplification of equipment juxtaposition was shown, and represents the basic interference problem in equipment. Energy can either be radiated or conducted away from a transmitter (here transmitter is used in the broad sense, irrespective of whether or not it is, in fact, intended to be a transmitter); energy can be received by a receiver (used in the broad sense) by either radiation or conduction. Therefore, transmitters should not radiate, or have unwanted energy, conducted away from them and receivers should not receive unwanted energy by radiation or conduction . To simplify this discussion, it should be noted that all problems associated with conduction are either grounding or cabling problems. These will be covered in detail in future chapters, as will conduction problems with equipment implications, e.g., the need for filters.

If it were always possible to isolate receivers and transmitters from one another, interference would be reduced to a manageable situation. As distances increase, radiation fields become weaker and energy along a conduction path becomes effectively dampened. But with high-powered equipment, physical isolation becomes difficult, because even small magnitudes of energy will be received by modern, highly sensitive receivers. However, within equipment, physical isolation becomes important.

Since some degree of unwanted energy will always be present, efforts should be directed toward reducing the level of unwanted energy to assure its reduction to such a small magnitude that it will not become an interference problem. *Between* equipments, this can be done by assuring that transmitters do not generate spurious harmonics of an intended transmitting frequency and, of course, that devices do not become unintended transmitters. *Within* equipment, the selection of good components and careful circuit design will minimize interference.

After the techniques of physical isolation and reduction of unwanted energy have been utilized to their fullest, there remains designing the equipment to operate free from interference. This can be accomplished by the following techniques

1. Shielding, which reduces the effects of unwanted radiation fields.
2. Filtering, which reduces the effects of unwanted conducted interference.
3. Bonding, which reduces the possibility of an equipment acting as though it were an antenna (either receiving or transmitting unwanted energy) and assures that shielding is continuous and effective.

The three techniques effectively *minimize* the problem rather than eliminate it; to eliminate it is, practically speaking, an almost impossible achievement.

If interfering and interfered-with devices have been sufficiently isolated, the degree of coupling between them should be so reduced as to render interference of no significance. Location and orientation are the two important parameters in physical isolation, and such isolation can be achieved by

1. Grouping
2. Shielding or shading
3. Spatial separation

It should be noted that these parameters take advantage of the physical attributes that exist within equipments and their installed locations.

Grouping is defined as the separation of circuits and components by identifying characteristics or classes. Circuits and components which will *not* affect one another can be grouped together; circuits and components which *will* affect one another should be kept physically apart. For circuits and components that can be grouped together, e.g., modules (a group of components mounted on a nonconducting board and wired together), and chassis drawers (groups of modules mounted in a rack), the following wiring rules should be followed

1. Power wiring, including d-c supply, filament heating, and grounds, should be run separately from signal-carrying wires.
2. Audio-frequency wiring should always be run separately from higher frequency wiring. If separation is not possible because of space restrictions, the audio-frequency wires should consist of twisted pairs with an outer shield.
3. Power ground return wiring should be as short as possible to the established ground.
4. Where unshielded antenna wires are used, they should be routed in the shortest, most direct way and separate from any other antenna wires.
5. If coaxial antenna wires are used, they, too, should be separated from other antenna wiring.

Shielding or shading is defined as the utilization of a barrier that will preclude penetration by electromagnetic radiation. Good shielding is expensive and, if utilized widely, adds to the weight and size of the equipment. The interest, here, is not externally introduced shielding, but shielding that is offered by the physical makeup of equipment. Dust covers used on chassis drawers, receiver cases, and functional separation of circuitry within a module by shield plates are all examples of various degrees of shielding that should be utilized to the fullest. Some of these shields have varying benefits at different frequencies, but are often available at no added cost and do not require additional parts.

Additional shielding, or, more properly, "shading effect," is realized when equipment is so installed as to take advantage of equipment racks, metal wall sections, metal structures and, on shipboard installations, bulkheads between compartments.

Spatial or space separation is defined as isolation by separation. Since electromagnetic radiation attenuates with distance, the greater the distance between a radiating source and a susceptible receiver, the less the opportunity for interference to develop. This is a particularly important consideration in connection with communication cable; if the cable has a good shield and the space separation between it and an interfering cable is of sufficient magnitude, the interference problem to the communication cable will be minimal.

If individual equipments are provided with outputs, as intended, no source of interference would exist. To achieve this is an ideal; however, if each component, circuit, module, etc., that makes up the equipment were treated individually, to minimize generation of unwanted energy, then each piece of equipment would approach this ideal. How carefully such detailed treatments are pursued will determine how successful the equipment will approach the interference-free ideal.

The components that make up the equipment's circuitry are the first important items to be considered. Careful selection of components can greatly enhance any effort toward achieving an acceptable, interference-free system. The most important sources of broadband interference are rotating machinery, switches, radar modulators, and ignition systems. The manufacturers of these devices are aware that these devices present interference problems and their efforts should be brought to bear to obtain for the designer devices that will be as trouble-free as possible. For example, military specification MIL-I-6181B imposes limits on conducted and radiated interferences for various equipments, which represents the maximum, practical interference control at the present time. Unless components which are interfering sources are eliminated, compliance with interference specifications will not assure that troublesome problems might not develop later as component performance degrades from its specification limits. Relays and other circuit switching devices should only be selected if contact areas are sufficiently large to assure that arcing will be minimized. Within the limitations of reliable operation, relay coils should have a low ratio of inductance to d-c resistance so that inductive kick and ringing will be minimized. Relays should have damping circuitry associated with them; electronic relays using thyratrons should only be used if they are completely shielded within the equipment.

When a design engineer decides to use a particular circuit, due consideration must be given to the development of noise interference. There are many facets to this problem, but those of primary interest to circuit designers are

1. Components should not be permitted to operate nonlinearly since this causes harmonics to generate. Overloading of the components also has this effect.
2. Multiple resonances of components, e.g., capacitors, coils, etc., which cause varying impedances and erratic circuit operation should be avoided.
3. The mixing of at least two signals in a nonlinear device which causes intermodulation distortion and results in the generation of harmonics should not be permitted.
4. Care should be taken to avoid too high or too low impedance levels which cause unwanted capacitive or inductive coupling.

5. Particular attention should be given to wiring between components or groups of components because bad wiring methods cause unwanted coupling to develop, resulting in unwanted feedback and spurious modes of oscillation.

There are four general rules that can be used as a guide for the selection of circuits so that interference may be controlled or reduced. These rules are basic and should be given careful attention

1. Circuits should be designed so that a margin of stability is achieved at all frequencies.
2. Circuits should always be operated in the linear range—nonlinear operation produces distortion and harmonics.
3. Unwanted feedback loops should be avoided, particularly those which can operate at noise frequencies generated as a result of interference.
4. Adequate filtering should be provided in the output of power amplifiers in Class C operation, so that the harmonic content will be reduced. Push-pull power amplifiers will reduce even-numbered harmonics; this will minimize filter design problems.

As noted, unwanted energy can either be conducted or radiated away from an intended or unintended transmitter, and can be conducted or radiated to an intended or unintended receiver. This, then, is the problem —to protect against radiation and conduction of unwanted energy. Conduction will be covered in connection with grounding, cabling and filtering. Radiation can be best understood by a discussion of the underlying theory of shielding against radiation.

3.3. Fundamental Theory

Every source of electric energy is surrounded by a field. The simple situation of an electric current flowing through a wire causes a field to exist around the wire, whose magnitude and direction follow well-known principles. Part of the energy in any field is propagated through space and eventually dampens to zero. The remaining part of the energy of a field either returns to its origin or is absorbed by some receiving source. A dipole antenna behaves in this manner: part of its energy becomes a radiation field; another portion (that periodically returns to the antenna) becomes the induction field. The general mathematical expression that describes an electromagnetic field is rather complex and usually discussed in texts on field theory.[1] It is easier to discuss this expression in terms of its electric vector **E** and its magnetic vector **B**, where **E** has the dimensions

---

[1]King. *Electromagnetic Engineering.* Vol. I, New York: McGraw-Hill Book Company, 1945.

of $\dfrac{V}{l}$ and units of $\dfrac{volt}{meter}$ and **B** has the dimensions of $\dfrac{VT}{l^2}$ and units of $\dfrac{volt\text{-}second}{meter^2}$. **E** and **B** can then be written as the sum of two components

$$\mathbf{E} = \mathbf{E_i} + \mathbf{E_R}$$
$$\mathbf{B} = \mathbf{B_i} + \mathbf{B_R} \tag{3-1}$$

The components of the induction field are $\mathbf{E_i}$ and $\mathbf{B_i}$ while the components of the radiation field are given as $\mathbf{E_R}$ and $\mathbf{B_R}$. $\mathbf{E_R}$ and $\mathbf{B_R}$ are proportional to B_o/R ($B_o = \omega/v_o$) or ω/v_oR where ω is the angular frequency of the field in radians and v_o is the velocity of propagation in meters per second. $\mathbf{E_i}$ and $\mathbf{B_i}$ are proportional to $1/R^2$ where R is the distance from the source in meters. The ratio of the two is B_oR or $\omega R/v_o$. It can be concluded from this that for very small values of R and any given values for ω and v_o, the induction field will be so much greater than the radiation field, that the latter may be neglected. If however, R is very large, the radiation field is important and the induction field can be discarded.

The induction, or near-zone field, is that area immediately around the source volume in which, and on which, charge and current density are non-vanishing, and where B_oR is very much smaller than one (1). If this is true,

$$\mathbf{E_i} >> \mathbf{E_R} \text{ and } \mathbf{B_i} >> \mathbf{B_R} \tag{3-2}$$

Then, if Eq. 3-2 is true

$$\mathbf{E} = \mathbf{E_i} \text{ and } \mathbf{B} = \mathbf{B_i} \tag{3-3}$$

Equations written to describe the components of $\mathbf{E_i}$, $\mathbf{B_i}$ and $\mathbf{E_R}$ and $\mathbf{B_R}$ all contain the term ϵ^{-jB_oR}. Since it has been noted that $B_oR \ll 1$, then $\epsilon^{-jB_oR} = 1 - j\,B_oR$, or $\epsilon^{-jB_oR} = 1$. This means that almost instantaneous action can be expected at very small distances. Since it has already been established that the induction field is important at very small distances, it can be stated that the induction field and an instantaneous acting state are almost identical. The instantaneous acting or stationary state has an electric field (known as an electrostatic field) and a magnetic field (known as a magnetostatic field) associated with it. Since ω must equal zero in this stationary state, there is no radiation field and only the induction field remains. At low frequencies $\omega R/v_o$ is so small that the induction, or near-zone fields, is the entire field as stated in Eq. 3-3.

The radiation, or far-zone field, is defined as that region where B_oR is very much larger than one (1).

Then

$$\mathbf{E_R} >> \mathbf{E_i} \text{ and } \mathbf{B_R} >> \mathbf{B_i} \text{ and } \mathbf{E} = \mathbf{E_R} \text{ and } \mathbf{B} = \mathbf{B_R}$$
$$\tag{3-4}$$

The relationships in the far-zone field that hold for electromagnetic fields show that these fields can be treated like a plane-wave phenomena.

Since the induction and radiation zones do not overlap, an intermediate zone exists between them; it is the region between $B_oR << 1$ and $B_oR >> 1$. Problems associated with this intermediate zone cannot be resolved in terms of a near or far zone, but must be treated in terms of the equations of the general electromagnetic field. This consideration is not important at this point because it does not directly affect the development of criteria necessary for the evolution of shielding principles.

So that the zones described may be pinpointed more clearly, numerical value can be assigned to $B_oR << 1$ and $B_oR >> 1$.

Where $B_oR << 1$ in the near zone, assumes a value of $\leqslant .01$,

then $\qquad B_oR \leqslant .01$

$$R \leqslant \frac{.01}{B_o}$$

$$R \leqslant \frac{.01 v_o}{\omega} \leqslant \frac{3 \times 10^6}{\omega} \text{ meters}$$

Where $B_oR >> 1$ in the far zone, assumes a value of $\geqslant 100$,

then $\qquad B_oR \geqslant 100$

$$R \geqslant \frac{100}{B_o}$$

$$R \geqslant \frac{100 \ v_o}{\omega} \geqslant \frac{3 \times 10^{10}}{\omega} \text{ meters}$$

(v_o is assumed to be 3×10^8).

If four angular velocities (ω) are assigned as follows:

low frequency $\omega = 10^3$—near zone $R \leqslant 3 \times 10^3$ meters

$\qquad\qquad\qquad\qquad$—far zone $R \geqslant 30 \times 10^6$ meters,

radio frequency $\omega = 10^6$—near zone $R \leqslant 3$ meters

$\qquad\qquad\qquad\qquad$—far zone $R \geqslant 30 \times 10^3$ meters

ultra-high frequency $\omega = 10^9$—near zone $R \leqslant 3 \times 10^{-3}$ meters

$\qquad\qquad\qquad\qquad$—far zone $R \geqslant 30$ meters,

very high frequency $\omega = 10^{12}$—near zone $R \leqslant 3 \times 10^{-6}$ meters

$\qquad\qquad\qquad\qquad$—far zone $R \geqslant 30 \times 10^{-3}$ meters.

From the foregoing examples, it is clear that in circuits where $\omega < 10^9$, the induction fields are the problems, while where $\omega > 10^9$ radiation fields are the problems. Transmitters operating at their intended frequencies are generally in the far zone with respect to their intended receivers.

Induction fields are either high- or low-impedance fields. A high-impedance field is defined as a field whose impedance is higher than the impedance of the dielectric in which it exists; a low-impedance field has an impedance lower than the impedance of the dielectric. High-impedance fields are associated with a voltage source and most of their energy is contained in their electric component, while low-impedance fields are associated with a current source and most of their energy is contained in the magnetic component.

This discussion of general properties of electromagnetic fields has been covered in great detail in some of the classical texts in the field and serves as background material for practical design considerations which will be developed later.

4 – SHIELDING

4.1. Introduction

Shielding is the only practical method of suppressing interference which is radiated directly from a source. A perfect shield will not allow the passage of either electrostatic or electromagnetic energy. Shielding action can be considered either from the viewpoint of field, or circuit theory. From the viewpoint of field theory, shielding partially reflects or absorbs the electromagnetic waves from the source with the absorbed portion attenuated as it passes through the metal shield. From the viewpoint of circuit theory, currents from the interfering sources induce currents in the shielding barrier, resulting in two external fields developed by the currents which are out of phase and cancel out.

Metals, such as copper and aluminum, have qualities of high electrical conductivity, but are not perfect conductors, and, therefore, it becomes necessary to study the nature of metallic shielding to establish the best approach to take for shielding susceptible equipment. It is usually advisable to shield at the interfering source to negate the possibility of interfering signals from radiating; however, in a practical sense, this may not be possible and the susceptible equipment may have to be shielded. Oftentimes both interfering sources and susceptible receivers may require shielding.

Shields of high conductivity, such as copper, aluminum, silver, etc., offer good shielding efficiency against high-impedance or electric fields. This does not, however, apply against magnetic fields; in some cases, with certain materials and at certain frequencies, the magnetic fields are practically not reflected at all. For plane waves, penetration loss is increased if magnetic materials are used for shielding, while reflection loss is increased with the use of highly conductive material. At audio frequencies, satisfactory shielding efficiency against magnetic fields is obtained by using shielding material with high permeability.

A good shield to contain the interference should satisfy the following general requirements

1. It must be able to confine undesired signals that are generated within the case or reduce them to such an extent that they do not cause malfunctioning of other equipment; malfunctioning can be caused by equipment feeding through the equipment case, discontinuities of the cases and control lines, or through the power lines of adjacent equipment.
2. It must be able to prevent susceptible equipment from receiving undesired signals that exist in the area. These signals can feed through equipment cases, discontinuities in the case, adjacent power lines, etc.

Together with these shield requirements, the following design criteria can be established

1. All sources of noise and potential radiation sources should be included.
2. The best materials for shielding are those with low surface impedance.
3. Good electrical continuity must be maintained throughout the shield.

4.2. Shielding Effectiveness

When a metallic barrier is inserted between the transmitting and receiving sources, the electromagnetic waves travelling between these two points suffer a loss in power. The insertion loss in power that occurs at a given point is the shielding effectiveness of the metal barrier and is based on the assumption that the insertion of the metal barrier does not affect the impedance of the interfering source, that electromagnetic waves that are transmitted or reflected do not return, and that the thickness of the metal barrier, in inches, is very much smaller than the distance, in feet, from the interfering source to the metal barrier.

Shielding effectiveness, S, is expressed in db by the following equation

$$S = R + A \qquad (4\text{-}1)$$

where R is the reflection loss in db,

A is the absorption (or penetration) loss in db.

This shielding effectiveness, the sum of the two factors (R and A), consequently represents the total insertion loss. The factor R represents the reflection of some of the electromagnetic energy which impinges on the metal barrier; the factor A represents the absorption (or penetration) of the remaining energy. The factor R is expressed by the following general equation for reflection loss on metallic surfaces:

$$R = 20 \log_{10} \left| \frac{(Z_s + Z_\omega)^2}{4Z_sZ_\omega} \right| \qquad (4\text{-}2)$$

Where Z_s is the intrinsic impedance of the metal barrier, Z_ω is the intrinsic impedance of the reflected electromagnetic wave.

From Eq. 4-2 it can be seen that reflection loss varies with different electromagnetic waves which determine the intrinsic impedance based on whether the wave is a high or low impedance field, etc.

If Z_s and Z_ω are expressed in other terms, some other basic facts are

$$Z_\omega = \frac{E}{H} \text{ (ohms)} = \frac{1}{V\epsilon} \times \frac{1 + j\beta r - \beta^2 r^2}{j\beta r - \beta^2 r^2} \qquad (4\text{-}3)$$

For a high impedance field, this becomes

$$r \gg \lambda; \ Z_\omega = \frac{1}{V\epsilon} = 377 \text{ ohms} \qquad (4\text{-}4a)$$

$$r \ll \lambda; \ Z_\omega = - j/\omega\epsilon r \qquad (4\text{-}4b)$$

For a low impedance field, this becomes

$$r \gg \lambda; \ Z_\omega = V\mu_0 = 377 \text{ ohms} \qquad (4\text{-}5a)$$

$$r \ll \lambda; \ Z_\omega = j\omega\mu_0 r \qquad (4\text{-}5b)$$

In Eqs. (4-4) and (4-5),

μ_0 = permeability of free space (1.26×10^{-6} henries/meters),

ϵ = permittivity of free space (8.85×10^{-2} farads/meter),

r = distance from source to barrier in meters,

$\beta = 2\pi/\lambda$,

V = velocity of light in free space, 3×10^8 meter/sec, and equals $f\lambda$.

Equation 4-5, therefore, is dependent on the basic physical constants of free space and the metal barrier material. The magnitude of the intrinsic impedance of the metal barrier can be expressed as

$$Z_s = (1 + j) \left(\sqrt{\frac{\mu f}{2G}} \times 3.69 \times 10^{-7} \right) \text{ ohms} \qquad (4\text{-}6)$$

where μ = relative permeability of metal referred to free space,

f = frequency in cycles per second,

G = the relative conductivity of metal referred to copper.

The second term of Eq. 4-1, A, is expressed as

$$A = 3.338 \times 10^{-3} \times t\sqrt{fG\mu} \qquad (4\text{-}7)$$

where f, G and μ have the same identification as in Eq. 4-6, and t is the thickness of the metal barrier material in mils.

From Eq. 4-7, it can be seen that A is independent of the type of field, but highly dependent on metal barrier material.

When penetration loss is less than 10 db, a compensating factor must be added to shielding to effectively compensate for wave reflections inside the shield and is expressed as

$$ B = 20 \log_{10} \left\{ 1 - \left(\frac{Z_s - Z_\omega}{Z_s + Z_\omega} \right)^2 \epsilon^{-2(\alpha + j\beta)t} \right\} \qquad (4\text{-}8) $$

where α is the attenuation constant,
β is the phase constant,
t is the thickness of the material.

Therefore, from the foregoing it can be seen that the effectiveness of a particular shield, with associated physical data, may readily be calculated. The important consideration is that shielding effectiveness depends on:

1. Frequency
2. Impedance of electromagnetic wave from interfering source
3. Physical distance from interfering source to shield
4. Metal barrier material

In the near-zone, shielding from a high-impedance field is accomplished relatively easily. The reflection loss for a high-impedance field is given as:

$$ R = 353.6 + 10 \log_{10} \frac{G}{f^3 \mu R^2} \qquad (4\text{-}9) $$

where R is the distance from the metal barrier to the source in inches; the absorption (or penetration) loss is given as

$$ A = 3.338 \times 10^{-3} \times t \sqrt{fG\mu} \qquad (4\text{-}10) $$

From Eq. 4-9 it can be seen that the magnitude of R would be largest at the lowest frequency (at dc, almost all the electromatic energy is reflected) and smallest at the highest frequencies. Since this is so, screens for metal barriers are needed at lower frequencies, while at higher frequencies, solid metal barriers ar required. From Eq. 4-10, it can be seen that highest attenuation is obtained as the frequency increases. From Eqs. 4-9 and 4-10, since both R and A are directly proportional to G (or conductivity), materials, therefore, with high conductivity always make the most effective shield. Materials such as brass, copper and aluminum are effective shields over a wide frequency spectrum ranging from 60 cycles to 1000 megacycles.

Low-impedance, or magnetic fields, are generally difficult to shield, particularly at low frequencies. Merely inserting a metal barrier would not offer an effective shield but, by a combination of methods, shielding can be accomplished. Materials that are excellent against high-impedance fields offer very little shielding to low-impedance or magnetic fields at low frequencies because of their conductivity. But, materials with high conductivity can attenuate a low-impedance field if its orientation, with respect to the field, is such that it presents a shorted-turn effect. It must be remembered that low-impedance fields have most of their energy contained in their magnetic component; this will induce eddy currents in the material. These eddy currents, in turn, produce a magnetic field of opposite polarity to the magnetic component of the source, cancelling it out. Limitation of this cancellation is due to I^2R losses in the material; manifestation of these losses results in the generation of considerable amounts of heat.

Another technique to shield against the low-impedance field is to interpose a material with high permeability between the metal barrier material of high conductivity and low permeability. This material would provide a path of low reluctance (or high permeability) for permitting the magnetic field to follow and, consequently, never effectively become an interfering source.

Shielding in the far zone is similar to that in the near zone except for a somewhat different calculation, necessary to establish its magnitude. Reflection loss for plane waves is given as

$$R = 108 + 10 \log_{10} \frac{G \times 10^6}{\mu f} \qquad (4\text{-}11)$$

From Eq. 4-11 it is apparent that R is directly proportional to conductivity and inversely proportional to permeability. Materials with these characteristics are, therefore, effective as metal barriers in this shielding application. The absorption loss in the far zone is given as

$$A = 15.35 \times t \sqrt{fG\mu} \qquad (4\text{-}12)$$

From Eq. 4-12 it can be seen that A is directly proportional to the square root of the product of the conductivity and the permeability of the material. This is interesting because materials with high conductivity usually have low permeability and only the use of certain materials would maximize the effect of attenuation. However, since shielding effectiveness depends on the sum of $R + A$, experience has shown that in the far zone, materials with very high conductivity and low permeability make the most effective metal barriers for shielding.

4.3. Shield Design

In the design of shielded enclosures, there are two prime considerations:

1. Is the shield designed to contain any possible interference within itself (rather than permitting it to radiate).
2. Is the shield designed to exclude interference that may affect the operation of the equipment within the shield.

The first case, *containing the interference* usually applies to transmitters; while the second case, *excluding the interference* usually applies to receivers.

In a shield designed to contain, shielding effectiveness must be dependent primarily on the attenuation of the shield, since reflections will have little or no effect. The shielding effectiveness equation becomes

$$S = R + A + B \qquad (4\text{-}13)$$

All radiated energy eventually enters the walls of the shield; it is the absorption loss through these walls that reduces the magnitude of the field. For a shield that must depend on the relationship shown in Eq. 4-13, the following steps should be followed when designing it:

1. The degree of required attenuation must be established. This is probably the key consideration, since the amount of attenuation is a function of the material used and its thickness in inches.
2. When specifying a particular material, the required thickness of the material must be calculated so that the degree of attenuation sought may be achieved. This computation can be made as follows:

$$t = \frac{A}{3.338 \times 10^{-3} \sqrt{fG\mu}} \qquad (4\text{-}14)$$

where t is the thickness of the material in mils,
    A is the required absorption loss in db,
    G is the conductivity of the shield material relative to copper,
    μ is the magnetic permeability of the material relative to the magnetic permeability in free space,
    f is the frequency in cycles per second.

When Eq. 4-14 is used, the value of f should be that of lowest frequency associated with operation of the equipment being shielded. Use of the lowest frequency is important, since attenuation is directly proportional to frequency and, consequently, attenuation will become larger as frequency increases.

Various materials used for shielding, with relative conductivity (referenced to annealed copper—which is unity), relative permeability at 150 kc, and penetration loss in db/mil at 150 kc, are listed in Table 4-1. Penetration loss in db/mil, for copper and iron, at several frequencies is listed in Table 4-2.

TABLE 4-1. CHARACTERISTICS OF VARIOUS METALS

Metal	Relative Conductivity	Relative Permeability at 150 kc	Penetration Loss (db/mil) at 150 kc
Silver	1.05	1	1.32
Copper—annealed	1.00	1	1.29
Copper—hard drawn	0.97	1	1.26
Gold	0.70	1	1.08
Aluminum	0.61	1	1.01
Magnesium	0.38	1	0.79
Zinc	0.29	1	0.70
Brass	0.26	1	0.66
Cadmium	0.23	1	0.62
Nickel	0.20	1	0.58
Phosphor—bronze	0.18	1	0.55
Iron	0.17	1000	16.9
Tin	0.15	1	0.50
Steel, SAE 1045	0.10	1000	12.9
Beryllium	0.10	1	0.41
Lead	0.08	1	0.36
Hypernick	0.06	80,000	88.5
Monel	0.04	1	0.26
Mu-metal	0.03	80,000	63.2
Permalloy	0.03	80,000	63.2
Steel, stainless	0.02	1000	5.7

TABLE 4-2. PENETRATION LOSS (IN DB/MIL)

Frequency	Copper	Iron
10 kc	0.34	4.4
150 kc	1.29	16.9
10 mc	3.34	36.3
100 mc	33.40	137.0

TABLE 4-3. REFLECTION LOSS (IN DB/MAGNETIC FIELD)

Frequency	Copper	Iron
10 kc	44.2	8.0
150 kc	56.0	18.7
1 mc	64.2	28.1
100 mc	84.2	56.5

Penetration loss is shown, graphically, in Figs. 4-1 and 4-2. Reflection loss at various frequencies for copper and iron is listed in Table 4-3.

The shielding effectiveness of iron and copper is shown graphically, in Fig. 4-3. Once the shielding material has been chosen, because of its effectiveness in the particular application, many other factors must be considered, depending on the complexity of the particular shielding situation. The mechanical and structural considerations are very important; also, cost, corrosion resistance, fabrication, etc. Finally, discontinuities and certain practical considerations must not be overlooked.

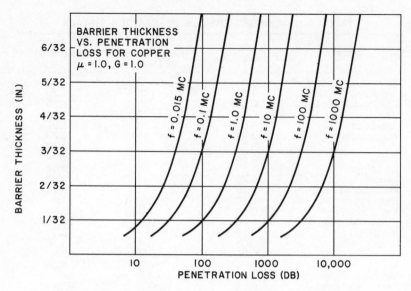

Fig. 4-1. Penetration loss vs. barrier thickness for copper.

Scrupulously clean and matched mating surfaces are very important to a good shield; also, the shield material must be rigid enough to prevent concaving between good contact points; concaving will produce a wave-guide action that becomes troublesome at certain frequencies. Conducting

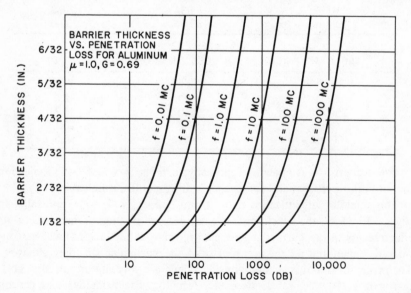

Fig. 4-2. Penetration loss vs. barrier thickness for aluminum.

gaskets and spring contact fingers must be utilized to assure good conductivity between removable panels and their mating surface. The best arrangement of spring contact fingers around removable panels or doors is to install two sets of fingers at right angles to each other; one is a wiping set, the other is in compression and makes good electrical contact when the door is closed. The pressure exerted by these springs is highly important and it should be carefully maintained.

Necessary holes in the shield must be kept small in area—the largest diameter being much smaller than the wavelength of the pertinent frequency —so as not to reduce the effective electrical area. Large holes such as ventilation ducts, must be covered by a fine copper mesh. Leakage from large holes can be reduced by using waveguide attenuators.

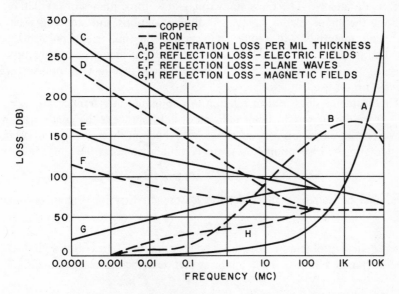

Fig. 4-3. Graph showing shielding effectiveness of iron and copper. (From C. S. Vasaka, "Shortcuts to R-F Shield Design," **Proceedings of the Conference on Radio Interference Reduction,** Armour Research Foundation, 1954.

Waveguides have a cut-off frequency — the frequency that can be handled without attenuation. Below cut off, attenuation becomes a function of physical length of waveguide and frequency. For 100-db attenuation in a circular waveguide, the length of the waveguide must be three times the diameter of the hole.

Mechanical and structural problems associated with shielding enclosures are sometimes solved by dividing the shielded enclosure into several compartments. This has the advantage of providing mechanical and structural stability. It also eliminates the formation of concave side walls and generally makes door accesses more rigid. The division of the compartment has the advantage of further shielding by presenting several different metal barriers of varying thickness and of varying barrier-to-barrier spacing to possible sources of interference.

We have mentioned that reflection is always present and, practically speaking, all energy ultimately penetrates the shielding barrier. At this point we should consider the condition of continual reflection within the shield—energy enters the shield, and reflects throughout the shield. The shield may then begin to act as a cavity resonator at various frequencies. A cavity resonator is described as a cylindrical box with perfect conductivity and containing within itself a nondissipative medium. An oscillation, once started within the box, should continue indefinitely since the walls are perfect conductors. These resonators may have three planes of oscillations. Altering the shape of the cavity will alter reflections and standing waves; absorbing materials will reduce reflection. The important point to be noted with this condition is that too good a shield may cause other problems, e.g., an unwanted oscillating field, which, in effect, is interference backing up on itself.

The problems discussed in relation to containing interference are essentially those encountered when exclusion of interference is the consideration. However, in exclusion of interference, reflection loss is an important consideration. Absorption losses are computed in the following manner:

$$A = 15.35 \times t \sqrt{fG\mu} \qquad (4\text{-}15)$$

This must be added to the reflection losses and Eq. 4-13 again becomes

$$S = R + A \qquad (4\text{-}16)$$

The practical problems of openings, discontinuities, structural soundness, etc., are handled in the same manner as that described for containment.

4.4. Bonding

Electrical bonding is a fixed union between two metallic surfaces resulting in a low-impedance connection. Such fixed union is a result of distributed physical contacts between any two conducting surfaces of two metallic objects, or from two objects being joined together by an electrical conductor. Bonds are made so there is no disparity between parts of a structure, and r-f currents are not likely to flow more in one part of the structure than in another, and thereby cause differences of potential which may in turn, result in interference.

Good bonding will produce a number of beneficial results. It will provide stability of conduction for r-f currents throughout the equipment structure, thereby assuring better transmission and reception. Bonding will preclude the buildup of a-c potentials on conducting frames of equipment, enclusures, and electrical conducting paths. Good bonding in the grounding system will assure adequacy of fault-current return paths and protect personnel that must work around the equipment from shock hazards. Also, it will prevent the accumulation of static charges that cause interference buildup, and discharge of these static discharges which cause explosion hazards.

All electronic equipment should have a continuous low-impedance path to ground; bonding will assure this. Bonding should be done on all clean, metal-to-metal contacts of equipment mounting plates, racks, shelves, brackets and mating surfaces so as to form this continuous low-impedance path to ground. To effect good bonding, jumpers should be avoided; their use should be restricted to limited situations such as having to cross non-metallic areas such as shock mounts.

A bond used to provide a low-impedance path to r-f energy should have low d-c resistance and reactance. When the size and material of the bond is known, the d-c resistance can be read from a chart found in a standard handbook. The inductive reactance is given by

$$L = 0.00508 \ (2.303 \ \log \frac{2 \ l}{10b + c} + 0.5 + 0.2235 \ \frac{b + c}{l})$$

(4-17)

where l is the length of the bonding strap in in.
  b is the length of the bonding strap in in.,
  c is the width of the bonding strap in in.,

If the bonding strap is not straight, or U-shaped, Eq. 4-17 is modified. A bent strap has the characteristics of a parallel LC circuit, that is operating far below its resonant frequency.

4.5. Bonding Effectiveness

Bonding effectiveness is a function of L in Eq. 4-17. Experience has shown that as the L exceeds 0.025 microhenries in magnitude, the effectiveness of the bond diminishes rapidly. Consequently, the ratio of 2l:10b + c in Eq. 4-17 is important, since it determines the value of L. As long as the value of L remains below 0.025 microhenries it makes little difference whether the bonding is accomplished by a single strap or by parallel straps suitably spaced. However, if a single bonding strap is used, its location could become quite important. If bonding is to be accomplished on a receiver that has an unshielded antenna, it would be best to locate the bond physically close to the antenna. If two racks are bonded, they should be bonded on the antenna side. Saturation bonding—where tradeoff occurs so that only less than 10% bonding is achieved with the addition of another bonding strap—occurs at about 0.018 microhenries.

In receivers that receive inputs by coaxial cables, bonding effectiveness is variable and unpredictable due to the effect of ambient electrical interference conditions on the coaxial cable. The signal-to-noise ratio of the receiver output may either change or remain constant when bonding is implemented. The most prevalent opinion is that the *length* of the bonding straps may have more significance than their impedances. But this is a problem that has to be "lived-with," because, despite the increase of noise in the output, with a consequent change in signal-to-noise ratio and a likely loss of intelligibility, the receiver must be adequately bonded to assure that electrical shock hazards to an operator will be minimized.

Since many equipments are presently being installed on shock mountings so they will not be affected by vibration, it is important to bond adequately across shock mounts. When doing so, thin strips of good conducting material should be used. These strips, in addition to their good conductivity properties, should be of such a size as to assure the lowest-impedance path to ground. The bond is put there to provide adequate metal-to-metal contact so that all parts of the equipment will be a single homogeneous conducting medium; however, in providing contact it must not act with a damping effect on the shock-mounted equipment.

Bonding is important to provide a low-impedance path to a ground plane in the transmission and reception of signals. All antennas, except those that have counterpoises as part of the equipment, must be provided with such a low-impedance path. This must be within the operating frequency ranges of the equipment and of sufficient physical size to obtain satisfactory radiation patterns.

If the operating efficiency of an antenna design depends on the existence of this low reactance current return path from the ground plane to the metal structure of the antenna, then the antenna must be of such a configuration that any r-f energy flowing in the external surface of the structure will allow a low minimum length impedance path to the metal portions of the antenna. Mating surfaces that have to be electrically homogeneous have to be clean metal surfaces. There should be no evidence of anodic film, grease, oil, paints, lacquer and metal finishes. Conductive metal finishes such as alodine, Iridite, Dow #1, and protective coatings such as silver plate, etc., do not offer problems, but most other finishes are nonconducting and destroy the low-impedance path. Bonding should also be provided for continity of a low-impedance path between the outer conductors of coaxial antenna leads and the ground plane.

For unshielded antennas, adequate bonding of associated equipment forms an important link in the low-impedance, r-f path from antenna to ground plane. When a receiver that is part of this equipment is bonded, it has a higher noise value in its output because its overall sensitivity to all signals has increased, whether they are wanted signals or not. This increased noise value is due to the receiver's increased sensitivity to radiated interference. When an *unshielded* receiver is bonded, however, a decrease in receiver output occurs, because the bond, by increasing the sensitivity of the antenna input circuit and, thereby, raising the signal-to-noise ratio, also provides a path to ground for conducted interference.

Bonding of equipment is very important in the prevention of hazards due to contact with energized parts of equipment that are at a higher potential than ground. All metal parts of equipment that can become energized (and this is practically all accessible parts) must have a low resistance bond of not more than 0.1 ohm to ground. If, in the design of electronic equipment, intrarack wiring connectors include a ground pin that is wired internally to all exposed parts, then a low-resistance ground wire connection to the particular ground pin will assure that this low-impedance path will be maintained. Metal conduits and trays that carry electrical wiring should have low-resistance bonds to the equipment of less than 0.1 ohm.

Bonding effectiveness is a function of application, frequency, current, and environmental conditions. Environmental conditions, such as vibration, temperature, humidity, etc., are important because they degrade or deteriorate the physical bonding device. Design criteria that satisfies the requirements of a good bond are as follows:

1. The bond must in no way degrade the quality of the bonded structure or bonded joint.
2. Bonds should always be made between the same metal. When different metals are bonded they should be close together in the electrochemical series, as listed in Table 4-4, to prevent corrosion. If two metals, widely separated in the series are bonded, such as aluminum and copper, there will be a continuous ion stream with an accompanying decomposition of the aluminum as it gradually goes into solution. If two such metals must necessarily be bonded, the bond should be carefully maintained and easily accessible for replacement.

TABLE 4-4. ELECTROCHEMICAL SERIES

1. Magnesium	9.	Tin
2. Beryllium	10.	Lead
3. Aluminum	11.	Copper
4. Zinc	12.	Monel
5. Chromium	13.	Some stainless steels
6. Iron	14.	Silver
7. Cadmium	15.	Platinum
8. Nickel	16.	Gold

3. Bonding, by means of jumpers, should not be considered satisfactory unless no other practical method can be utilized. Jumpers should be as short as possible; and the ratio of width to length as high as practical so that impedances at high frequency will not increase. Also, jumpers should be of a material satisfactorily placed in the electrochemical series in relation to the surfaces to be bonded, to reduce corrosion.

4. Bonds should be installed in places accessible for maintenance.

5. Bonds should be of a sufficient cross-sectional area to carry any potential current densities that may develop.

6. Bonds should not be held in place by self-tapping screws, since these generally cause high-resistance contacts.

7. Bonds that might possibly be required to carry large currents due to lightning surges entering the equipment, should be of minimal size; not less than 7000 circular mils for stranded copper cable, and not less than 10,000 circular mils for stranded aluminum cable.

8. If practical, bonds should have a width-to-length ratio of more than 0.2.

9. Any conductors in cabling that is terminated in equipment should have less than a 1-ohm resistance to the equipment structure to eliminate shock hazards.

10. All bonds should be clean metal-to-metal contacts.

11. Bonds should be made without weakening the bonded surfaces.

12. Bonds should not be affected by vibration, shock, expansion or contraction that might damage, break or loosen the bonding connection.

13. Bonds should not be installed where they will interfere with any movement within equipment required for normal operation and maintenance.

14. Required bonding that will interfere with movable parts, necessary for either operation or maintenance, should be made by slip rings or some other self-correcting device.

4.6. Corrosion Bonding

Corrosion is a very important problem to consider when discussing bonding. It will render bonding completely ineffectual by the development of high resistance joints and increased joint impedance to radio frequencies. Corrosive action can be either electrolytic or galvanic. Both types of corrosion are accelerated by moisture. Therefore, in addition to selecting the materials for the bond in close proximity (in the electrochemical series, Table 4-4) to the kind of material to be bonded, it is also important to protect the bond from moisture.

For galvanic corrosive action, bonded materials with moisture present develop a chemical reaction similar to that which develops when two metal electrodes are immersed in a salt solution. A potential develops across the bonded material much like that between two electrodes in a chemical cell. If the bonded materials are the same metal, no practical potential difference will develop. If the bonded materials are different, a metal with a low-potential difference should be chosen. A copper bus on an aluminum structure would develop a deadly corrosive action on the copper. If the copper bus were tin-plated, the corrosive action would rapidly slow down. The reason for this is readily apparent from Table 4-4.

Electrolytic corrosive action occurs when a d-c current is allowed to pass from one metal surface to another with an electrolytic solution present. This occurs with the same material, if the current is present and moisture available. If, however, a bonded joint is physically tight, clean, and care is taken to prevent moisture from entering, the problem should be reduced.

Bonding jumpers for power-return currents should be used only where the materials involved are stainless, cadmium or zinc-plated steels, copper, brass, and various bronzes. Cadmium or zinc-plated steel clamps should be used on steel, copper and brass conduit or tubing. For aluminum or magnesium conduit or tubing only aluminum alloy clamps should be used. Non-anodized aluminum separators should be used between any two dissimilar metals except if one of the metals is stainless steel, copper, brass or bronze. Bonding to magnesium should always be avoided. If magnesium must be bonded, aluminum separators should be used between the magnesium and other metal.

If bonding is to be made to tubing or any cylindrical object, the bonding jumper should be attached by means of a clamp. Cadmium-plated steel clamps should be used on all steels, copper, bronze, brass tubing or conduit. Stranded bonding braid should never be used for bonding when r-f currents are involved. Jumpers that are easily and quickly disconnected should never be used except if required for maintenance purposes.

Bonding becomes a very important consideration when the main equipment grounding system, the prime power system, and the building (that houses the equipment) grounding is discussed, and will be covered in considerable detail in the discussion of grounding system bonding methods. The problem is essentially the same—to achieve a low-resistance joint with the assurance that the grounding system is electrically continuous and homogeneous. To make these ground connections, an exothermic process appears to do the most satisfactory job. There are several manufacturers who can supply bonding materials. The exothermic process is essentially a process whereby the oxides of the metal to be deposited and another metal are ignited in a mold; a reaction takes place and a metal with a low-resistance joint is formed that is mechanically strong and has excellent electrical properties.

In addition to bonding, which effectively assures that disconnected sections of equipment can be joined together so that they are electrically homogeneous, conductive r-f gaskets can be used. When these gaskets are used where openings occur at joints or removable partitions, an effective shield is produced. R-f gaskets should be made of such material that has excellent resiliency and, of course, high conductivity. The basic design problems are:

1. Providing minimum gasket thickness for surface discontinuities that probably will occur.
2. Providing for correct pressure necessary to make the gasket effective.
3. Providing for the wavelength of a frequency that would be the same as the physical distance of the opening.

To overcome these problems, gasketing material must be highly conductive, used advantageously in connection with other materials in the electrochemical series, and be highly resilient.

Monel metal is widely used for gasketing because it has remarkably good resistance to the formation of nonconductive films as well as excellent mechanical properties; its conductivity, however, is not very good, and this is a disadvantage. Aluminum has poor corrosion resistance properties but excellent conductivity. This is typical of nonalloyed metals; they are a compromise between various good and bad qualities. Alloys, such as silver-plated brass, represent an excellent compromise and are widely used. Silver-plated brass, e.g., has high conductivity, resiliency, and generally good mechanical properties, and is not apt to form nonconducting film.

Commercial gaskets are generally held in place by sidewall friction, an attachment device, or by a shoulder or collar. They are available in various physical sizes and shapes—round, rectangular and combination types.

5 – FILTERING

5.1. Introduction

Since it has been shown that radiated interference can be successfully coped with by suitable shielding methods, the next problem to be attacked is the minimization of the magnitude of conducted interference. Equipment must be connected to other equipment; equipment must be connected to common power systems; and equipment must be connected to common ground systems. In the case of equipment interconnection and connection to power supplies, means must be devised to permit only the intended energy to be brought into the equipment. Elimination of unintended signals is the function of filters. In the case of connection to common grounds, the design objective is to reduce the flow of any current in the grounding system to a level that will not cause interference. This will be treated in detail on the chapters devoted to grounding. A further note must be added that equipment interconnection is intimately involved in the cable problem; certain techniques can be applied in cable design to minimize conducted interference in cables. This will be treated in the chapter on cables.

There are many techniques that can be employed in filtering out conducted interference. Essentially, the particular technique employed depends on the bandwidth of the intended signals, how much attenuation is required to give a satisfactory signal-to-noise ratio, how much space can be taken up within the equipment by the filters, and, what is the complexity of the waveform of the intended signal. Each of these parameters is a limiting factor and must be weighed against one another. In many cases, poor planning may make one of these parameters so intolerable, that filtering becomes a major equipment redesign consideration. This occurs when no attempt is made to suppress interference until a cable is brought into an equipment and it is discovered that the filtering has to be so complicated, that large portions of the equipment must be utilized to house the filters. This is a specific example of the "crisis" approach that has previously been discussed.

Filtering of a specific nature can be accomplished by utilization of the basic electrical parameters of capacitance, inductance, and resistance. Combinations of the three parameters can be made in many different ways, and these combinations are what is generally known as filters. Each of these parameters effectively accomplishes the filtering-out action by a different method: capacitance, by short circuiting; inductance, by open circuiting; and resistance, by dissipation.

In discussing filters of any variety, it is most important to understand the concept of insertion loss. This concept is important because the effectiveness of any filter cannot be measured solely in terms of the impedance offered to the interfering currents. It must be noted that filters eliminate interference by introducing a high impedance into the path of an interfering current; filters may shunt an interfering current to ground through a low impedance; or filters may function by combining these two methods.

Insertion loss is defined as the ratio of voltages that are measured across the line immediately beyond the point that the filter is inserted in the line. The insertion loss is always given at a specific frequency and is measured in decibels (db). The ratio of input voltages is required to obtain a specified constant output voltage. The ratio is given as:

$$\text{Insertion loss (in db)} = 20 \log_{10} \frac{E_1}{E_2} \qquad (5\text{-}1)$$

where E_1 is the output voltage with a filter in the circuit,

E_2 is the output voltage without a filter in the circuit.

It can be seen from this ratio that insertion loss is practically an exact measurement of filter suppression effectiveness. A typical insertion measuring loss circuit for a shunting-type filter capacitor is shown in Fig. 5-1. Its

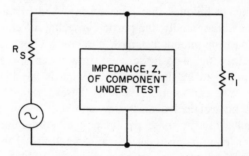

Fig. 5-1.   Insertion loss measuring circuit for a capacitor.

insertion loss is given as:

$$\text{Insertion loss} = 20 \log_{10} \left| 1 + \frac{R}{Z} \right| \qquad (5\text{-}2)$$

where R is the effective parallel combination of the source and load impedance,

Z is the complex impedance of the shunting component under test. For applications to military systems, it is now general practice to follow the standard measuring method as specified in MIL-STD-220 and as shown in Fig. 5-2. It will be noted that in this military standard the source and load impedance are both 50 ohms.

There are a number of important and decisive factors that must be known before an effort is made to minimize interference in equipment by the use of components such as filters. The frequency range over which suppression

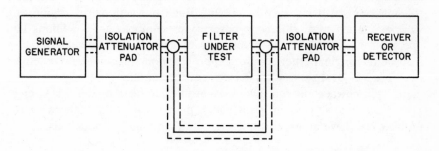

Fig. 5-2.   Circuit for measuring loss of filters (as per MII-STD-220).

is required is of prime importance. For filters, frequency range is the factor that, for the most part, determines most of the key parameters in their design. Another consideration is to determine whether the circuit involved can still satisfactorily operate in its intended manner when the suppression component is introduced: what will it do to the overall circuit impedance; what will its effect be on line drop, etc. Finally, the mechanical and environmental factors must be considered in relation to how they will affect the filter.

Unfortunately, no filters constructed of ideal suppression components exist. Each component, or combination of components, have their own inherent limitations. For example, an ideal low pass filter should have a negligible insertion loss on all frequencies below the cut-off frequency, and an infinite insertion loss above this cut-off frequency. Bluntly, it should "cut off." But the inherent component limitations make such a sharp cut off almost impossible to achieve. Capacitors have varying impedances depending on frequency; they show an almost infinite impedance to d-c and low frequencies, and practically zero impedance to radio frequencies. Coils and inductances are almost the opposite: they show no impedance at low frequencies and almost infinite impedances at r-f frequencies. Resistors have practically constant magnitudes of resistance at all frequencies. Technological limitation is the key consideration in the use of various components for suppression. The better the components—the more stable their operation—the better the opportunity to achieve the objective of any radio interference control program viz the reduction of unwanted energy to a level that will be relatively harmless in relation to the operation of the equipment.

It is well to note at this point that most of the problems associated with filters can be solved with comparative ease, when a strictly theoretical approach is taken. As long as ideal components, ideal combinations of components, ideal ambient conditions, etc., are postulated; then complete solutions are relatively easy to obtain. But from a practical engineering viewpoint, such ideal situations never exist: components, conditions and operations vary widely; the practicality of any solution depends on how realistic the original criteria were. Approximations that can be overlooked in theoretical treatments—key factors that are omitted so that the mathematics will not become too involved—are the problem of the design engineer when he must come to grips with a practical solution. Otherwise, the problem will have an excellent solution on paper and not much else.

5.2. Simple Filters

A number of individual components used *individually* may be considered simple filters, since they actually perform a filtering action and, generally, whether they are, for example, only capacitors, contain the other electrical parameters of inductance and resistance. The first of these components to be considered will be a capacitor used as a filter. The ideal capacitor has an impedance which is calculated as:

$$X_C = \frac{1}{\omega C} \qquad (5\text{-}3)$$

But no ideal capacitor exists; though it is a component that is primarily capacitance, it also has an inherent inductance due to the capacitor itself and due to the capacitor lead-in wires. It is obvious, then, when X_L becomes equal to X_C, the capacitor becomes a series resonant circuit with characteristics that are of practical use. When $X_L = X_C$, the impedance of the capacitor is minimum and the insertion loss is maximum. Past the point of resonance, the inductive reactance continues to increase and the capacitor is no longer effective as a bypass filter. A typical bypass filter made up of a capacitor component is shown in Fig. 5-3; the inductance of the capacitor is depicted—the internal inductance of the capacitor and the inductance of the capacitor lead-in wire. The resonant frequency of such a circuit is given as

$$f = \frac{1}{2\pi\sqrt{LC}} \qquad (5\text{-}4)$$

Consequently, the smaller the total inductance, the higher the resonant frequency. From this it can be seen that the frequency range will have a higher upper limit and, thereby, be more useful. Since no change can be implemented to the internal inductance of a capacitor component once it

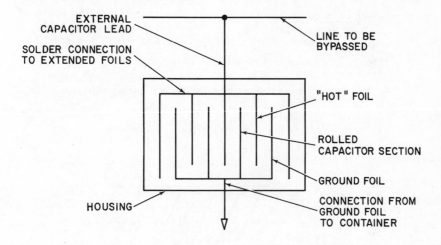

Fig. 5-3. Construction of a typical bypass capacitor.

has been specified, the total inductance will change with a change in length of the lead-in wire. Figures 5-4, 5-5, 5-6, and 5-7 show (for various types of capacitors) how the insertion loss varies with the length of the lead-in wire.

It can be seen from the illustrations, that a close control of the length of the lead-in wire will enable a designer to have strict control in changing the resonant points for a specified capacitor component. Figure 5-4 shows the curves for a commercially available paper tubular capacitor. Assume that there is a design requirement which specifies that the capacitor filter be used in an application at 3-mc bypass. As shown in Fig. 5-4, the following possibilities exist:

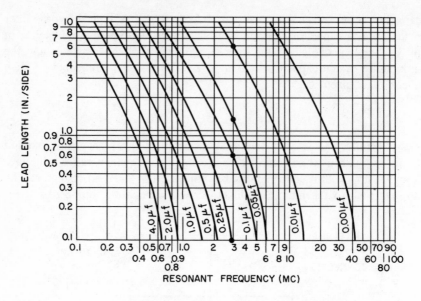

Fig. 5-4. Resonant frequency as a function of lead length for paper tubular capacitors.

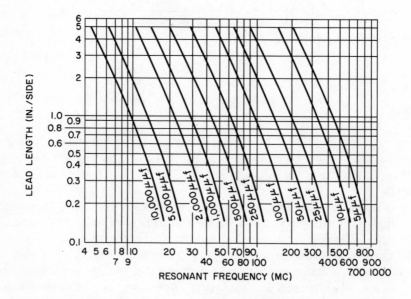

Fig. 5-5. Resonant frequency as a function of lead length for mica capacitors.

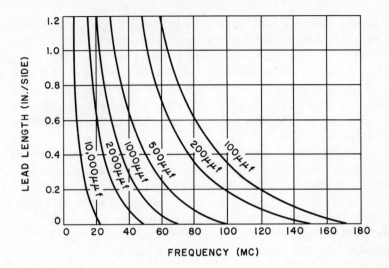

Fig. 5-6. Resonant frequency as a function of lead length for disc ceramic capacitors.

1. 0.25 μf with 0.1 in. lead length.
2. 0.10 μf with 0.6 in. lead length.
3. 0.05 μf with 1.2 in. lead length.
4. 0.01 μf with 6 in. lead length.

The insertion loss of the 0.25 μf capacitor will be greater over a wider

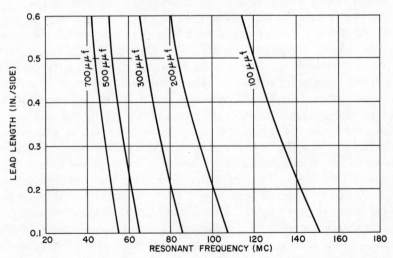

Fig. 5-7. Resonant frequency as a function of lead length for the standoff type ceramic capacitor.

range of frequencies, but, with its impractical length of lead-in wire—
0.1 in.—it is clear that it cannot be used. The next value—0.10 μf—is the
capacitor to be used because the length of its lead-in wire is within practical
limits. Similar examples can be shown by reference to Figs. 5-5, 5-6, and
5-7. The important consideration to be noted is that the capacitor value is
determined theoretically; it will not give a practical solution. The resonant
frequency depends implicitly on the geometry and construction of the
component.

Component manufacturers have developed the ceramic stand-off, or
stud-type, capacitor in an effort to reduce the internal and lead-in inductance of the capacitor, and, thereby, raise the resonant frequency. This
particular capacitor development still retains the construction of the comparatively long length of lead-in wires replaced by a short thick stud terminal with a minimum inductance. This new construction does improve
the insertion loss characteristics, but this is traded for only a slight improvement in the resonant frequency value.

From the foregoing it can readily be seen that with added inherent inductance as part of its geometry and construction, a capacitor with lead-in
wires is, in a measure, superior, for various applications to an ideal capacitor. This superiority is demonstrated up to and a little beyond resonant
frequency. Of course, beyond the point of resonant frequency, the capacitor
with lead-in wires almost completely loses its effectiveness as a filter.
Another consideration is that a limited amount of manipulation can be
made using the lead-in wire length, since the internal inductance of the
capacitor cannot be altered once the component is specified.

Another component that can be used as a filter is a feedthrough capacitor. Though it has many applications it is essentially useful where interference is of a broadband variety. For broadband interference, many
capacitors cannot be used because their resonant frequency is far below the
required frequency for resonance. This, then, is the design problem that is
overcome by the feedthrough capacitor. Its geometry and construction is
such that the total inductance of the component is greatly reduced by eliminating the length of the lead-in wire and by reducing, appreciably, internal
inductance. From Eq. 5-4, it can be seen that f increases as L becomes
smaller. Commercial feedthrough capacitors are designed with resonant
frequencies of over 1000 megacycles, with impedance characteristics so
excellent that they appear to be almost ideal. A comparison of three types
of capacitors is shown in Fig. 5-8. It can be seen that for frequencies up
to about 20 megacycles, the feedthrough capacitor is equivalent—in attenuation—to the ideal capacitor. On the other hand the lead-in capacitor's
attenuation is equivalent—in attenuation—to the ideal capacitor up to
about 1 megacycle. The deviation of the feedthrough capacitor after 20
megacycles is attributed to transmission line resonance which occurs when

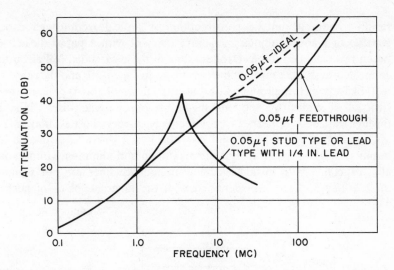

Fig. 5-8. Insertion loss of a feedthrough capacitor compared with an ideal and a lead type capacitor. (From **Proceedings of the Second Conference on Radio Interference Reduction,** Armour Research Foundation.)

the capacitor foil thickness is identical to the particular wavelength.

Figure 5-9 illustrates typical insertion loss curves of feedthrough capacitors of varying inductances.

As noted, the basic advantage of the feedthrough capacitor is in the elimination of a lead-in wire, and reduction of the inherent inductance,

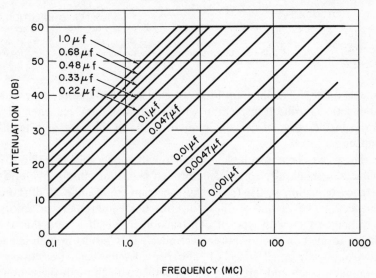

Fig. 5-9. Insertion loss curves of a feedthrough capacitor.

resulting from its unique construction. A typical feedthrough capacitor consists of a rolled tubular capacitive element with a paper dielectric between two extended foil electrodes. One of these extended foil electrodes is connected to the feedthrough bus, as shown in Fig. 5-10, and the other to the metal case which is grounded. Some capacitors of this type are also constructed of capacitive sections made up of alternate discs. The feedthrough capacitor appears to be, effectively, a very short section of a very low-impedance coaxial line, and insertion loss is due to a mismatch at the terminals of the capacitor. But the maximum and minimum voltages normally associated with mismatched low-impedance lines are not seen, since these voltages effects are identified with the inherent losses of such mis-

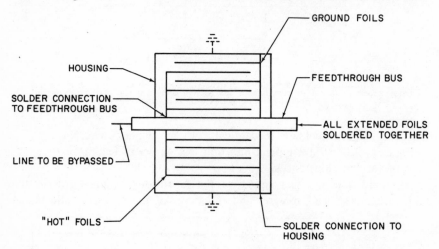

Fig. 5-10.   Construction of a feedthrough capacitor.

matched lines. The inherent losses of a mismatched line produces a marked attenuation during transmission which does not show up when plotted as a dip in the curve at certain frequencies, as in the case of a feedthrough capacitor.

There are now available, commercially, low voltage, high capacity, physically small, electrolytic feedthrough capacitors that provide for interference reduction in the frequency spectrum from audio to ultra-high frequencies. The design of these electrolytic feedthrough capacitors takes advantage of interval-type of construction in which a very thin dielectric film is formed on one, or both, electrodes. This results in high capacitance in a physically small space. It also provides the center electrode with a terminal at each end, creating a conductive path through the center of the capacitor. The outer metallic case then acts as both the third terminal and the second electrode. Insertion loss characteristics of the electrolytic feed-through are, practically speaking, identical with ordinary feedthrough capacitors, but the electrolytic has the decided advantage of providing these characteristics in a smaller physical package. The small package becomes a key consideration, especially when filtering has to be implemented when the design is so far along and there is very little space remaining in the equipment.

In the application of these feedthrough capacitors as suppression components (it should be noted that their attenuation characteristics are similar to any low pass filter—to be discussed later—except that more capacitance is needed for a given insertion loss), the method of installation is important. The best mounting practice is to mount the capacitors on a wall, utilizing the walls of the shielded container to shield the input from the output. This type of wall mount will assure that the insertion loss characteristic curve of the feedthrough capacitor will approximate that of an ideal capacitor. To calculate the insertion loss achieved by the use of a feedthrough capacitor in a matched line, the following relationship is used:

$$\text{Insertion Loss (in db)} = \frac{Z_0 \omega C}{2} \qquad (5\text{-}5)$$

This relationship is only valid if

$$\text{Insertion Loss (in db)} >>> 0 \qquad (5\text{-}6)$$

The current rating of the feedthrough capacitor is based on its ability to carry all the current through the center conductor.

The limitations that have been discussed in connection with the use of capacitors with lead-in wires and feedthrough capacitors, both electrolytic and nonelectrolytic as suppression elements, leads naturally to the development of a component that circumvents these limitations and satisfies the suppression function. Such a component is the L-Cap, which is actually an artificial transmission line with lumped parameters. Its construction is illustrated in Fig. 5-11.

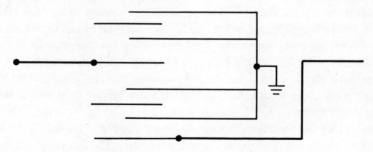

Fig. 5-11. Construction of an L-Cap.

It has been shown that the feedthrough capacitor is very similar to the ideal capacitor, but even this similarity is not desired because the "ideal" capacitor has disadvantages. For example, its attenuation characteristics are functions of load impedances. This is no problem as long as these load impedances are of appreciable magnitude, but as they become smaller, insertion loss becomes small, and, accordingly the feedthrough capacitor loses its effectiveness as a suppression element. To eliminate this problem, it is necessary to increase the impedance of the series circuit of the capacitor by increasing the inductance of the circuit. Considerable performance improvement is gained by taking inductance from the bypass circuit and adding it to the series circuit. The addition of these small inductance increments are key considerations because of the difficulty in incorporating them in the design to improve circuit characteristics.

The use of the turns and length of the through-load carrying conductor as the source of inductance is one approach in using these small values of inductance. It should be noted that since this is inherent inductance, its effectiveness per unit of material is enhanced. Also the isolation offered by the turns eliminates resonant effects. Frequency is of no consequence, and, therefore, we have a broad suppression device that is only a capacitor, yet has qualities that are not associated with an ideal capacitor. This device actually gives a much higher insertion loss for a specified capacitive loading on a circuit, since the inherent distribution of the inductance with the ground plane capacitance is utilized.

A comparison of the electrical circuit equivalents of lead-in wire, feedthrough, and L-Cap is shown in Fig. 5-12. Note the progression in the use of inductance in the various capacitors.

If we further compare the construction of the feedthrough and the L-Cap capacitor at this time, we will note differences in the "live" or "hot" foil. In the L-Cap, the edge of foil is not extended beyond the dielectric paper, as in conventional construction, but is a long, spirally-wound inductor because its edges are not joined. Circuit connections are provided to both the inside and outside ends of the foil; this unique feature makes the L-Cap a series inductance capacitor. The capacitor is enclosed in an hermetically sealed container and mounted by a terminal stud type of device, which also gives a good ground connection. Best installation practice dictates that the capacitor be mounted so that output and inputs are separated.

Fig. 5-13 shows typical insertion losses that can be obtained with the L-Cap. Unlike the feedthrough capacitor, there are no drop offs to deteriorate performance.

The L-Cap is constructed to satisfy any voltage and capacitance rating that is normally required by the circuit designer. Physically, it compares favorably with a standard capacitor of the same capacitance and voltage

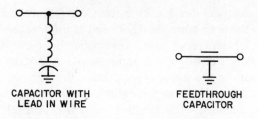

CAPACITOR WITH
LEAD IN WIRE

FEEDTHROUGH
CAPACITOR

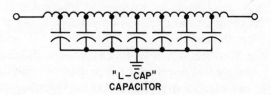

"L-CAP"
CAPACITOR

Fig. 5-12.   Electrical circuit equivalents for capacitor suppression devices.

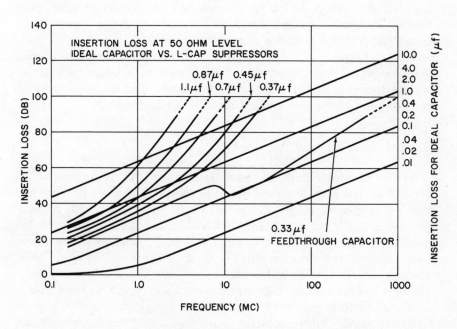

Fig 5-13.   Insertion loss curves of an ideal and L-Cap capacitor at 50-ohm level.
(From **Proceedings** — Second Armour Conference)

rating. Like all electrical devices, its current carrying capacity is affected by thermal considerations since the "hot" foil is used as the through conductor and has inherent resistance. Consequently, the L-Cap is more effective in low and medium current applications. A current rating of one ampere is adequate if no heat sink is provided to dissipate the internal heat. But, because of the usual wall mounting practice, a current rating of twice this rating can be tolerated. This doubled rating is practical if the device is mounted on six inches of metal. With such a mounting the ambient temperature may reach as high as 160°F.

To satisfy particular applications, the L-Cap can be varied. The current-carrying capacity is increased by increasing the thickness of the hot foil, and this with only an insignificant increase in physical size. It has been estimated that doubling the foil thickness only increases, by 20 percent, the volume needed for the capacitor.

Another design variation would be to add a series inductance element. This is added to the normal distributed LC portion by continuing the turns of the hot foil and insulation. This added section may be electrically incorporated between the interfering source and the device, isolating the capacitive portion of the device so that very little capacitive loading is added to the interfering circuit.

Another design variation is to wind the capacitor with thin foil. This improves attenuation, the LC ratio is increased, and a more effective device results. Physically, for maximum attenuation, the L-Cap should be a square rather than a long, thin rectangular shape.

This rectangular capacitor, with its increased efficiency, will bring increased attenuation characteristics that cannot be obtained with a conventional capacitor of the same bulk. Materially, it assists in the achievement of a low cost, highly efficient capacitor suppression unit.

5.3. Four-Terminal Networks

So far, suppression of unwanted interference, that is transmitted by conduction, has been discussed from the viewpoint of three-terminal networks that consist, essentially, of capacitive components with inherent inductance and resistance. Manipulation of these inherent parameters has made it possible to use the capacitors to the best advantage. These essentially capacitive networks are filters in the broad sense of the term. Now, however, filters, as such, will be discussed.

Filters are, essentially, four terminal networks which transmit energy over a given frequency band, but attenuate energy outside of this given frequency band. Filters combine bypassing capacitive action with the impeding action of the inductances and are the most effective device for providing high insertion loss over an extremely wide band, ranging from frequencies from 14 kc to 1000 mc. Filters are generally classified as to whether they are low pass, high pass, bandpass or bandstop; they are combinations of inductance and capacitance, see Fig. 5-14.

We must digress at this point to discuss the general problems relating to noise interference, and the selection of the proper filter to enable one to suppress the noise. The key consideration is to maintain a sufficiently high signal level. If level is high, the signal-to-noise ratio will be beneficially affected, i.e., if the signal level can be raised without also raising the noise level. But there are built-in design limitations of voltage, power, etc., which restrict the increase in signal level, and, from a system viewpoint, this increasing signal level may act as an interfering source to other equipments which are part of the system. This problem is sharpened in intensity when

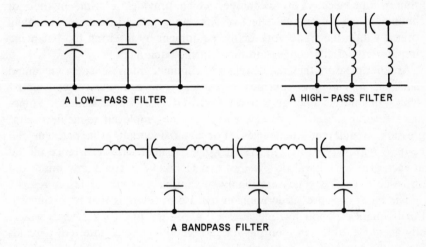

A LOW-PASS FILTER   A HIGH-PASS FILTER

A BANDPASS FILTER

Fig. 5-14. Types of filters.

discussing servosystems, since in these devices, the operating signal level is normally quite small. For such devices, the key factor to be considered is the noise interference that is inherent in the device, and the signal-to-noise ratio which must be coped with if the error rate requirements of transmission are to be met.

Interference susceptibility can be reduced by lowering the signal circuit impedance if the interference is being caused by resistance or capacitive coupling; it is not too worthwhile if the interference is caused by impedance coupling. A good design criteria for a maximum tolerable impedance level, within equipment, is that it be 100,000 ohms for standard construction,

3 megohms for hermetically sealed equipment and 500 ohms for signal transmission lines between equipment. These are practical design values that are known to give good results.

Interference susceptibility can also be reduced by limiting the bandwidth because unwanted signals which are accepted from a flatband source vary directly with the width of the band. The narrower the bandwidth, the less the probability of receiving unwanted signals. This method of reducing susceptibility to unwanted signals is commonly used in radio communication where bandwidths of a few hundred cycles are used for carrier wave (cw) transmission, and is also useful on servosystems.

If it can be predicted, as a result of a system analysis, that susceptible interference will be at a constant level, balancing circuits can be used to neutralize this constant interference. This method is particularly useful when the interference is provided by mutual impedances, such as a common ground impedance. This technique, which provides a prime method of eliminating the detrimental effect of circulating ground currents, is usually applied within the framework of the equipment by inserting the balancing circuit after the interconnection point in the equipment.

Another measure that can be taken to eliminate interference by unwanted signals is to eliminate spurious responses. For equipment receiving r-f signals, this means a design with a sufficient degree of preselectivity. Sometimes several stages of preselectivity must be employed to achieve suppression at different frequencies. For non-r-f circuits, the problem can be dealt with very easily. In the a-f range, a small series resistance placed in each grid circuit will do the job; this technique is commonly employed on ac-dc radio sets which are highly susceptible to spurious responses.

The basic design consideration in the use of filters is that of frequency. For frequencies below five megacycles, a constant pi-section filter is generally adequate, although multiple-derived sections may be inserted, depending on the required attenuation. The values of capacitance and inductance are relatively large and their magnitude is determined by the cut-off frequency.

For frequencies between five and fifty megacycles, the associated distributed capacitance of the inductor becomes important. The inductor may have to be wound spirally to reduce this parameter. A toroid inductance is commonly employed to minimize distributed capacitance; the toroid inductor used should have a core material not nearly saturated at rated load conditions.

For frequencies above fifty megacycles, high-quality r-f capacitors are the essential components. Most attenuation is due to the action of the capacitor since the inductor is almost completely bypassed. Even small amounts of inductance at the bypass circuit will greatly reduce the value of a filter; consequently, at these frequencies, feedthrough capacitors are recommended and care must be taken in their installation.

The major functional limitations of filters—since they are made up of capacitors—are the same as those of capacitive suppression elements. Also, filters utilize inductances whose distributed capacitance at high frequencies is also a limitation. But these limitations can be "lived-with" and the design of a low-pass filter can be made so that it will have good suppression characteristics up to 1000 megacycles. Another difficulty is that most standard filters do not dissipate energy within their operating range, but, merely reflect, or send it to some other place. Consequently, while the filter may be serving its intended function in the specific circuit by suppression, the rejected energy still appears at another circuit as worse interference. Furthermore, there may be a load impedance, which at a particular frequency, presents an ideal condition for some filters to pass on the maximum rejected energy to the circuit. This is equivalent to a negative insertion loss. A dissipative filter, using a ferrite core, resolves this difficulty by taking advantage of the loss vs. frequency characteristics of ferrites.

Modern, commercially available filters have a number of common, important characteristics: the input and output are always separated; the input capacitor is shielded from the output capacitor which precludes r-f coupling. Capacitors with lead-in wires always have the shortest practical length; the foil ends are always swedged to reduce the inherent inductance of the capacitor. Toroid inductors are employed to keep the distributed capacitance to minimum levels within the physical limitation and magnitude of the inductance.

The equivalent circuit of an inductance coil in addition to the inherent parameters is shown in Fig. 5-15. To effectively use such an inductance

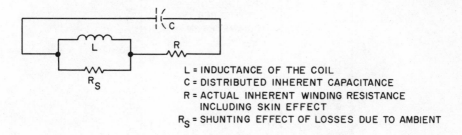

Fig. 5-15. The equivalent circuit of an inductance coil.

as part of a filter network, the distributed capacitance should have as small a value as possible so that the anti-resonant frequency will be as high as possible, since, above this anti-resonant frequency, the inductance acts as a capacitor. The reactance of L should be small for wanted frequencies, and large for unwanted, interfering frequencies. Winding resistance, R, should be small enough not to cause a large voltage drop. The R_s, which is the shunting effect due to ambient conditions, determines the Q of the coil. The R_s is not of interest for operation above the cut-off frequency. Because of the requirement to minimize the distributed capacitance, mutiple layer coils, which have a high distributed capacitance, should not be used; single layer coils are preferred when wound with a wire size that can safely carry 100 percent overload. If not restricted by physical require-ments, an air dielectric can be used for coils up to 1000 microhenries. The value of inductance for a single-coil air core can be calculated from the following

$$L = \frac{0.5d^2 1^2 T^2}{9d + 20\,1} \tag{5-7}$$

where L is the inducance in microhenries,
   d is the average coil diameter in inches,
   1 is the length of the winding in inches,
   T is the number of turns per inch.

To facilitate calculations, nomographs may be constructed based on Eq. 5-7; such a nomograph is shown in Fig. 5-16. To find the distributed

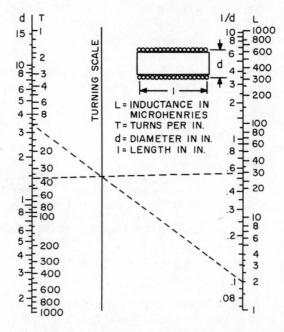

Fig. 5-16.   Nomograph for single-layer coil design.

capacity of a coil, a nomograph such as that shown in Fig. 5-17 can be constructed. The necessary data to use this nomograph is d—the diameter of the coil; a—the diameter of the wire used for winding; and s—the distance between the centers of adjacent turns.

As noted, air core coils have limited use because of their physical bulk, especially when their values go above 1000 microhenries. To gain more

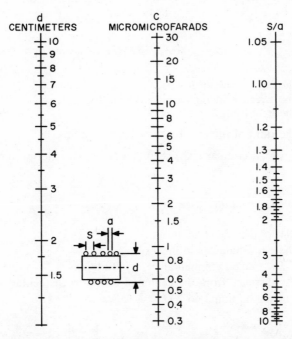

Fig. 5-17. Nomograph for determining the distributed capacitance of single-layer coils.

inductance in a limited physical space, a magnetic material core must be used in place of the air core. However, the use of such magnetic material introduces another limiting factor: the insertion loss must be specified as that insertion under load, since magnetic core materials, without external air gaps, saturate when drawing appreciable currents in d-c circuit application. The effect of saturation can be determined by examining Eq. 5-8, which is for a toroid-shaped coil of rectangular cross-section and without an external air gap:

$$L = 0.00508N^2b\mu_d l \ \frac{r_2}{r_1} \ (\text{in } \mu h) \qquad (5\text{-}8)$$

where N is the total number of turns,

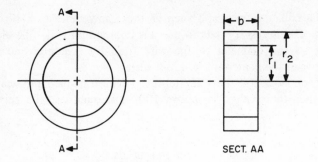

Fig. 5-18.   Toroid of rectangular cross-section.

b is the core width in inches,
μ_d is the average incremental permeability,
l is the length in inches,
$\dfrac{r_2}{r_1}$ is the ratio of the outside to the inside radius.

For a toroid with a circular cross-section without an external air gap (see Fig. 5-19)

$$L = 0.0319N^2\mu_d \left(r_m - \sqrt{r^2_m - \frac{b^2}{4}}\right) \qquad (5\text{-}9)$$

where N is the total number of turns,
b is the core diameter in inches,
μ_d is the average incremental permeability,
r_m is the distance from the center of toroid to the center of the core in inches; is equal to $\frac{1}{2}(r_1 + r_2)$

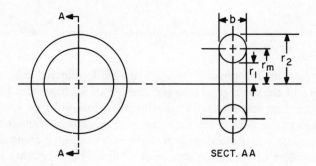

Fig. 5-19.   Toroid of round cross-section.

From equations 5-8 and 5-9, it can be seen that

$$L \propto \mu_d \qquad (5\text{-}10)$$

μ_d is a function of magnetization and this varies according to

$$H = \frac{NI}{2\pi r_m} \qquad (5\text{-}11)$$

where H is magnetization in ampere turns per inch,
I is the direct current in amperes,
r_m is as above.

The μ_d, or incremental permeability, varies widely with magnetization for different materials. Curves for various materials are shown in Fig. 5-20.

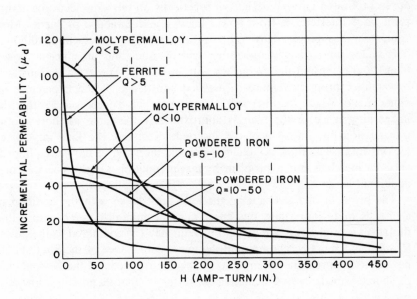

Fig. 5-20. Incremental permeability as a function of magnetic field intensity for different core materials. Q's given are at 200 kc.

Ferrites have the highest initial permeability, however, saturation is rapidly reached. Molypermalloys start with lower initial incremental permeability but their curves are flatter. In fact, Molypermalloys represent the best core materials where high values of inductance are needed with low losses at high frequencies.

5.4. Commercial Filters

There are many specific kinds of commercially available filters that are generally identified by the functions they are to perform. They can be classified by their frequency characteristics: low-pass, high-pass, bandpass and bandstop. These frequency classifications are then subdivided into sections; e.g., low-pass filters are divided into L, T and pi sections. Pi-section filters usually provide the best attenuation characteristics, considering the physical size of the filters, but are usually the most expensive. Low-pass filters are used mainly for suppression of r-f inerference from equipment power lines and other low-frequency interference sources which may be conducted into the equipment. These power line filters are usually a pi network made up of two capacitors and an inductor designed to give maximum insertion loss for a specified frequency range. Power line filters are very widely used, and are incorporated into the designs of practically all modern electronic equipment since interference from power lines is so common a problem. Most equipment has power delivered to it at 60 cycles per second, although 400 cycles power is already rather widely used, and an efficient power filter should transmit this frequency with little loss. To design and install a power filter properly requires a detailed knowledge of the impedance on either side of where the filter will be inserted. This is necessary so that the image impedance of the filter is approximately the same as those of the transmission line into which it is inserted. Restated, the load impedance looking into a line must not change with the insertion of the filter. Impedance mismatch is not a problem in the attenuation range since it brings additional losses.

The problem of not changing the load impedance with the addition of a filter is quite important; this effect must be minimized. To assure that this effect is minimized, a high cut-off frequency (as compared to the power frequencies) must be chosen, and the image impedance of the filter should be selected approximately equal to the geometric mean of the Z_R load and Z_S source impedances. Calculations have shown that the loss in a low pass constant K pi filter is:

$$\alpha = 124f^3LC^3Z_R \qquad (5\text{-}12)$$

From Eq. 5-12 it can be seen that the insertion loss of the filter is directly proportional to Z_R. If a filter designed for 60 db of insertion loss in a line with 50-ohm impedance over a specified frequency range is used with a 20-ohm line, the insertion loss will be decreased by 8 db.

For many applications in the suppression of 60-cycle power, a simple shunt capacitor or series inductor, or some combinations of these is effective in suppressing conducted interferences across most of the frequency spectrum. Such an approach is the "brute force" technique, and is so called because of is relatively unsophisticated solution. This technique, which utilizes any type of suppression network, though not designed to give a degree of attenuation across any specifically defined band, still effectively solves the suppression problem for the specific application. Most brute force applications consist of only a single capacitor, inductor, LC or even pi section, which is used for its capability for providing a bypass to ground, or, at least, a series impeding action.

The simplest suppression network that can be applied using the brute force technique, is a single capacitor connected from the conducting interference line to ground. As long as the capacitance is the predominating parameter, it is the most useful technique known. Such a capacitor presents a minimum impedance to ground for conducted interference and an open circuit to direct currents. The installation, however, is quite important: it should be located physically, as close to the interfering line as practical, and, if it is shielded, it must be located within the shielding or "wall-mounted" through the shield.

A single capacitor has the biggest benefit associated with its use, but, in some applications, a single inductor might be used. If an inductor is used, however, installation is sometimes a problem, because its physical size, for the same attenuation, will be much larger than a capacitor. Other disadvantages to the use of an inductor as a single element in the brute force technique are:

1. The inductor, since it is series inserted, must carry the full line current at the transmission frequency.
2. A rather large amount of copper is required in the inductor to obtain adequate suppression of r-f interference.
3. If, to obtain larger values of inductance, a magnetic core is used in place of an air core, unwanted losses are then produced at power frequencies, and core saturation may become a problem with direct currents.

If these inductors are used, it must be borne in mind when considering their installation, that inductors are placed outside the interfering field. If this cannot be accomplished in the installation, the inductor itself must be shielded.

The technique of "brute force" may also be expanded to include combinations of inductances and capacitances in various kinds of sections as shown in Fig. 5-21. This application would be used if there was a requirement for greater attenuation. Certain restrictions, however, govern the use of these combination devices. If an LC section is used, it should be used as a capacitor-input L section; this will assure greater attenuation. The rule is modified, however, and an inductance-input L section is used to prevent overloading a source. An inductance-input L section presents a higher input impedance to the interfering current, and, consequently, reduces the currents before the actual suppression network comes into the picture.

Another important filter is an antenna r-f filter, used to suppress spurious

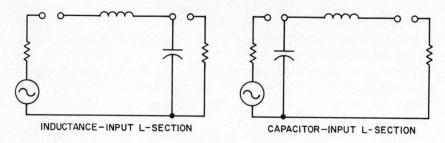

INDUCTANCE–INPUT L-SECTION   CAPACITOR–INPUT L-SECTION

Fig. 5-21.   Brute force filter sections.

and harmonic transmissions from high-power antennas, and known as "frequency-gate" networks. These filters transmit, with maximum power, wanted energy from the transmitter to the radiating antenna and prevent unwanted energy from reaching the antenna. This type of filter, which has a relatively inexpensive passive element, improves the capability of the transmitter efficiency to increase on its intended radiation frequency. This efficiency is increased because of the high-rejection nondissipative action on spurious and harmonic frequencies.

It has been recognized for some time that these spurious and harmonic frequencies of wanted signals have been cluttering up the frequency spectrum. Because this spectrum has finite limitations, its space had to be conserved. Consequently, users of frequency spectrum space have had restrictions imposed on them. The Department of Defense has specified requirements and some typical examples of detailed requirements are given as follows:

1. From military specification MIL-I-6181B, par. 3.4.1.1.2: "Under key down or transmit conditions, the r-f output of any transmitter, at other than fundamental shall be at least 80 db below the power of the fundamental or less than 0.02 microwatts for 0.15 to 1000 megacycles, whichever is greater."

2. From military specification MIL-I-16910A, par. 3-6.1.2.3: "Radio-frequency radiation, under key down or transmit condition, on frequencies other than the fundamental shall not be greater than a level equivalent to 50 db below the full power carrier output as measured across the output terminals of the transmitter when terminated in an impedance equivalent to the normal operating load."

The Federal Communications Commission has also specified requirements that apply to commercial users. Examples of these are:

1. Broadcast Services, Part 3, par. 3.687(1) specifies that spurious

emissions be attenuated 60 db below the fundamental and that in the event of interference caused to any service, greater attenuation will be required.

2. Public Radio Communication Services Parts 6, 11, 16, par. 16.104(c)(2) specifies that any spurious emissions be attenuated as in the table below:

Maximum authorized plate power input to the final r-f stage	Attenuation (db)
3 watts or less	40
3 watts to 150 watts	60
150 watts to 600 watts	70
over 600 watts	80

3. For international broadcast there is the proposed Part 3, par. 3.756(a): "All spurious emissions (including harmonics) shall be attenuated below the level of the unmodulated carrier at least to the limits derived from the following formula: Attenuation in db $= 80 + 10 \log_{10} P$ where P is the transmitter output power (unmodulated) in kilowatts."

So that these harmonic filters, as the antenna r-f filters are usually identified, may be used to their best advantage, a number of important considerations must be thoroughly explored. When used as a passband, the filter should perform as a conventional transmission line section; it should not cause an insertion loss greater than 0.5 db and, if there is any mismatch, it must not reduce the power output of the source. When used as a band-stop, the attenuation should be enough to meet the requirements of the regulatory body that apply, or, at least 60 db, if no other requirements exists.

The most widely used of these harmonic filters is usually the low-pass type because of the lower power magnitude of harmonics of a fundamental frequency. Where harmonics are of sufficient magnitude, a bandpass filter is used. Also an important consideration, is the determination of cut-off frequency. Generally, the cut-off frequency should be lower than the frequency of the second harmonic. This is rather easily accomplished with a fundamental frequency of 100 megacycles and its second harmonic of 200 megacycles, for here the cut-off frequency can be set at a figure which is 0.75 times the frequency of the second harmonic. This problem becomes more involved if there is less of an interval between the fundamental and second harmonic as, e.g., between 10 megacycles and 20 megacycles.

Filters that are constant K, m-derived, using lumped parameters, can be used and will perform adequately up to 100 megacycles. "Constant-K" filters are those that have the product of the shunt and series impedances equal to K^2; i.e, $z_1 \times z_2 = K^2$. K is independent of frequency and its, value is taken from the nominal value of the terminal impedance of the network, $R_T = K$. Figure 5-22 illustrates this definition. "M-derived" means filters that are made up by multiplying the elements of a constant-K

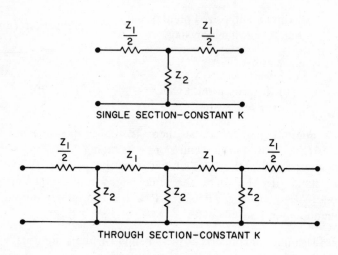

Fig. 5-22.   Diagrams of constant-K filters.

filter by a factor m or some function of this factor. The m-derived filter usually uses more shunt and series elements which provide sharper cut-off and more uniform attenuation in the pass region. M-derived filters also enable one to select frequencies outside the passband where very large attenuation may be obtained.

For higher frequencies, the use of lumped parameters is severely limited, since generally, these are not commercially available at high frequencies. Consequently, at high frequencies, short lengths of transmission lines are used for these lumped parameters. Since the use of these short lengths of line becomes important, detailed calculations will be shown as to how these substitutions for lumped parameters may be made.

Figure 5-23 shows the equivalent circuit for a uniform, lossless transmission line which has a characteristic impedance, Z_o, and its electrical length is θ radians. Its L parameter of inductance, in henries, and its C parameter of capacitance, in microfarads, is given as:

$$L = \frac{Z_o \sin \theta}{2f} \qquad (5\text{-}13)$$

$$C = \frac{\tan\left(\dfrac{\theta}{2}\right)}{2fZ_o} \tag{5-14}$$

If θ is less than $\dfrac{\pi}{12}$, approximations can be made for Eqs. 5-13 and 5-14:

$$L \text{ (in henries)} = 84.7 \ Z_o \ d$$

$$C \text{ (in microfarads)} = \frac{42.3d}{Z_o} \tag{5-16}$$

where d is the actual physical length of the line in inches.

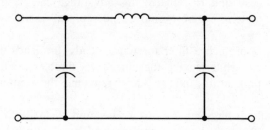

Fig. 5-23. Equivalent circuit of a transmission line.

From Eqs. 5-15 and 5-16, it can be seen that for an electrically short line ($\theta < \dfrac{\pi}{12}$), frequency is not a consideration. This condition is necessary if the filter is to function in the intended manner. The characteristic impedance of various kinds of transmission lines may be obtained from

$$Z_o = \frac{138}{\sqrt{\epsilon}} \log_{10} r \tag{5-17}$$

where ϵ is the dielectric constant of the medium between the two conductors,

r is the ratio of the inner diameter of the outer conductor to the outer diameter of the inner conductor.

5.5. Practical Considerations

It should be apparent that most modern electronic equipment of even moderate complexity will require many filters to assure that it will operate in the intended manner. When an equipment requires a number of filters, there are two practical alternatives: group all the filters into a single black box, or filter unit, or perform each filtering function from the viewpoint of its need, and use the single filter necessary to accomplish this need. Each of these approaches has advantages and disadvantages which must be traded off against one another to establish the optimum method for the particular design consideration.

All the required filters can be grouped together in a black box—this can be either a chassis, a drawer, or a hermetically sealed box that has an input lead consisting of compressed solder sealed terminals, and an output terminal that extends through the wall, as shown in Fig. 5-24. This type of filtering package has important advantages:

1. It is an easy unit to replace; this advantage can be used on many military systems where "remove and replace" maintenance is practiced.
2. In the use of such a filter for power leads, the leads can be routed to one area while leaving the unit at yet another area. This allows the grouping of the power leads, reducing the scattering of interference.
3. The resultant physical size of the filter unit is smaller, thereby reducing overall weight because of decreased packaging requirements.

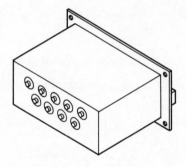

Fig. 5-24. Input and output connections to the multisection filter are solder-sealed terminals and an A-N connector.

However, there are certain disadvantages in grouping the filters into one package:

1. Replacement of the entire package is mandatory if a single section filter fails. Hermetic sealing does not permit easy repairs on the field.
2. The package units are less reliable than the individual units. The dependence of multi-pin connectors which have a relatively high failure rate is the cause.

3. Use of such package units requires advance planning as to the use of suppression components. Since such planning is usually very difficult, it is important to consider the filtering problem as an integral part of the equipment design, and not simply to correct marginal design.

The use of individual filters, with solder-type terminals at both input and output leads, has advantages opposed to the packaged unit:

1. Replacement of the entire unit is not mandatory when failure occurs.
2. There is no failure due to faulty connectors.
3. Individual units are readily available, while the packaged unit requires extra time and cost to construct.
4. The units can be used to correct design deficiencies that occur because of inadequate planning.

Also there are certain disadvantages:

1. Failure of an individual unit requires time and the use of a highly trained technician to locate the trouble.
2. Extensive, and complex wiring increases the problem of locating failure plus increasing the size that is required to house the filter package.

The advantages of both the package and individual filters have been considered in designing a filter package. This has resulted in the use of individual filters within a common enclosure, enabling "remove and replace" maintenance, and enabling correction of design problems by the addition of individual filters. Figure 5-25 shows a typical construction employing this concept.

It has been noted at various points in this discussion of filtering that filter installation is highly important; that there must be isolation between the input and output terminals of the filter and the r-f impedance of the filter case to ground must approach zero.

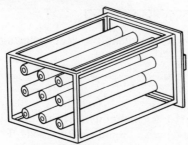

Fig. 5-25. Open type construction of a multisection filter shows termination of output leads in a single exit point.

Figures 5-26 and 5-27 show examples of correct and incorrect filter mounting installation. Figure 5-26A shows a common installation error: input and output leads are physically crossed, rendering the filter completely useless. In Fig. 5-26B, complete isolation does not exist. Mountings as shown in Fig. 5-27 have proven very effective.

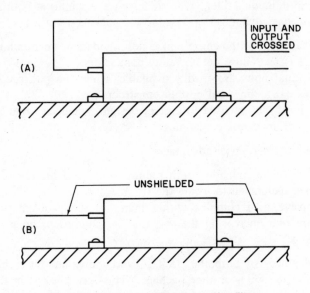

Fig. 5-26.   Incorrect method of mounting filters.

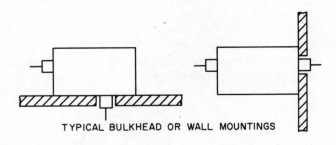

Fig. 5-27.   Correct method of mounting filters.

It must be noted that filter mounting surfaces must be clean and bright. No metal finishes, iridite, etc., should be tolerated. The mounting surface of the filter must also be clean and bright, as well as mounting studs, so that firm positive contact may be made over the entire area.

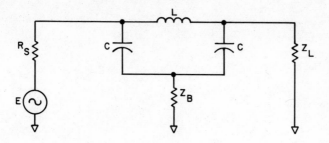

Fig. 5-28.   Effect of poor r-f ground on a filter.

A poor r-f ground from the filter case will render the filter ineffective. Figure 5-28 depicts such a situation. The impedance to ground can become sufficiently large to cause an interfering voltage to be developed and the filter itself to become an interfering source.

6 – INTERFERENCE REDUCTION
IN CABLES

6.1. Introduction

In the previous chapter, it was established that filtering is an important technique toward minimizing the effect of conducted interference. Filtering prevents unintended signals from being conducted into equipments along with the intended signals. There are many ways in which the filters can be made to work more effectively. Probably the most important consideration is never to permit unwanted signals to enter the conducting line in the first place. This is accomplished in variety of ways:

1. Control of the input to the conducting medium, so that the unwanted signals are never allowed to traverse the conducting material.
2. Control of the conducting medium, so that it does not pick up unwanted energy from stray fields that may exist.

The ideal situation is for a conducting medium to have only a wanted signal impressed on it at the transmitter, have the signal travel to the receiver without picking up any unwanted signals, and have only the wanted signal delivered to the receiver. Such a simplification is dangerous however, since the whole problem of interference reduction in conducting media varies greatly, depending on the nature of the particular equipment involved.

A number of general ideas can be reviewed by way of introduction. The magnitude of interference, to which a single-conducting medium may be subjected, is usually directly related to:

1. The physical length of the exposed conducting medium.
2. The intensity of unwanted signals, or fields, to which they are exposed.

3. The particular types of interfering fields involved.
4. The impedance of the terminations to which the particular conducting medium connects.

These same conducting media are, on the other hand, causes of interference, depending on length, the fields they induce, the nature of these fields, and impedances of terminating equipment. It can be seen then, that the complexity of the situation easily manifests itself: a conducting medium is a "two-way street"—it is interfered with, and, by its very nature, causes interference.

A key consideration in discussing the question of interference in a conducting medium is that the problems are vastly different in every kind of equipment and system. A conducting medium is defined as a copper path connecting two points, A and B, which must transmit energy between the two points. When so defined, a short piece of an r-f lead wire, on a chassis of a simple radio receiver, is a conducting medium; likewise, a large multi-conductor cable connecting a control center, and the launching pad of a complex weapon system is also a conducting medium. It is this common property, and yet very different means of implementing this property, that is at the hub of the interference problem in a conducting medium, and the problem grows in complexity as systems become more extended. In a small system, as in a single receiver, for example, interference problems can be minimized, in most cases, by maintaining a proven, good wiring configuration. R-f leads are kept short and point-to-point, direct connections are made; wiring leads that have different frequency signals are kept separate; the sensitivity of the equipment assures a good signal-to-noise ratio; and, the nature of the reception is usually noncritical. However, as systems grow in size, these important guide lines collapse rapidly; wires cannot be run directly and kept short; they cannot be kept separate, but must be cabled together; equipment has broadband frequency characteristics; and, the nature of the equipment function may become highly critical, as in a weapon system. So it can be seen that most of the interest in the interference problem of a conducting medium would be critical in large systems where wires are bundled into cables.

To illustrate the differences between the problems associated with relatively simple systems and complex, extended systems, an example of each of the systems will be described.

Considered first, a commercially available mobile radio transmitting-receiving set that is widely used in automobiles and trucks. This equipment consists, essentially, of a transmitter-receiver, control head, microphone and associated power supply and cabling interconnection. A layout of these parts and cables is shown in Fig. 6-1. In such a layout, the cabling routing is important. Usually, such cabling is run under the chassis, and along the

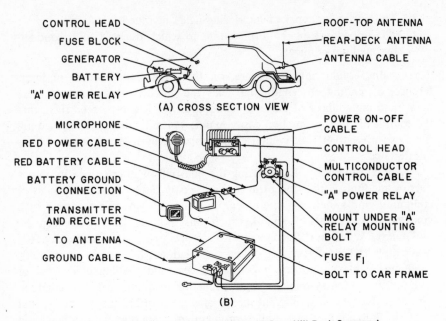

Fig. 6-1.   Layout of parts and cables. (From McGraw-Hill Book Company)

side of the car. Since the equipment is usually installed at the dashboard of the vehicle, some cables will have to be run on the engine side of the fire wall. When this is done, the installing technician will usually position them where they receive the least amount of pickup from the ignition. The fuse-mounting and relay assembly is usually mounted close to the power source so the power cable can be run as directly as possible to the transmitter-receiver. A typical cable layout for an automobile is shown in Fig. 6-2. It can be seen from the foregoing that even for comparatively simple equipment, careful attention must be given to minimizing the interference problem of component interconnection. It should also be noted that no

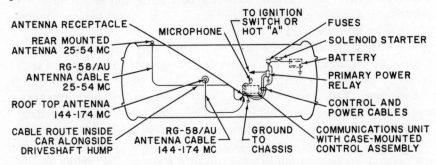

Fig. 6-2.   Typical cable layout for mobile radio in an automobile. (From McGraw-Hill Book Company)

consideration was given to the transmitter-receiver itself, because experience has shown that such commercial equipment is generally available with industry standards.

Now consider a large extended radar system, such as the Ballistic Missile Early Warning System. It was reported that a typical site consisted of many radar and support buildings interconnected by shielded passageways.[1] These passageways (shielded for the protection of personnel from radiation) were approximately 10-12 feet wide, with an average length of 650 feet between adjacent buildings, and sometimes joined together to form a continous, mile-long passageway. All of the power, telephone, data cables, and waveguides carrying r-f power from the high-powered transmitters to the antennas were run in these tunnels. The design objective was to minimize the internal, mutual interference effects in such a passageway. To accomplish this, the following criteria were established:

1. The power leads were twisted.
2. Inherent shielding of armor trays and structure were utilized.
3. The effected communication lines were always balanced, twisted pairs.

The estimated effect of these criteria were:

1. Twisted power leads, −26 db,
2. Inherent shielding, − 6 db.
3. Balanced, twisted pairs, −80 db.

These criteria proved effective and it is a matter of record that the BMEWS sites are operational.

Further consideration of the preceding examples makes clear that as systems grow in size, so does the interference problem. The major problem lies within large systems. When cabling these systems, certain rules have wide application. Low-level, medium-level, and high-level signal-carrying wires should be isolated and grouped together to form cables. Low-level is defined as circuits carrying signals with a magnitude of less than 1000 microvolts; medium-level, from 1000 microvolts to 3-5 volts; high-level, all a-c power circuits and radar pulse circuits. These different levels, having been grouped according to signal level, should be physically separated from one another by as much distance as is practical; shielding and shading from separate wireways should be employed. If these wireways are connected with a good low-impedance path-to-site ground, their shielding effectiveness will substantially reduce interference between the various levels of signal.

---

[1]H. G. Schwartz. "Design of a Wire Communication System in a Shielded Passageway of the BMEWS Radar System," *Proceedings of the Fifth Conference on Radio Interference Reduction and Electronic Compatability,* Armour Research Foundation, (October 1958), p. 398.

Connection of points A and B, via a conducting medium, can be done within an equipment (intraconnection wiring), or between equipments (interconnection wiring). Intraconnection wiring is important in some equipments, but in modern, electronic equipments it is usually used only to connect functional drawers that make up racks of equipment. Interconnection wiring is the area of primary interest in this chapter. In Fig. 6-3, we have an equipment rack consisting of drawers that are made up of modules, or printed circuit cards. These modules, or cards, are plugged into a connection block; a group of the modules and connection blocks

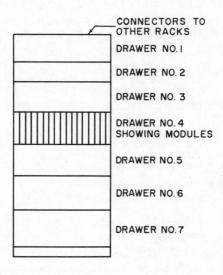

CONNECTORS TO
OTHER RACKS

DRAWER NO. 1

DRAWER NO. 2

DRAWER NO. 3

DRAWER NO. 4
SHOWING MODULES

DRAWER NO. 5

DRAWER NO. 6

DRAWER NO. 7

Fig. 6-3.   Rack of equipment.

make a drawer. The wiring from these drawers then goes to connectors to which other equipment is connected. Therefore, all wiring in typical, modern equipment is cabled.

6.2.   Basic Considerations

The general problem of interference reduction in cables is divided into three separate subproblems all relating to unwanted signals conducted where they cause interference. These are:

1. Inductive coordination subproblem: the effect of power circuits on signal circuits.

2. Crosstalk subproblem: the effect of one signal circuit on another.
3. Environmental subproblem: the effect of all other interfering sources, such as cosmic noise, nuclear blasts, etc.

The first two of the subproblems interests us; the third is beyond the present area of interest.

The principal sources of interference in cables are those caused by magnetic fields, electric fields, electromagnetic radiation, and direct coupling. When a closed electric loop is placed in a magnetic field, a voltage is induced in the loop proportional to the normal vector component of flux and the area of the loop. The normal vector component is one of two flux components attributed to the existing magnetic field which may have been generated by any number of different sources. The interference from such a magnetic field depends on the nature of the field that is picked up, the pick-up loop, and the distance from the loop to the source of the magnetic field. From these facts, three rules can be followed to reduce inductive pickup to permissible levels:

1. The loop can be shielded.
2. A wider physical distance between the loop and the source can be implemented.
3. The loop area can be reduced as close to zero as is practical.

If a potential difference exists between two circuits, these circuits may be coupled, under proper conditions. This potential difference is transmitted to the effected circuits by the electric field, and the resulting capacitance between the two circuits depends on the usual capacitance parameters: the potential difference and the physical geometry of length, spacing, etc. If two circuits are physically close together, and their individual circuit impedances are high, coupling usually develops. Consequently, to minimize the coupling problem, sufficient physical separation should be maintained, the magnitude of the voltage of the interference source can be reduced, and the affected circuit impedance can be lowered.

Electromagnetic fields are considered another major source of interference in cables. These fields prevail when a particular combination of physical circumstances exists which causes the affected circuits to behave as though they were receivers. This occurs when the physical length of the cable is such that it happens to approximate the wavelength of an unwanted signal present in the general vicinity. This problem becomes especially troublesome at higher frequencies.

Another source of interference in cables occurs when circuits are directly coupled either by direct physical connection, or by resistive coupling. This interference develops as a result of improperly designed grounding circuits which can be detected by a careful examination of the schematic.

Figures 6-4 and 6-5 show examples of circuits that are unintentionally resistively coupled, and the corrective measures that may be taken to eliminate this problem.

6.3. Shielding of Cables

Reduction of interference in cables can be accomplished by eliminating the effect of electromagnetic fields, and by reducing the susceptibility of the cable to reception of unwanted electromagnetic fields. Shielding of the

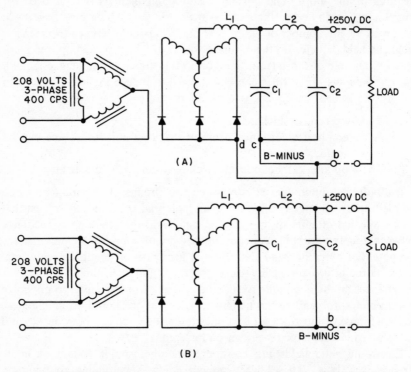

Fig. 6-4. Interference caused by direct coupling. (A) Schematic diagram does not show that resistive coupling may cause trouble. (B) Point-to-point diagram indicates by removing lead bd and connecting c to d that pickup can be prevented.

cable is the most effective way to eliminate the effects of electromagnetic fields, and the use of balanced lines, twisted pairs and coaxial cable is the best way to reduce the susceptibility of the cable. It will be shown how these two approaches can be used to reduce interference on a communication cable, first from another communication cable; then from a power cable. Whether the interfering source is a power or another communication circuit actually makes no difference, because the problem is the same; in the case of the power circuit, since the level of its energy is so large, the magnitude of the interfering field is much greater; in the case of the communciation cable interfering, its frequency is important.

A good continuous metallic shield will completely screen out an electric field, thus preventing it from having an influence on the conductors within the shielded cable. It will also reduce the magnetic field within the cable since eddy currents will flow within the shielding material (when subjected to alternating fields), and these currents will tend to neutralize the disturbing field. A shield made of magnetic materials will protect the conductors inside the shield from any magnetic field which may exist.

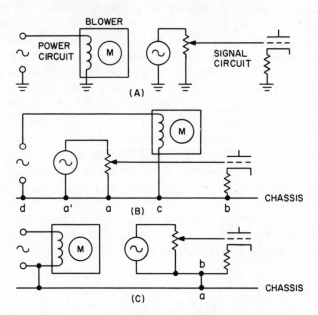

Fig. 6-5. (A) Power circuit and signal circuit in an instrument. (B) Connections of circuits as assembled in the instrument. (C) Proper method of grounding to avoid pickup. Chassis is a unipotential electrostatic shield.

At frequencies over three megacycles, it is most convenient to study electric and magnetic fields separately. Electric fields depend on capacitive coupling, or mutual capacitance, between interfering and interfered-with circuits; the magnetic fields depend on magnetic coupling, or mutual inductance, between the circuits. At frequencies above three megacycles, energy, in radiation form (the magnitude of the energy increases as the square of the frequency), becomes important since it causes interference at far greater distance than the electric or magnetic fields. This radiation penetrates through spaces within the cable braid, or metal tapes, and even, although attenuated, passes through the solid shield material itself.

Shielding has many complex ideas that must be fully pursued for complete understanding in its present state. However, a short digression is necessary at this point, to clarify the principles of shielding as applied to communication cable.

It is a well-known fact that reductions of more than 90 percent can be achieved in the magnitude of interfering voltage induced along cables; even in the most unwieldy field installation, appreciable reductions can be achieved.

Shielding is defined as the action of diminishing the action in an interfered-with circuit that is induced by current flowing in an interfering circuit. The amount of shielding is expressed by the percentage of voltage reduction in the interfered-with circuit. For making calculations, a shield factor is used which is defined as the ratio of the resultant voltage in the interfered-with circuit, after the shielding is used, to the nonshielded interfered-with voltage; in both cases the voltages are related to the same magnitude of current in the interfering circuit. The shield factor is a vector quantity, but, generally, only its absolute value is of interest. Therefore, the effective coupling between interfered-with and interfering cables, in which the interfered-with cable is shielded, is equal to the mutual impedance between these cables without any shielding multiplied by the shield factor. Low shield factor is a desirable design objective in cables, because it indicates a large reduction in voltage.

The effect of shielding is shown in Fig. 6-6. Current identified as I_1, flows and induces voltages which can be measured at E_2 and E_3. Current I_2 flows in the shield; this induces a counter voltage in circuit C and results

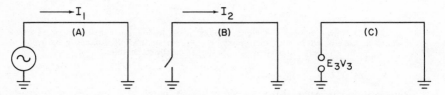

Fig. 6-6. A shielding system. (From Report No. 26—EEI/BTS Joint Subcommittee)

in a lower voltage than originaly induced by I_1. This is the basic principle of electromagnetic shielding. Voltages for circuits B and C can be written as:

$$0 = I_1 Z_{12} + I_2 Z_{22} \qquad (6\text{-}1)$$

$$V_3 = I_1 Z_{13} + I_2 Z_{23} \tag{6-2}$$

where Z_{12}, Z_{13} and Z_{23} indicate mutual impedances of circuits A and B, A and C and B and C, respectively, and Z_{22} indicates the self-impedance of circuit B. All these are per unit length. The voltage in circuit C is then

$$V_3 = I_1 Z_{13} (1 - \frac{Z_{12}Z_{23}}{Z_{13}Z_{22}}) \tag{6-3}$$

Without a shielding circuit, Eq. 6-2, this equation would have been

$$E_3 = I_1 Z_{13} \tag{6-4}$$

This reduction of the interfering voltage by the action of the shield to the fraction η is the shield factor

$$\eta = \frac{V_3}{E_3} = 1 - \frac{Z_{12}Z_{23}}{Z_{13}Z_{22}} \tag{6-5}$$

Since shielding is generally built into a communication cable (e.g., with a 5- or 10-mil copper shield) the ideal situation of a shielding conductor being quite close to the interfered-with line prevails. Shielding may also be placed around the interfering conductor, however, this would mean that a large shielding current would flow; shielding, placed equally separated from the interfering and interfered-with conductor, would have an equal shield factor. Shielding also varies with the resistance of the shielding circuit; it is most effective when the total resistance, including both its inherent resistance and ground connection, is small. For this reason, a good conductor, with a low-impedance ground, makes an excellent shield. Also, a reactance is determined by other system constants, which makes the shielding action most effective. The optimum shielding reactance can be determined as follows:

$$X_{22} = \frac{1}{2X_{12}} \left[R_{12}^2 - 2R_{22}R_{12} + X_{12}^2 + \sqrt{(R_{12}^2 - 2R_{22}R_{12} + X_{12}^2)^2 + 4X_{12}^2 R_{22}^2} \right] \tag{6-6}$$

Finally, the shield factor is affected by changes brought about by the addition of mutual impedance, and by increasing the frequency.

A relatively large amount of experience has been gathered relating to the shielding effectiveness of various kinds of cable shields. The shielding effectiveness is dependent upon a number of factors that have been described, but to underline the effectiveness of shielding, results of tests on open lines will be discussed first.

A 2-conductor, ten-foot length of flat television antenna cable, was put under test with a two-wire interfering circuit parallel to it and one in. of separation between them. This flat television cable was used to obtain the necessary magnitude of conduction, and to simulate the lack of uniform twisting in a long length of twisted-pair cable. In such a test, it should be noted that the electric field interference is due to capacitive coupling between the interfering and interfered-with cables. Magnetic coupling is eliminated by leaving the far end open and grounding one wire of each circuit. Interference is measured in this test by the number of millivolts induced into the interfered-with circuit by one volt of potential on the interfering circuit. With a metallic shield on the interfered-with wires, a millivolt reading could not be taken. Various other voltages are shown in Fig. 6-7. Where the interfering fields are of high frequencies and of small magni-

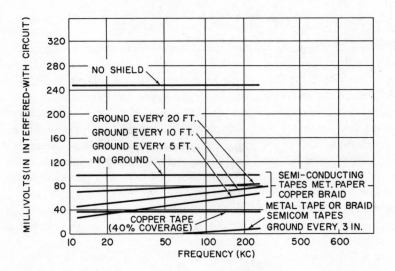

Fig. 6-7. Induction due to electric field. (From Gooding and Slade, "Shielding of Communication Cable")

tude, a metallic shield can be replaced by one that is only a fair conductor. Fair conductors are usually tapes and braids in which a good ground wire is run through. This type of shielding is highly effective against electric fields, less expensive, and very flexible to use. The ground wire makes contact with the tape, or braid covering, all along its length and is grounded frequently at relatively close intervals. Figure 6-7 shows how effective grounding is at various intervals. It can be seen that if a metallic shield is used, grounding every 20 feet will improve the shielding from electric fields; if a braid, or tape, that conducts partially is used, it is best to ground the ground wire (running through the braid) every few inches.

A metallic shield that is ungrounded will reduce at least one half of the interference, whereas, a metal shield with a good ground, will reduce about three quarters of the interference. The circuit described above was used to establish these facts with the exception that the far ends of the wires were shorted to each other. Figure 6-8 shows a comparison of the efficiency of various types of shields against magnetic fields. The interfering circuit has

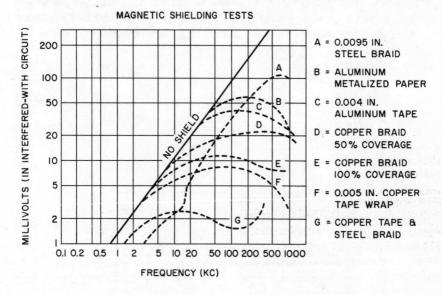

MAGNETIC SHIELDING TESTS

A = 0.0095 IN.
    STEEL BRAID

B = ALUMINUM
    METALIZED PAPER

C = 0.004 IN.
    ALUMINUM TAPE

D = COPPER BRAID
    50% COVERAGE

E = COPPER BRAID
    100% COVERAGE

F = 0.005 IN. COPPER
    TAPE WRAP

G = COPPER TAPE &
    STEEL BRAID

Fig. 6-8.   Induction due to magnetic field. (From Gooding and Slade, **op cit.**)

one ampere flowing in it. The solid line is for unshielded conditions, and changes, of course, if the spacings of the interfering and interfered-with wires change. It should be noted that steel braids are effective at lower frequencies, and 5-mil copper is very efficient at higher frequencies. There is no comparison to be drawn from this chart for cable enclosed in steel conduit. Experience has shown that steel conduit is a most effective shield. The use of steel conduit is a good, practical solution where a sensitive area must be traversed with a piece of communication cable with only moderate shielding. Steel conduit has also been highly effective in underground installations, where large ground currents are present.

The effectiveness of shielding has been discussed so far in reference to open lines; now, it will be concerned with circuit lines terminated in an impedance generally equal to their inherent impedance. In such a case, both the electric and magnetic fields are of interest, particularly the phase sum of these two fields. To analyze this effect, tests were made to simulate operating conditions, see Fig. 6-9. An oscillator was used to supply an interfering voltage, but the principles involved are equally applicable whether a power of communication circuit is interfering, or whether a communication circuit (a "worst case") is interfering. The lines were terminated in 100-ohm impedances, and an unbalanced, grounded circuit was used to simulate the "worst case." Voltages, measured at both the transmitting and receiving ends, were unequal. Most of the inductive effects occurred between the ungrounded conductors nearest to each other at Area A. The value of I was measured as was the voltage E_R at the

SENDING END   RECEIVING END

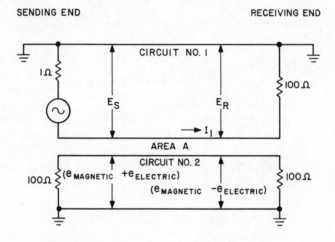

Fig. 6-9. Circuit to test the effectiveness of shielding.

receiving end of circuit No. 1. Then, $e_{MAGNETIC}$ in circuit No. 2 is dependent on the current I_1 in circuit No. 1 and the value of $e_{ELECTRIC}$ is dependent on E_R. Total induced voltage is the sum of these, or $e_{MAGNETIC} + e_{ELECTRIC}$. With the receiving end of circuit No. 1, i.e., with the 100-ohm terminal impedance shorted out, the transmitting and receiving end voltages of circuit No. 2 were equal to each other, and equal to $e_{MAGNETIC}$ which is induced by the magnetic field. If circuit No. 1 was open circuited, i.e., with the 100-ohm terminal impedance removed and no short placed across it, the voltages at the sending and receiving ends of circuit No. 2 could also be determined; these voltages were caused only by the electric field.

If the relative magnitudes of the electric and magnetic fields, and their sums, are properly plotted against frequency, it will be seen, from Fig. 6-10, that the relationship is linear. The sum of the two fields is different at the receiving than at the sending end of the line. This difference is accounted for by the difference in direction of the current flow in the circuits, depending upon whether the circuits are capacitively coupled, as is the case of the electric fields, or inductively coupled, as in the case of the magnetic field. As previously mentioned, the total induced voltage as the transmitting end is $e_{MAGNETIC} + e_{ELECTRIC}$; while at the receiving end it is $e_{MAGNETIC} - e_{ELECTRIC}$.

Magnetic induction is, generally, of greater importance than electric induction over the entire frequency range. This is the case when discussing lines which terminate with the same value of impedance, since the interference will be dependent on the circuit-terminating impedance as well as the frequency. If, as shown in Fig. 6-9, the terminating impedances were 200 ohms instead of 100 ohms, and all other conditions were identical, the current, and, consequently, the magnetic induction, would be halved. Likewise, the electric induction would have become twice as much, and the lower curve would have to be labelled magnetic induction, and the middle curve electric induction. (See Fig. 6-10.)

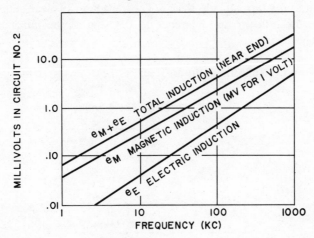

Fig. 6-10. Induction curves for circuit shown in Fig. 6-9. (From Gooding and Slade, **op. cit.**)

6.4. Crosstalk

It has been shown how the effect of energy in one cable produces electric and magnetic fields which, in turn, produces unwanted energy in other cables. The effectiveness of shielding on the interfered-with cable has been reviewed and the various shielding methods discussed.

The discussion has been limited to the effects between pairs of conductors, and in modern electronic systems, most cables are made up of many pairs. Each of these pairs, when bundled together in a multiconductor cable affect one another. This effect, described as crosstalk, is the signal from one circuit being picked up by an adjacent circuit. Crosstalk is caused by electric and magnetic fields surrounding the wires. Two circuits so affected are said to be coupled electrically by these fields. Crosstalk coupling is a measure of the magnitude of crosstalk current flowing in the interfered-with circuit as compared with the current flowing in the interfering circuit.

Crosstalk can occur at either the near or far ends of the line, and is caused by combinations of electric and magnetic couplings by way of different paths. Figure 6-11, shows a simplified version of how near- and far-end crosstalk is propagated. It should be noted that, as shown, the paths are indicated as originating at one point, although many paths may actually exist. Even when different frequencies are used for transmission, near-end crosstalk is a problem. This is so because mismatch between the two lines causes reflection which appears at the far end of the line and adds to far-end crosstalk already there. The reflection of near-end crosstalk is equal to the ratio of the difference to the sum of the impedances of the mismatched lines:

$$\text{Reflection (in \%)} = \frac{Z_2 - Z_1}{Z_2 + Z_1} \times 100$$

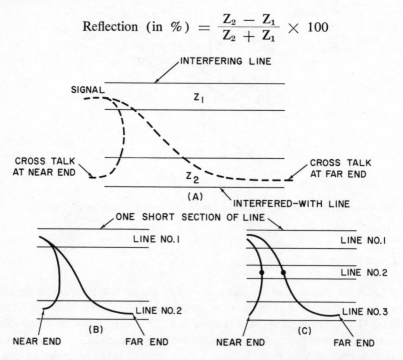

Fig. 6-11. Diagrams illustrating crosstalk: (A) How crosstalk is propagated; (B) Direct transverse crosstalk; (C) Indirect transverse crosstalk.

where Z_1 is the impedance of the interfering line,

Z_2 is the impedance of the interfered-with line.

Practical experience has shown that this reflection varies from a few to as much as 30 percent.

Transverse, and interaction crosstalk, occurs between two 2-pair cables within a short section of line. It can be either direct or indirect crosstalk and is shown, simplified, in Fig. 6-11B and C. Total transverse crosstalk is the sum of the direct transverse crosstalk plus the sum of the indirect transverse crosstalk. Interaction crosstalk is similar to indirect transverse crosstalk, except that it involves two short sections of line rather than one. There are four kinds of interaction crosstalk:

1. Near end, near end
2. Far end, far end
3. Near end, far end
4. Far end, near end.

Near end, near end means that interaction crosstalk is via a near-end coupling path from the first cable to the third, and via a near-end path from the third cable to the second. Other terms, such as far end, far end, etc., have comparable meanings.

From a practical viewpoint, certain kinds of crosstalk-coupling are more important than others. In near-end crosstalk, the direct transverse component of coupling is the most important. In the case of far-end crosstalk, the interaction component is most important.

Calculations of crosstalk between two cables may easily be carried out by computing the electric and magnetic effects from the magnitudes of the capacitances and inductances between cables. Figure 6-12, illustrates how the effects of electrical field induction may be analyzed. Capacitances between wires of balanced pairs No. 1 and No. 2 neglecting the ground capacitances are shown in Fig. 6-12A. This is also shown by a network of impedances (Fig. 6-12B). If the inductive effects in the line containing C_4 and C_1 are equal, there will be no resultant voltages in line No. 2 due to line No. 1. This is expressed as:

$$K = (C_4 - C_1) - (C_3 - C_2) \qquad (6\text{-}7)$$

The crosstalk in Fig. 6-12A is proportional to unbalance capacitance K. If Figs. 6-12C and D are examined, it will be seen that when a voltage, V, is applied across 1a-1b, the voltage across line No. 2 will be proportional to the ratio of the impedance $\dfrac{Z}{2}$ has to the total impedance across 1a-1b. From this can be written:

$$\text{Crosstalk ratio} = \frac{8 \times 10^{12}}{\omega KZ} \qquad (6\text{-}8)$$

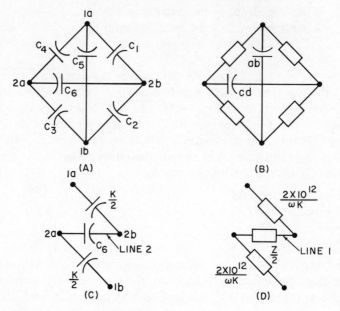

Fig. 6-12.   Circuits for analyzing the effects of electric field induction.

where K is the unbalance capacitance in $\mu\mu$f,
 ω is $2\,\pi f$,
 Z is the characteristic impedance of the two lines.
Converted into decibels (db) Eq. (6-8) becomes:

$$\text{Crosstalk ratio} = 20\ \log_{10} \frac{8 \times 10^{12}}{\omega KZ}\ (\text{db}) \qquad (6\text{-}9)$$

A similar analysis can be made for total magnetic induction; between line No. 1 and line No. 2:

$$\text{Crosstalk ratio} = 20\ \log_{10} \frac{2 \times 10^6 \times Z}{\omega M}\ (\text{db}) \quad (6\text{-}10)$$

where M is the effective resultant magnetic induction in microhenries. The inverse of the crosstalk ratio gives the voltage in the interfered-with line when 1 volt is applied to the interfering line. The voltages from Eqs. 6-9 and 6-10 may then be added to give the total induction referenced to 1 volt.

For electric induction:

$$V' = \frac{\omega KZ}{8 \times 10^{12}} \qquad (6\text{-}11)$$

For magnetic induction:

$$V'' = \frac{\omega M}{2 \times 10^6 \times Z} \qquad (6\text{-}12)$$

where V' and V'' are voltages in the interfered-with line for 1 volt in the interfering line. These two voltages add, at the near end, with reasonable accuracy, at least up to a megacycle.

From Eqs. 6-11 and 6-12 it can readily be seen that frequency affects crosstalk. Total crosstalk is a direct function of frequency. The characteristic impedance of the two lines (Eqs. 6-11 and 6-12) is directly proportional to the electric induction, but, inversely proportional to the magnetic induction. Therefore, if the impedance varies, and the two types of induction are equal, there will be no change in the total crosstalk.

A practical example will illustrate the above analysis: given a cable pair, shielded with a single 0.0063-in. copper wire braid that completely covers the pairs, with the operating frequency at 100 kc. If this copper wire braid is at ground potential, the electric induction field will be zero. It can be seen that the magnetic field is reduced by the shielding in a ratio of 20 to 120, or 1/6; if both pairs are shielded, 1/2 of 1/6 or 1/12.

Then

$$\text{Total cross talk voltage} = \left(\frac{\omega}{2 \times 10^6 \times Z}\right) \times \left(\frac{M}{12}\right) \times V \quad (6\text{-}13)$$

where V is the voltage applied to the interfering circuit, and M is the resulting unbalance mutual inductance when unshielded. For a length of 1000 feet of this cable, a typical value for M would be 0.1 μh; a typical Z would be 100 ohms; then Eq. 6-13 becomes

$$\text{Total crosstalk voltage} = \frac{2\pi \times 10^5}{2 \times 10^6 \times 10^2} \times \frac{0.1}{12} \times V$$

$$= 26 \ \mu V \text{ per volt in the interfering circuit.}$$

To express this in decibels, the interfered-with line would be 92 db below the interfering line.

If there were no shielding, however, the electric field would then have to be included. Using Eq. 6-11 and inserting a typical value of K such as 20 $\mu\mu$f for a length of 1000 feet,

$$V' = \frac{2\pi \times 10^5 \times 20 \times 10^2}{8 \times 10^{12}}$$

$$= 157 \ \mu V \text{ per volt in the interfering circuit}$$

and from Eq. 6-12

$$V'' = \frac{2\pi \times 10^5 \times 0.1}{2 \times 10^6 \times 10^2}$$
$$= 314 \ \mu V \text{ per volt in the interfering circuit.}$$

The total crosstalk would be the sum of 157 μV + 314 μV or 471 μV, and would be an attenuation of 67 db. The effect of the shielding can clearly be seen from: 26 μV instead of 471 μV or a 25 db advantage.

So far, the discussion has been concerned with electrically short lines, but the principles are fundamentally the same for long lines. It would be simple indeed, if all the short sections of line could be added arithmetically. Crosstalk currents are affected by attenuation along long lines. The basic equations and calculations are valid for lines up to several thousand feet in length, and, with proper consideration given to the effect of frequency on the terminating impedance, can readily be used for longer lines.

If the shield on a line is grounded at both ends, reduction of voltage exists in the interfered-with line because the electric field has been eliminated and the magnetic field reduced (by some of its effect being cancelled by the eddy currents in the shield). Figure 6-13 shows, graphically, how

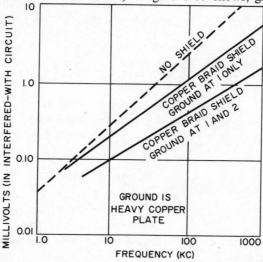

Fig. 6-13. Total induction tests showing effect of grounds applied to shield over cable pair. (From Gooding and Slade, **op. cit.**)

this develops: the voltage is higher if the shield is grounded at point 1 than at points 1 and 2. Grounding at points 1 and 2 shows the lower value, because the electric field is eliminated. It should be noted also that frequent grounding at lower frequencies is not nearly as important as at higher frequencies.

When discussing coaxial cable, the problem of shielding is somewhat different. Consider the following: If two coaxial cables were running alongside each other, their inner and outer sheaths would be connected and grounded at both ends. The sheath current of the interfering cable would have a parallel path through the interfered-with cable sheath. Coaxial cables usually affect one another by a voltage from the interfering cable either directly or by induction being impressed across the outer braid of the interfered-with cable. Calculations of these effects are performed using this formula:

$$Z_{\alpha\beta} = \frac{2e}{I} \text{ ohms} \qquad\qquad (6\text{-}14)$$

where $Z_{\alpha\beta}$ is the transfer impedance due to the voltage in circuit α causing another circuit β to have a current flow,
   I is the interfering current,
   $2e$ is the total voltage in the interfered-with circuit.

6.5. *Commercial and Military Cable*

Modern communication cabling is available, commercially, with a wide variety of coverings for various shielding requirements, and ranges from a group of simple, insulated pairs with a copper shield around them, to a highly sophisticated cable (as used, e.g., on a weapon system), made up of several plastic jackets with separate shields for protection against the effect of electric and magnetic fields. A typical cable, widely used by the Rural Electrification Administration of the U. S. Department of Agriculture, and one of a less complex variety, includes the following specifications for the shield: fully annealed, corrugated, copper material with a thickness of 0.005 ± 0.0004 in. for standard cable; 0.010 ± 0.0008 in. for gopher-protected cable. Compare this to a newly developed cable, used by the U. S. Air Force, that has an inner shield of fully annealed copper, with a thickness of 0.010 in. and two ten-mil helically-wound steel tapes.

The shielding effectiveness of various types of metal coverings is not easily calculated because of the many variables involved: lack of continuity of covering; radiation between the wire braids; variation in contact resistance between the braids, etc. However, test results have been published that prove these types of shielding effective. The empirical results are illustrated in Figs. 6-14, 15, and 16, and cover such diverse situations as differences in frequency, kinds of shielding materials, etc. Figure 6-14 shows the differences in shielding effectiveness when a coaxial cable has one copper braid for a shield as compared to two or three braids. Tests have indicated that considerable improvement can be achieved with this combination copper and steel braiding. Figure 6-15 shows the improve-

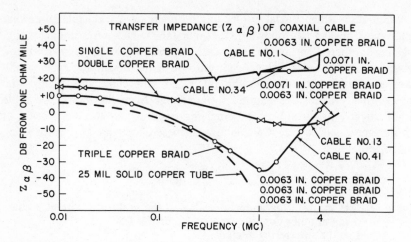

Fig. 6-14. Measured transfer impedance of coaxial cable with copper braid shields.
(From Gooding and Slade, **op. cit.**)

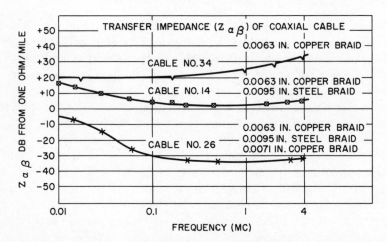

Fig. 6-15. Measured transfer impedance of coaxial cable with copper and steel braids.
(From Gooding and Slade, **op. cit.**)

ment of this combination braid over the copper braid even though the former is a triple braid. Because of the presence of the steel, the combination braid is an effective shield even at relatively low frequencies.

Because of the problem associated with braiding in cable manufacturing, steel tapes were tried as well as aluminum braiding as substitutes for copper braiding. Helically-wound steel tapes proved an effective barrier against radiation due to the very small openings in the braid.

Another cable improvement to provide more effective shielding, was attempted in the development of a coaxial cable with two shields insulated from on another. As shown in Fig. 6-16, this is effective, especially at low frequencies. This kind of cabling is constructed with a steel braid over a copper braid and with the outer shield of the copper braid insulated from

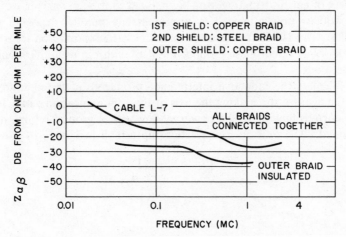

Fig. 6-16.   Measured transfer impedance of triaxial cable. Outer braids insulated from each other. (From Gooding and Slade, **op. cit.**)

the steel braid. This, of course, is not as effective a shield at higher frequencies, where the inner and outer shields become electrically connected effectively because of the high capacitance between them.

Shields are a highly important and critical factor in the reduction of interference in interconnecting cables. At low frequencies, it is usually satisfactory if shields are constructed of metallized paper and semiconducting (fair conducting) media, that are effective against electric fields. The magnetic field is unimportant at low frequencies. Copper shields are practically never used at low frequencies. At higher frequencies, the types of shielding discussed will be effective against both the electric and magnetic effects. It should be noted that even with shields, the effect of physical separation is highly important. This is particularly true in the case of interference from power systems in which large magnitudes of current are involved.

6.6. Power and Communication Cable

The problem of shielding effectiveness will be concluded with a discussion of a practical problem concerning the effect on a communication cable from a nearby high-voltage transmission line. The communication cable is described as a multiconductor cable, comprising an inner polyethylene jacket around the bundle of conductors, a 10-mil copper shield, a middle polyethylene jacket, two 10-mil helically-wound steel tapes, and a final outside polyethylene jacket. This cable was buried with a cover of about three feet of earth. Running, roughly parallel to it, with varying exposures, was a 100-kv power line. This approximately parallel exposure ran for 2.7 miles. The 100-kv power line (an aerial line supported on transmission towers), was a three-phase grounded system with the usual harmonics and variable loads.

To calculate the inductive interference produced in the communication cable, the average force along the axis of the communication cable, induced by the current flowing in the power system with a ground return, must be determined. The first obvious relationship established is

$$M = -j \ \frac{i}{\omega \sigma I} \qquad (6\text{-}15)$$

$$\omega \sigma I M = -j \ i \qquad (6\text{-}16)$$

where ω is $2\pi f$,
   σ is the inducing current in amperes from the power system,
   M is the mutual inductance in H/m,
   i is the current density in the soil.

Since the value of I is known from the characteristics of the power system (in this case, the current used was the worst case—that of a fault current of 1500 amperes—and a common case—a residual current flowing in the neutral when there is unbalance in the power system), the value of σ can be assumed, the value of ω is known ($2\pi f$), and an evaluation of M must be made to find the value for i.

A good approximation for M is[1]:

$$M = \frac{\mu_o}{4\pi} \left(12.981 - 2\ln P_d \right) \frac{H}{m} \qquad (6\text{-}17)$$

where μ_o is $4\pi \times 10^{-7}$,
   P_d is $\alpha'd$ where $\alpha' = \sqrt{\sigma f}$,
   d is the actual distance between the power line and the communication line in meters.

Experience has shown that the induced voltage around the conductor in the cable is less than the induced voltage around the cable. This is due to the following reasons:

---

[1]H. R. J. Klewe. *Interference Between Power Systems and Transmissions.* New York: Edward Arnold, 1958.

1. The shielding effectiveness of the cable sheath was found to be —6 db.
2. The pairs within the cable were balanced; this was estimated, conservatively, to have a —60 db effect.

Consequently, it was found that in typical sections of exposed lines, if a voltage of 321 millivolts was induced around the cable (because of a fault current of 1500 amperes in the power line), it would be attenuated to 0.16 millivolts around the conductor.

It has been noted that the entire section of exposed communication line was 2.7 miles, or 4370 meters. Over this length of line, the total voltage induced by a fault current was 635 mv, which is far above the permissible level on most systems.[1] Only the fundamental frequency has been considered; harmonics are also worth considering if their current magnitudes are sufficiently large.

6.7 Other Techniques

There are a number of methods other than shielding that are useful in reducing the susceptibility of interference in a communication cable. A very effective, and, rather obvious method, is to increase the signal strength so the signal-to-noise ratio is higher, and the noise has less magnitude and, consequently, would become less important. This technique, however, is a very perilous one to use, because when the signal itself is increased, it may become a further source of interference to other cables. On the other hand, this method has its merits on small, restricted systems, but, as can be seen, if every subsystem on a large system used this method to its utmost, the subsystem would become inoperable: each subsystem would have to overcome the unwanted effects of all the large signals that would exist in the electronic environment.

Another way to reduce susceptibility to unwanted signals in cables is to use various signal-processing methods to improve the signal-to-noise ratio. These methods are well adapted for transmission over long lengths of cable but, unfortunately, require the use of specialized equipment for implementation. The first signal-processing method is signal modulation. This is useful on amplitude-modulated signals where the signal output and the input signal amplitude are the same. If an amplitude limiter is used and the signal gain is adjusted so that it operates slightly under limiting conditions, the high peaks of impulse noise can be chopped off. Another method is to use a coding technique to transmit digital data, and, by so doing, provide a means of parity checking to determine whether good signals are

---

[1] CCIF standard.

being transmitted. It is obvious that this last method requires considerable equipment for implementation, but it a very reliable means of eliminating interfering signals on highly critical systems. Finally, if all analog signals were transmitted as digital signals, the accuracy of transmission would improve in the presence of interfering signals.

It has been noted that balanced lines go a long way toward reducing susceptibility to unwanted signals in a cable. Some authorities have stated that balanced lines cause an attenuation of as much as —80 db, although a more widely accepted conservative figure is —60 db. A balanced system is shown in Fig. 6-17. As illustrated, required isolation between sending and receiving circuits is achieved and interference, arising from differences in ground potential, is eliminated. Induced voltages and currents caused

Fig. 6-17.   A balanced line for reducing susceptibility to interference.

by interfering fields are also eliminated. "Balance-to-unbalance" transformers are used at both the receiving and sending ends. These transformers are normally grounded at the center tap of their secondary windings. This effectively limits the voltage rise above ground potential. With this arrangement, the primary and secondary windings must be shielded from each other. If the voltages on the lines are different, they produce a voltage on the secondary winding equal to their difference. This keeps interference to a minimum. If the pairs are perfectly balanced, one end could be left ungrounded, however, experience has shown that perfectly balanced lines are an aspiration rather than an easily achievable fact; consequently, grounding at both ends is highly desirable.

The use of twisted pairs can be helpful in minimizing the effect of interference due to magnetic fields, and is accomplished by minimizing the loop area of the signal circuit. This is not a good technique to use, however, if the signal circuit is grounded at more than one point, or when used at VHF frequencies, or above.

As noted, coaxial cable is very effective in minimizing interference. An important consideration in the use of coaxial cable is that the terminal impedance be matched with the characteristic impedances of the coaxial cable. If a coaxial cable with a 50-ohm characteristic impedance were terminated in a 25-ohm impedance at each end, disturbing reflections introduced into the line would result. This problem, which was covered in the discussion of crosstalk, is of minor importance on short sections of line, but becomes quite important on long lines.

From a practical viewpoint, it is always advisable to ground cable shields. This assures that potential differences will be minimized and as little current flow as possible will occur within shields. In small systems, where lines are short, only one point of the shield need be grounded to the common ground point of the system. This is a very good solution for a small system as long as the common ground lead itself does not become a source of interference. However, it is well to note that even in small systems, high impedances and current-return grounds, in common with shield grounds, can cause trouble in sensitive circuits.

In longer, shielded lines, the shield impedance introduces a shield ground-return impedance problem in that section of the shielded cable that is far from the grounded end of the cable. Should this occur, electromagnetic energy can be coupled from the current flowing in the shield to the conductors to be shielded. This situation can be resolved by either limiting the level of energy made available near the shield (in other words, shielding the source of interference), or by reducing the impedance of the shield to ground by providing more than one grounding point; a combination of both, within practical limitations, often turns out to be the best solution.

Studies relating to cables on large missile systems have shown that all cable grounds should be connected to the equipotential plane of the system. This should be done at both ends of all cables and at all intermediate connection points where the cable may run through a piece of equipment. These studies have shown that such a procedure results in a minimum amount of coupling and considerably reduced interference. Use of such procedures is often objected to on the basis that circulating currents on multiple grounded cable shields will cause interference to be generated. However, the impedance of the shield and ground between grounding points must be considered. If a potential difference exists between grounding points, the relatively low impedance of the shield means that it will carry only a small part of the ground current and, therefore, not become an interference source.

7 – INTERFERENCE CONTROL
IN EQUIPMENT

7.1. Introduction

The techniques discussed in the previous chapters have been used to solve many of the interference problems. Many problems are straightforward, not warranting further discussion, while others are so complex that they require extensive considerations. In this chapter the solutions of these complex problems will be considered with respect to actual pieces of equipment that are used extensively by both the military and industry. These are:

1. A transmitter
2. An electric drill
3. Fluorescent lighting
4. Rotating electrical equipment
5. Arcing devices
6. A solid-state digital computer
7. Radar
8. A commercial mobile radio

7.2. A Transmitter

Utilization of the principles of interference control in the design of equipment will be shown by considering the design of a hypothetical communication transmitter. To begin, the design engineer will have at hand the following: frequency range, required amount of r-f power to be delivered to the antenna, limitations of physical size, and specifications of the prime power supply. With these parameters in mind, the engineer develops his design, the objective being to emerge with an optimum design for a transmitter. As a result of his studies and cost trading, one of his conclusions was that he would use vacuum tubes in the final amplifier stage. It was decided that the selected tubes will require forced air cooling so that the ambient temperature around the final amplifier tubes will not rise above a critical value. Another design decision was to minimize the number of frequency multiplying stages, by tripling on the final r-f stage and driving all preceding multiplying stages to their maximum power limits. In still another design decision, the engineer chose to use all tubes with the same heater voltage; this was done in an effort to keep down the physical size of the power supply. The heater voltage idea was implemented by grounding one side of the heater winding of the power transformer and "chasing" a single lead to all the tubes in the final stage. As noted, forced air cooling would be required. To provide this forced air cooling, a blower would have to be included in the design; since this was one of the last items considered, only a restricted amount of space remained in which to mount a blower. Consequently, a small, compact, high-speed blower, of the ac-dc universal type, with brushes and commutator was the only kind that would satisfy this need. The design of the transmitter was completed and incorporated into the design.

A first class interference problem became apparent when the transmitter was constructed. Various techniques were used, all eliminating some of the interference, but none really solving the problem. A filter was inserted in the input power line, but proved ineffective. Another filter was then inserted on the leads on the blower motor, but because of the small space available, metallized capacitors had to be used which, in themselves, are interference-generating components.

A bad rejection filter, tuned to one-third of the transmitter output frequency, was placed in the final amplifier tank circuit to try to reduce radiation of the crystal harmonics from the antenna.

Break-in operation of the transmitter was impossible because of keying the stage after the crystal oscillator, and because of the r-f radiation developed with the key-up condition.

Carbon dust from the brushes in the blower motor entered the forced air from the blower impeller and shorted out the insulators in the final amplifier.

The transmitter, simply, would not work.

This hypothetical case illustrated how relatively small problems contribute to the major interference problem. Fortunately, situations rarely get this bad. A design criteria, introduced early in the design, would have minimized the effect of interference. This criteria would be:

1. More low-level frequency-multiplying stages should have been included so that tripling in the final stage would not have been necessary.

2. All filament leads should be twisted pairs.
3. Low-power stages should be separated and effective shielding isolation between stages in common connections provided.
4. Early allocation of sufficient space should be made to provide for an a-c induction motor.
5. Each stage after the oscillator should be tuned so that harmonics in the transmitter output are reduced. Parallel tuning or pi-network coupling is preferred from an interference viewpoint.
6. Low power stages should not be overdriven as this will tend to produce unwanted harmonics. An adequate number of lower power stages are mandatory so that overdriving will not be necessary.
7. Provide the transmitter with an effective shield.

Criteria for the routing of internal leads will have to be developed: low and high level leads, separate; low level leads not laced into harnesses but running directly from point to point and perhaps shielded; shields on wires to be grounded.

If the design criteria were followed, the "comedy of errors" would never occur. It must be remembered that mere compliance with a specification requirement is not enough. A design guide that has been given much careful thought must be spelled out.

7.3.   The Electric Drill

A portable electric drill is now considered. The drill is driven by a universal electric motor, with commutator and brushes, and will operate from 115-volts dc to 60-cps ac. This drill, in addition to performing the intended function of driving a drill point, unfortunately, also generates electromagnetic energy which becomes part of the electronic environment of any electronic equipment operating nearby. This electromagnetic energy can vary in intensity between extremely wide limits. Test results have indicated that two apparently similar drills have generated levels of electromagnetic energy that varied by as much as one thousand-to-one when tested at the same frequency. Laboratory analysis of many of these drills has resulted in the following list of factors which influence the generation of this electromagnetic energy:

1. Arcing at the brushes. It has been estimated that 90 percent of the interference produced by portable electric tools is because of this.
2. Capacitance and inductance of the field and armature coils form local resonating circuits for multiples of line and commutator frequencies.
3. Discharges of electrostatic energy built up between moving parts.

This is particularly true of high-speed parts such as between the inner and outer races of ball bearings where the grease or oil film acts as the dielectric through which the discharge takes place. Use of a conductive lubricant will eliminate this. All sorts of additives to grease and oil can be used. Some of these are ineffective as a conductor, or if they are good conductors, the service life of the bearing is shortened. A good, dependable, conducting lubricant is still not generally available, however, reliance can be placed upon the inner races of ball bearings grounded using grounding brushes to the outer races and to the frame of the motor or tool. This is not an ideal solution, but when properly used, does reduce the generation of interference.

4. Poor concentricity between the commutator and bearings. This causes brush bounce.

5. Too few commutator segments. An example of this is the motor-driven drafting room eraser. It operates from 115-volts ac-dc and has three commutator segments. Interference levels, as high as 15 volts, were measured at 150 kilocycles between power supply lines of this device.

6. Too little or too much brush spring tension.

7. Lumped windings in the motor fields. Series motors are usually employed in portable electric drills because of the desirable torque and speed characteristics. The conventional method of interconnecting armature and fields is to connect one brush to one side of the power line, and the remaining brush to the remaining field terminal. It has been determined that in such cases, the interference levels from one line terminal to the frame of the tool may be one hundred times the interference level from the other line terminal to the frame of the tool. Obviously, the higher levels were found on the line terminal connected to the brush. However, connecting the outer leads of the field coils to the line terminals and placing the armature in between the two field coils, will provide from ten-to-one to one hundred-to-one decrease in interference level previously measured on the line terminal connected to the brush.

8. Poor mechanical balance of the armature has been found to result in armature shaft "shipping" particularly at high speeds. This results in brushes bouncing on the commutator and arcing between the brushes and the commutator.

9. Armature shaft of too small diameter resulting in shaft shipping, particularly under load.

10. Radiation of interference from air vents adjacent to the commutator and from the plastic covers of brush holders. It would be approp-

riate to provide fine mesh screen over the air vents to the motor to confine the interference to the interior of the tool as well as to prevent foreign materials from being drawn into the motor by the air stream. Metal caps over the brush holders would prevent the radiation of interference.

It is apparent that many factors are highly critical and can be controlled only by proper design of the offending devices. Some manufacturers have followed these guide lines, in addition to their own specific rules, for interference control and have produced such devices that can be operated in areas adjacent to sensitive electronic equipment.

When these rules are followed in basic equipment design, not only is the generation of unwanted electromagnetic energy reduced, but the motor is better from an electrical viewpoint: brush area on the commutator is adequate, the motor shaft is sufficiently sturdy, bearings and commutator are concentric, and an additional degree of protection against contamination of the motor by small flying particles is realized.

7.4. Fluorescent Lighting

Widespread use of fluorescent lighting has been an important source of radio-frequency interference. Because of its efficiency, means must be uncovered which makes it possible to use such lighting in the same areas where various receivers, etc., are being operated. The most important point in considering fluorescent lights is that any such installation should be operating properly and have no defective parts. This broad rule will assure a good lighting system and a big stride in minimizing the effect of this interference source. In a fluorescent lighting installation, if there is an intermittent flashing lamp, it should be turned off until a replacement bulb is installed. All bulb contact areas should be maintained regularly so that there is always a good contact and that arcing does not occur during the switching-on operation. This regular periodic maintenance is of prime importance since potential sources of interference can be eliminated before they do any damage.

Radio-frequency interference from fluorescent lighting usually affects electronic equipment because of direct radiation from the bulb, the fixture supply line, and line feedback from the fixture, through a common power supply with the susceptible equipment.

Direct radiation from the fluorescent bulb, or lamp, can be minimized by adhering closely to the following straightforward rules:

1. There should never be an installation of fluorescent lighting in which any of the fixtures are installed within ten feet of the equipment.
2. The lead-in wires to the fixtures should be shielded.

3. The equipment that is near the fluorescent lighting installation should be periodically checked to assure that it has a continuous low-impedance r-f ground. If the fixtures are installed over a test work bench, or similar facility, a metal screen that is bonded to the reflector on the fixture will be a useful corrective measure.

Line radiation from the fixture power supply line can be controlled by employing the same techniques used to suppress bulb radiation. The major difference between the effect of line radiation and bulb radiation is that the interfering effects, due to line radiation, may be conducted away a considerable distance by the supply line and cause a problem a considerable distance from where they are being generated. Line feedback into other equipment is best controlled by inserting a device in the line close to the suspected point of origin of the interference and bypassing any energy to ground. Experience has demonstrated that control is best if each fixture is handled as an individual problem and suppressed individually. In installations where this line feedback can potentially conduct interference into other remote parts of the overall installation, it is best to suppress each lighting panel board (that feeds fluorescent lights) with a filter at that point.

Interference generated by fluorescent lamps is generally in medium wave bands. For fluorescent fixtures with a starter switch, a single capacitor filter, connected as shown in Fig. 7-1, will give the best overall protection.

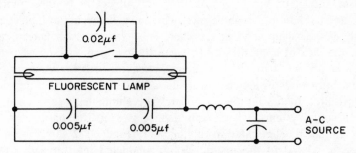

Fig. 7-1.   Fluorescent fixture with starter switch.

The value of the capacitance across the lamp must not be of greater magnitude than the value noted in Fig. 7-1 or the operating life of the tube will be severely reduced. Where the suppression problem is such that large values of capacitance are needed to cause this effect, an LC filter can be used.

7.5.   Rotating Machinery

Generally, rotating electrical equipment (all types of motors) are important sources of electrical interference. Depending on the particular kind of electrical equipment, it can be of more or less importance. A positive offender is any kind of rotating machinery that utilizes commutators; next in importance as a source of interference, is equipment that uses slip rings; and, least important, is, generally, electrical equipment with no intentional conducting path between the rotor and the stator. However, from the different types of equipment, two important causative factors can be identified: the process of commutation and the use of brushes in the device.

Commutation is a problem because wherever it is employed, there is always a good chance that arcing may occur between the commutator and the brushes. If this commutation process is carefully designed, the interference problem can be minimized. If interpoles or compensating windings are introduced in the design, the commutation process will usually become more efficient and interference will be minimized. Obviously, unless the design of the machine considers these sources of interference there is little that can be done when the rotating electrical machine is installed in an electronic system. Some "fixes" can be made: commutation can be improved by rotating the brushes with respect to the orientation of the field, although this can only be done at certain loads and speeds; commutation arcing can be reduced by using laminated brushes and a lower brush current density.

Brushes are a problem because they are subject to bounce, vibration, chatter and oxidation. Brush bounce, which usually occurs at high speed, is a result of the "whipping" of the shaft due to a poorly balanced design, and by the lack of concentricity between the commutators (or slip rings) and the bearings. If brush pressure is increased, brush bounce is usually reduced, but results in increased maintenance due to the sharp decrease in the brush life. Increasing the brush pressure eliminates interference, however, on some systems, where maintenance is a critical parameter, interference cannot be eliminated in this manner. Figure 7-2 shows how brush pressure is related to the magnitude of conducted interference; Fig. 7-3 shows the relation for brush current density. By showing several curves, in each case, the variations with different frequencies may be observed.

Oxidation is a perennial source of interference in rotating machinery and is especially important because it becomes more serious with the increased operation of the equipment. It never shows itself in checkout after installation, and is more insidious because of this. Oxidation film is generally formed irregularly causing variations in the sliding control resistance which, in turn, causes the d-c current to vary, resulting in r-f interference. The oxidation film also sets up a rectifier condition which makes transients possible since the resistance varies nonlinearily, depending on whether the brush is positive or negative. Fortunately, this rectifier action can easily be

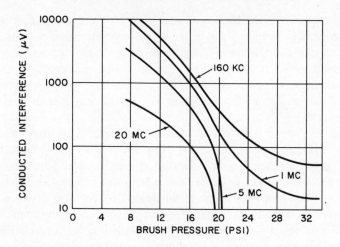

Fig. 7-2.   Effect of brush pressure on generated interference.

overcome by plating the commutator with 0.001 in. of chromium.

When the rotor and stator of a machine are not electrically connected, interference develops because of the discharges of the electrostatic energy which builds upon the separate moving parts. This situation becomes especially bad at high speeds where, for example, the grease, or lubricant, between the inner and outer cases of a ball bearing acts as a dielectric. Energy builds up on both sides and eventually discharge takes place across the dielectric. Naturally, a conductive lubricant would eliminate this build-

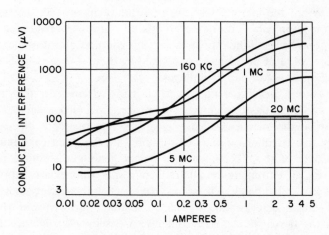

Fig. 7-3.   Effect of brush current on generated interference.

up of charge, however, this is a new technique and its application is limited to commercially available products. A more positive and successful technique is to ground the rotating shaft by use of a slip ring and, connecting this through two grounding brushes that are connected directly to the frame of the machine. The grounding brushes should be so spaced around the slip-ring that one grounding brush, at least, is making contact to ground at all times.

Capacitors are used when suppression is required on two commutator motors. They are connected across the brush holders and from each brush holder to the machine frame. Short lead lengths should be employed to keep the resonant point high. To obtain the most suppression, feedthrough capacitors should be used. The metal frame of a rotating device will serve as an excellent mounting place for these capacitors, since the frame encloses the source of interference and, when so installed, noise currents flow away from the capacitor, radially, in all directions, and the current path will have zero inductance. The metal frame of the motor, when used to this advantage, should be without long slots or large openings and, if made of several pieces, should be homogeneously bonded.

Finally, if it is possible to use rotating devices that do not use commutators or brushes, all of the problems discussed will become academic. All types of induction motors fill this requirement and should be used whenever possible, since they produce very little r-f interference.

7.6. Arcing

The scope of this discussion on arcing is limited to low energy switching circuits (power less than 10 watts and voltages less than 300 volts) because these are the circuits that are of primary interest in the design of electronic equipment. Furthermore, this discussion is restricted to the phenomenon of arcing directly at the switch contacts and does not include any consideration of interference generated by these source circuits because of fluctuation in power supply voltages.

The "making" or "breaking" of an electrical circuit carrying a current through switch contacts, usually causes a phenomenon known as "arcing" to develop at the switch contacts. It is this phenomenon that dissipates the energy that is either supplied to, or stored in, the electrical circuit. The primary effect of this phenomenon is that it generates a source of interference with an extremely broad frequency spectrum, whose upper limit is beyond the visible band. The secondary effect of this arcing phenomenon is that it causes deterioration of the arc contact surfaces and ultimately results in the destruction of the contacts. Consequently, in the design of equipment containing switching devices, some means must be taken to suppress interference that is generated, and secondly, additional measures must be taken to assure that contact deterioration does not develop to a point to compromise the operational capabilities of the equipment.

Oftentimes, a gross approach to the problem of arc suppression is taken; some standard technique is applied and a recommended component used without ever really probing into the nature of the problem itself. Such an approach will, when given a superficial examination, appear to give satisfactory results, however, associated problems have been generated; these are changes in circuit reliability, costs, system effectiveness, etc. With careful consideration some principles can be evolved which will go a long way toward minimizing the problem.

The source of electromagnetic energy that becomes an interference problem is either the energy supplied to, or stored in, the electrical circuit during the switching operation. Typical circuit loads that are switched are resistive, lamp, motor, capacitive and inductive loads. These various types of loading can be classified into two distinct types to facilitate discussions on arcing:

1. Current surges which occur when the transient current is greater than the steady state current, and which are a characteristic of a capacitive load.
2. Voltage surges which occur when the induced voltage is greater than the supply voltage and which is characteristic of a inductive load.

Generally, resistive loads are not subjected to current or voltage surges.

Special networks can be designed for arc suppression. These special networks accomplish this suppression by delaying or eliminating any transients that may occur during a switching operation. In selecting a suitable design, the following parameters must be considered:

1. Release time: this is important for inductive loads. Nearly all suppression networks delay the release time of relays by permitting a circulating current to flow. Generally, the greater the reduction in surge voltage, the slower the discharge of current through the inductance. This delaying action causes the ampere turns to decrease at a slower rate, thus causing a delay in the action of the drop-out ampere turns of the relay.
2. Physical location of suppression networks: Fig. 7-4 shows these suppression networks across the relay coils; equivalent circuits may also be connected across relay contacts. These networks generally can be located either across the contacts or across the load, but, practically, one position is preferable to the other in specific applications. An example of this preference in a specific application is the use of a relay for switching a number of loads connected in parallel. In this

case, suppression at the components is more advantageous because overall circuit reliability is improved by the use of fewer components. Conversely, the suppression network acros the load would be better for the same reason.

3. Contact protection: a contact, protection-type network is employed to assure the same reliability for an inductive or capacitive type load as for a resistive type load and, is employed in cases where the signal-to-noise ratio is such that the interference generated can be tolerated.

4. Minimizing noise: suppression networks that reduce arcing also reduce the peak of the surge voltage and, consequently, reduce interference. Therefore, it may be feasible to suppress the arc and, thereby minimize interference with one network.

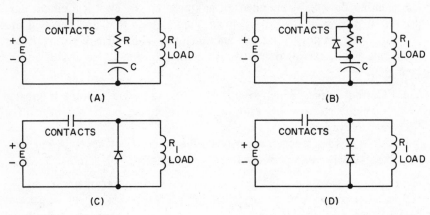

Fig. 7-4.   Arc suppression networks: (A) resistor-capacitor; (B) diode-capacitor-resistor; (C) diode; (D) two diodes wired back-to-back.

Many suppression networks can be designed based on the parameters that have been stated. Each of these suit specific requirements, but generally they can be categorized into four general types: resistor-capacitor, diode-capacitor-resistor, diode, and two diodes wired back-to-back.

1. Resistor-capacitor. (See Fig. 7-4A.) When contacts are closed, the value of the instantaneous current flow is a function of the magnitude of the applied voltage and the value of the resistor, R. As capacitor, C, charges, the suppression network current falls off to zero. This is the steady state condition that is achieved after the contacts are closed. When the contacts are open, voltage source, E, is disconnected from the load, the capacitor discharges through the resistor, and current flows through the load. The magnitude of the charge on

the capacitor will determine the amount of current flow, and voltage drop across resistor R. The voltage drop across R should be less than the minimum arcing voltage across the contacts. The size of resistor R must be calculated so that its value limits the current to less than the minimum arcing current on the "make" and to less than the minimum arcing voltage on the "break."

2. Diode-capacitor-resistor. (See Fig. 7-4B.) On contact closure, this circuit acts in the same manner as the resistor-capacitor network; the diode is equivalent to an open circuit. When the contact is open, the capacitor discharges through the diode and current continues to flow through the inductance. This magnitude of current flow determines the voltage drop across the diode; it is this voltage that appears across the contacts. A large value of R on the resistor limits the current when the contact "makes"; when the contact "breaks," the diode shorts out the resistor, causing a lower voltage drop across contacts than that of the resistor-capacitor network.

3. Diode. (See Fig. 7-4C.) When the contact "makes," the instantaneous current is low because of the diode action; the rate at which the current through the inductance builds up is slow. When the contact "breaks," the current through the inductance changes quickly and produces a negative surge voltage across the load. When this voltage decreases to approximately one volt negative, the voltage at which the diode starts to conduct, current circulates through the diode loop. At this point the instantaneous voltage across the contacts is the supply voltage plus the small voltage drop across the diode. This technique has the greatest effect on the delay of the release time.

4. Two diodes wired back-to-back. (See Fig. 7-4D.) When the contact "breaks," one of the diodes shorts and the second diode acts as a nonlinear resistor. The functioning of this network depends on the inverse resistance characteristic of the diode, and this characteristic, in turn, depends upon the reverse voltage applied across the diode. The voltage that appears across the contact "break" is a combination of the supply voltage and the voltage drop across the diode. This type of network is commonly used for switching a-c loads.

The specific applications of the suppression networks discussed depend upon their being able to vary the circuit parameters involved. By so doing, specific solutions to arc suppression problems can be developed.

7.7. Computers

Many of the present day, large extended systems require that some kind of a digital computer be utilized somewhere within the system. This is particularly true with large military systems such as Atlas, BMEWS, etc., which employ digital computers. When these devices are used, the question of compatibility is quite important: how much interference they generate and how susceptible they are to other parts of the system. Determinations of the interference generated and propagated by these computers have been made and the susceptibility of such a computer to the worst case type of electromagnetic fields — radar — has been established.

A computer, comprising an arithmetic element, instruction control, program control, test memory, input-output controls and magnetic drum and ferrite core storage will now be considered. Its associated device is an IBM card reader and an IBM electric typewriter. The logical operations of the computer are accomplished by d-c level circuits and pulse gating. Standard signal levels are ground and —3.5 volts and the pulses are approximately 35 nsec. wide and —3.5 volts in amplitude. The computer has a 20-bit word length, operates with a clock frequency of 6.25 mc, and has 23 instructions designed to operate with two overlapping core-storage units.

The prime sources of interference that computers will radiate from are the repetitive operation circuits. These repetitive operating circuits are, usually, the basic oscillator, time pulse distributors, register counters, drums, etc. The results of the interference generated by these sources is shown in Fig. 7-5. The values indicated are the maximum for each fre-

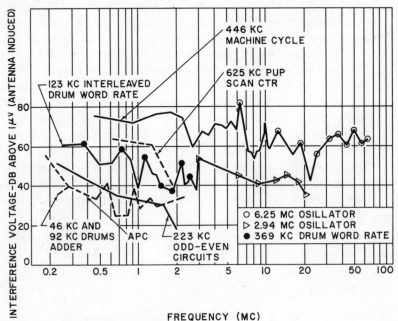

Fig. 7-5. Composite cw radiated interference spectra. (From Harder and Powers, Sixth Armour Conference)

quency. If the basic timing and logic information of a computer is known, the frequencies at which interference will develop are easily determined. However, determination of the amplitude of the interference is quite complex and, at the present time, this problem is being investigated, thus no general rules for the prediction of the amplitude of interference can be given.

The second most important aspect in the consideration of digital computers is to determine how susceptible they are to interference. Operation of a digital computer depends upon properly predetermined in-time pulses and standard voltage levels. A capability is usually built into the circuitry to assure that its signal-to-noise ratio will be such that it will have smooth, efficient and normal operation. But, when this operation is of the worst-case type (the computer has to operate in an environment loaded with strong r-f pulses from a radar), it is important to know if these radar pulses will affect its operation. Tests have shown that radar pulses have a deleterious effect on the digital computer. Low signal amplifiers used to boost core storage output and drum output signals are affected by radar pulses. These pulses sometimes appear as valid inputs to the amplifiers and sometimes as degraded true signals going through amplifiers. Figure 7-6 shows the accumulator flip-flop when the simulator pulse is sufficiently

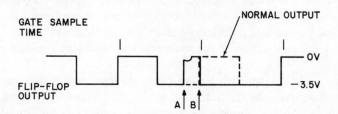

Fig. 7-6. Effect of radar signal on flip-flop output. (From Harder and Powers, op. cit.)

strong to cause the flip-flop to change to its alternate pulse state. At point A, an error pulse and a voltage are received until point B is reached, where the true pulse is now received. This additional pulse, from A to B, causes the error rate to increase rapidly and, consequently, severely reduces proper operation of the computer. Figure 7-7 shows flip-flop output affected by the radar pulse at gate sampling time. In this illustration there is no change on the time axis, but the flip-flop has introduced into it a voltage step resulting from the radar signal. The capacitively-coupled gate conducts, and the sample pulse will produce an erroneous output. Certain general rules can be stated that will reduce the susceptibility of a digital computer to interference. If all circuits are transistorized, packaging can be made more

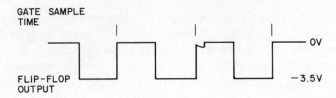

Fig. 7-7.   Accumulator bit 1 flip-flop output (condtion causing gate error). (From Harder and Powers, **op. cit.**)

compact with the enclosure of the computer assisting in the shielding. This more compact packaging will also decrease signal line lengths and thereby reduce antenna action. If the computer "black boxes" are made as compact as possible, using as much shielding as possible, the susceptibility of computers can be reduced to a manageable level.

7.8.   Marine Radar Set

Another practical approach to eliminating r-f interference in equipment can be illustrated by considering a common commercial marine radar set. This equipment contains a number of troublesome interference-generating devices such as microswitches, drive motors, and magnetrons. The magnetrons are particularly troublesome since they generate harmonics that are caused by the modulation of the magnetron pulses by the pulse repetition rate.

It was first found that such a piece of commercial marine radar generated broadband interference from 150 kc to 75 mc. This level averaged 100 microvolts above the ambient average noise. Motor noise was detected up to 35 megacycles and the pulse repetition rate of 800 cps was clearly detected across the band. Considerable r-f energy leakage was detected around the edge of the transmitter cabinet and at the ventilation openings; radiation was detected around the waveguide entrance to the transmitter cabinet.

Obviously, some modifications had to be made to equipment to assure that these interference sources would either be suppressed or the radiation contained. A 0.25 μf capacitor was inserted in the antenna drive motor circuit; shield braid for bonding was placed around the edges of the cabinet, and the ventilation opening was covered with screen wire, but, despite all of these measures, the interference was not eliminated. A pi network was inserted in the main power leads and interference was sharply reduced, but it was still possible to detect noise from the microswitches every time the heading flasher fired and every time the synchro-locking switches closed.

Additional modifications were now necessary. Cable grips were added so that all cable shields could be grounded with the use of grounding lugs. An RC network was inserted in the synchro-locking switch circuit, switch cams were modified to reduce voltage spikes, and a resistor was inserted in the ground side of the heading flasher switch circuit. Following these modifications, approximately two microvolts of noise, above the ambient, was detected in the frequencies of the standard broadcast band, in the region of 2.2 megacycles.

For the final elimination of remaining interference, additional modifications were made. All high level signal leads were shielded and tube filaments bypassed with 0.01-microfarad capacitors. All spaces in the interconnecting cable harnesses were ungrounded at one end to eliminate the possibility of circulating currents. The system trigger level was reduced by the ultilization of a voltage divider network, and an amplifier stage was inserted in the indicator to bring the trigger voltage to the utilization level. A modification also had to be made to the sweep multivibrator to compensate for this lowering of the trigger voltage level. After these things were completed, a slight amount of interference was still detected at 3.3 megacycles, but it was possible to tune this out and to come out with an essentially interference-free piece of radar equipment.

It should be readily apparent that all of these modifications that had to be made to eliminate interference in this radar set could have been eliminated by a closer control of sound design practices. Every change that had to be made was based on what can be considered good interference-free design techniques.

7.9. The Automobile

A very important and widely available source of r-f interference is the automobile. There are many sources of interference in such a vehicle and they are of varying importance. Friction effects, produced by rotating parts such as shafts, wheels, belts and pulleys, are a source of "static" interference, and can generally be controlled by the use of either conductive or insulating material, or by careful design of these sources. The automobile electrical system is the major source of r-f interference; its generation of unwanted signals can be minimized by careful selection of components, shielding, and by the use of filters in the electrical lines.

An important, major part of an automobile electrical system is the generator and its associated regulation device. This is so important a source of interference that measures have to be taken to control its unwanted signals so that the automobile's own broadcast receiver might function properly. This is usually accomplished by using a bypass capacitor at the generator and regulator, so that r-f energy will be bypassed, and by giving due care to the wiring configuration. This technique will not be sufficient, however, when a vehicle is equipped with a two-way radio. Feedthrough, or coaxial capacitors, are usually substituted for the bypass capacitor. The most reliable and economical method based on sound experience, is to use both coaxial and bypass capacitors and shielding available commercially in a kit. This kit includes a metal regulator shield assembly with universal characteristics, shielded cables for connecting generator to regulator, and a 0.1-microfarad bypass capacitor. The shield reduces radiation of r-f energy from contact chatter in the regulator, permits the capacitors to be bulkhead mounted, and provides a ground termination for the shielded cable that will be used to connect the generator and regulator. The shielded cable is for protection against radiation from the generator armature and field cables. The 0.1-microfarad capacitor effectively assists the shielding action against radiation. The use of such a kit will reduce r-f interference to a level of 0.5 microvolts (per kilocycle of bandwidth) over the 0.15-mc-1000-mc frequency spectrum. Additional elimination of r-f interference can be accomplished by adhering to the principles outlined for rotating electrical machines.

The automobile ignition system is another important problem area. It is capable of producing 1000 to 8000 voltage pulses per minute with peak amplitudes up to 35 kv. This generated interference is very irregular and has a broadband effect. The pulses are nonsinusoidal, with steep leading and trailing edges and with wide variations in frequency, phase, and amplitude. Such interference in vehicles equipped with two-way radios causes these otherwise well performing equipments to have their operation degraded. The first corrective measure that can be used to minimize this i-f interference is to keep the ignition system well maintained: rotor and spark plug gaps properly adjusted; no pitted, burned or improperly adjusted distributor primary contacts; and good high voltage wiring so that there will be no leaky or poor contacts. A resistance inserted in the high voltage wiring, between distributor and coil, and between distributor and spark plug gap, has proven another effective suppression technique. A high voltage, distributed resistance-type of wiring is now standard for practically all American automobiles. An even better refinement of this technique is to use lumped and distributed resistances. Lumped resistance is usually 10,000 ohms added to the connection between distributor and coil, and a 10,000-ohm resistance-type spark plug. With lumped resistance, total circuit resistance may become 30,000 ohms. When this is done, a coaxial-type capacitor, of perhaps 2 microfarads, is usually added at the battery input terminals. Shielding of the ignition system is also employed, some of which is obtained by the sheet metal around the automobile engine, but, which, because of its discontinuities, openings, etc., has limited effect. The most effective shield is to enclose the ignition system itself, paying particular attention to the insulator portion of the distributor. A self-shielded distributor cap is available commercially that makes use of the same physical configuration as a nonshielded cap, but which has electrically deposited pure copper on its outside surfaces and is electrically continuous with the threaded cable adapter. Low-impedance r-f grounding of this shielded cap is accomplished by means of a flexible bonding strap. The shielding of the ignition coil is accomplished by means of a universal clamp-on type of metal shield. It includes a 1.75-microfarad bulkhead-mounted feed-through capacitor. This capacitor filters conducted interference and isolates the ignition coil from the ignition battery. The spark plug cables incorporate integral snap-on spark plug shields. The shielded spark plug cables conform to military specification MIL-C-3162. The techniques used for shielding an automobile's ignition system make it possible to achieve a measured interference level of 0.5 microvolt (per kilocycle of bandwidth), and can be accomplished with an expenditure of not more than one-half hour of a technician's time.

7.10. Measurements

In all of the preceding discussions concerning specific pieces of equipment, there were repeated references to the fact that knowledge of *how much* interference could be permitted in the operation of equipment was necessary. This knowledge is primarily needed so that the level of interference might be compared, as in the signal-to-noise ratio, and further so that one can be assured that the particular specification goal that is involved for the particular piece of equipment is achieved. The whole question of measurement of electrical interference levels is an extremely thorny problem area, since standardized procedures and universally acceptable measures of interference simply are not available. One of the early investigators in this field has written:[1] ". . . the most difficult problem in radio noise measurement is to select from the many types of measurements which might be made, the ones which are most significant for the purposes desired. It is easy to obtain numerical measures of radio noise; the problem is the interpretation of the values after they are obtained."

Since the area of interest in this chapter is the measure of interference in operating systems, only the techniques of measurement and measuring devices that can be described as field measuring devices and practices will

[1]C. M. Burrill. "Progress in the Development of Instruments for Measuring Radio Noise," *Proceedings of the IRE* (August 1941).

be of interest. These are the techniques and devices used by equipment manufacturers to determine if the equipment satisfies a particular specification requirement (such as military specifications MIL-I-6181B and MIL-I-16910A).

The first measuring device for r-f interference was developed about thirty years ago and consisted of a tuned r-f receiver, a full wave, copper oxide rectifier for a detector, and a meter indicator. Measurement was made by comparing the interference reading with an internal 120 cps reference. About twenty years ago, a new approach to the problem of measurement was taken when it was stated that the most practical type of noise-measuring instrument is, essentially, a radio receiver with an indicating means. A modern typical r-f measuring device is shown in Fig. 7-8.

The heart of the device is essentially a standard receiver, the differences being that the input circuits must accommodate a number of different

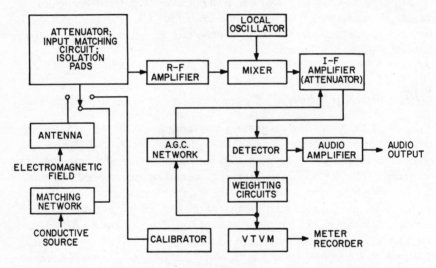

Fig. 7-8. Typical RIFI meter (The nucleus of the device is a standard receiver) (**op. cit.** p.111, Electronic Industries, March 1961)

pickup devices and the outputs must have special detectors and metering devices. A list of commercially available devices is shown in Table 7-1[1].

It has been noted that there is at present no standardized method for measuring the interference susceptibility of equipment. There are, however, several widely accepted methods in general use. One method is to simply operate the equipment in its intended application and determine if there is any interference present which causes a degradation to its intended

---

[1]Electronic Industries, March 1961.

TABLE 7-1. CHARACTERISTICS OF SEVERAL COMMERCIAL RIFI METERS

Manufacturer	Type Designation		Frequency Range	Bandwidth 6db(5)	Sensitivity Limit(6)	Detector Function (7)	Calibrator Source	Pick-up Devices
	Commercial	Military						
Empire Devices	NF-105		0.014-1000mc/s with 5 tuning units as follows T-X/NF-105 14kc-150 kc	600-1000cps(3)			variable prf impulse generator;	loop, 12"; rod, 1/2 meter
			TA/NF-105 150kc/s-30mc/s	5-15kc/s(4)	1μv			
			T-1/NF-105 20mc/s-200mc/s	100kc/s(3)	10μv			
			T-2/NF-105 200-400mc/s	200kc/s(3)	10μv	A P SBP	fixed frequency sine wave generator	tuned dipole, Broadband conical
			T-3/NF-105 400-100mc/s	300kc/3	10μv			
Empire Devices	NF-112		1-10kmc/s with 4 tuning units as follows T-1/NF-112, 1-2kmc/s	1mc/s and 5mc/s(3)	10μv	A P SBP	impulse generator 1000pps	Horns
			T-2/NF-112, 2-4kmc/s					
			T-3/NF-112, 4-7kmc/s					
			T-4/NF-112, 7-10 kmc/s					
Ferris	32B		150kc/s-350kc/s, 550kc/s-20mc/s	10kc/s(3)	1/2μv	QP2	random noise generator	1/2 meter rod, inductive probe
Ferris	32D		550kc/s-25mc/s	6.4-9.6 kc/s(2)	1μv	QP1 SBP	multi-vibrator	1/2 meter rod; loops: one per band 5"-6 1/2" "Square"; loop probe 2" dia.; Dummy antenna.

TABLE 7-1. CHARACTERISTICS OF SEVERAL COMMERCIAL RIFI METERS (CONT'D)

Manufacturer	Type Designation Commercial	Type Designation Military	Frequency Range	Bandwidth 6db(5)	Sensitivity Limit(6)	Detector Function (7)	Calibrator Source	Pick-up Devices
Ferris	32J		any 40kc/s interval in range 500-1600kc/s is available	10kc/s (estimate)	1μv	QP1 QP2 QP3	multi-vibrator	1/2 meter rod;
Measurements	58AS		15-150mc/s	140kc/s(3)	1μv	A QP1 SBP	random noise source	loop 9″ dia., Tuned dipole, loop probe, 3″ dia., capacitive probe, r-f probe
Polarad	FIM		1-10kmc/s with 4 tuning units as follows FIM-L, 1-2.4kmc/s FIM-S, 2.14-4.34 kmc/s FIM-M, 4.2-7.74kmc/s FIM-X, 7.36-10.0kmc/s	5mc/s(3)	20μv	A SBP QP1	internal sine wave signal generator	Broadband Conical, Horns
Stoddart	NM-40A	AN/URM-41	a. Selective: 30cps-15kc/s b. Wideband: 30cps-15kc/s ± 0.5db	13-90cps(1) variable	1μv 15μv	A A SBP QP1	400cps tuning fork ocsillator	loop: 30″ dia.; capacitive probe with dipole
Stoddart	NM-10A	AN/URM-6B	14kc/s-250kc/s	100-cps-600cps (2)	1μv	A SBP QP1	neon bulb random noise source	rods: 1 meter and 1/2 meter; loops: 30″ and 5 3/8″ dia.; r-f Probe
Stoddart	NM-20B	AN/PRM-1A	150kc/s-25mc/s	2-6kc/s(2)	3μv	A SBP QP1	random noise source	rod: 1/2 meter; loops: 30″ dia, and 7″ x 8″ rect. loop probe; r-f Probe

TABLE 7-1. CHARACTERISTICS OF SEVERAL COMMERCIAL RIFI METERS (CONT'D)

Manufacturer	Type Designation		Frequency Range	Bandwidth 6db(5)	Sensitivity Limit(6)	Detector Function (7)	Calibrator Source	Pick-up Devices
	Commer-cial	Military						
Stoddart	NM-30A	AN/URM-17	20mc/s-400mc/s	138kc/s-(2) 175kc/s	1µv to 145mc 2µv to 240mc 6µv to 400mc	A SBP QP1	impulse generator 60pps	tuned dipole, tuned vertical rod, loop probe 3" dia.
Stoddart	NM-52A	AN/URM-17	375mc/s-1000mc/s	510kc/s(3)	1.6µv to 610mc 2.0µv to 1000mc	A SBP QP1	impulse generator 60pps	tuned dipole, Broadband "Bowtie"
Stoddart	NM-60A	AN/URM-42	100mc/s-10.7kmc/s	1.5mc/s(3)	15µv	A SBP QP1	impulse generator 60pps	Broadband conical, Horns

1. The bandwidth of this instrument is continuously variable over the range shown.
2. The bandwidth of this instrument depends upon the frequency to which the device is tuned.
3. The bandwidth of this instrument is virtually constant over the tuning range.
4. This unit is tuned in 6 bands; within any one band the bandwidth is said to be virtually constant.
5. The bandwidth quoted in this column is either the 6-db bandwidth or the "effective impulses bandwidth" defined as the peak output voltage at the detector to an impulse divided by the impulse strength. The latter is for circuits nearly equal to the 6-db bandwidth.

6. The sensitivity limit is not defined rigorously in most manufacturing bulletins. It may be viewed as the rms amplitude of a sine wave input signal required to equal the detector output obtained from the internal receiver noise.

7. Dector functions are designated by the following

    A = Average of envelope
    SBP = Slide Back Peak
    P = Peak
    QP1 = Quasi-Peak, 1msec charge - 600msec discharge
    QP2 = Quasi-Peak, 10msec charge - 600msec discharge
    QP3 = Quasi-Peak, 1msec charge - 160msec discharge

operation. Another method is to operate the equipment in its intended manner but to substitute a high intensity interfering source for what are suspected to be potential interfering devices. For measuring purposes, low frequencies can usually be obtained by standard power sources together with power amplifiers. Standard audio amplifiers, inverters, etc., are adequate. Special measurements can be made by modifying vibration equipment of the moving voice-coil type.

In the evaluation of the r-f interference problem in electronic equipment, there are some basic problems that are always present: the r-f leakage from the equipment must be considered, and the evaluation and control requirements of the susceptibility of the equipment to extraneous signals must be investigated. The susceptibility of a piece of electronic equipment may be measured by following a basic procedure based on practical considerations. Such a procedure requires the use of test equipment including standard signal generators with 50-ohm internal impedance, a length of RG-9/U cable 20 feet long; and a one turn, electrostatically shielded loop, three inches in diameter, used as a probe. This loop probe is rigidly attached to the equipment under test at its point of maximum r-f leakage. This point of maximum r-f leakage is easily located. Since the loop probe is used as a signal source, high intensity magnetic fields are created which have a low wave impedance. These are the most difficult types of fields to shield effectively. These magnetic fields penetrate the equipment case more easily and, consequently, provide a "worst case" type of test. They represent a far more severe test than if a rod antenna is used as a signal source. The open-circuit voltage of the signal generator must be carefully recorded since this establishes the limits for the control. Tests that utilize this method can be classified into two types: threshold susceptibility tests, and tests of the effect of actually occurring equipment leakages. Threshold susceptibility tests are those that reveal an unwanted signal that is barely discernible from a wanted signal, resulting in a degradation of intended quality of operation. In this test, a record is made of the signal generator open-circuit voltage fed into the loop probe; this, in turn, is used to establish limits to prevent this threshold susceptibility. A record is also kept of the signal generator open-circuit voltages since this is a simulation of the voltages which actually cause equipment leakage. From this, can be determined the degree of resistance to susceptibility which the equipment under test must be able to withstand in order to operate with a specified level of equipment leakage present.

The measurement of a high-intensity magnetic source is often done with a pickup device that has poor sensitivity to the field being emitted. Such measurements are usually not very successful, since the measuring device must be sensitive to the magnetic field. The use of a loop probe to obtain an estimate of the magnitude of the electric field is only a satisfactory procedure when the antenna is located at such a point in the radation field where the ratio of the electric to magnetic components is constant and equal to the intrinsic impedance of free space. Where the point to be measured is physically close to the radiating source, the technique is not satisfactory and the results are useless. The fields emitted by a loop in free space are basically similar to fields emitted by low-impedance, interference-producing sources. Since almost all r-f interference measurements are made in the induction field, the only correct way to use the loop antenna is to assume that it measures the magnetic field and state results in terms of magnetic field units (amperes/meter). This gives good practical results for most distances from the interference source and for measurements that are made in the radiation field. A good empirical procedure is to make an approximation for the electric field by multiplying the results obtained by 377.

Since filters are used so widely to suppress conducted interference, it is necessary to measure their effectiveness. The effectiveness of a filter is usually expressed in terms of insertion loss in decibels (db). This effectiveness is intimately influenced by the characteristics of the noise source to be filtered and the supply circuit. From a practical viewpoint, the insertion loss of a filter should be 10 db in excess of what is the estimated required effectiveness. Frequency must also be specified since insertion loss and effectiveness depend on it.

The insertion loss of r-f filters is often measured with rated current applied. A common military standard is that this measurement should be performed between a 50-ohm source and low resistive impedances. The insertion loss is given by:

$$\text{Insertion loss} = 20 \, \log_{10} \frac{V_{50\Omega} \text{ (before inserting filters)}}{V_{50\Omega} \text{ (after inserting filters)}}$$

$$(7\text{-}1)$$

Such a measurement is a little restrictive because it only approximates the attenuation of the filter because of its reference to an arbitrary standard. In practical use, the insertion loss depends on load impedances which may vary widely. Insertion losses of typical feed-through capacitors are given in Table 7-2.

Figure 7-9 shows the method for measuring the insertion loss of filters with a rated load applied. The $L_1 C_1$ and $L_2 C_2$ networks form high-impedance shunts across their sources and 50-ohm load impedances. These shunts block the passage of r-f currents that would otherwise shunt the filter under test. Any r-f currents near the d-c source are shunted to ground through C_1 and C_2. The d-c source has been restricted to passage through

TABLE 7-2.   INSERTION LOSS OF FEEDTHROUGH CAPACITORS

CAPACITANCE	INSERTION LOSS (db)		
(in microfarads)	f = 150 kc	f = 400 mc	f = 800 mc
1.00	27	96.0	102.0
0.68	24.5	92.7	98.7
0.47	21.0	89.5	95.5
0.33	19.0	86.4	92.4
0.22	14.5	83.0	89.0
0.10	7.5	76.0	82.0
0.047	1.5	70.0	76.0
0.010	0.0	56.5	62.5
0.0047	0.0	50.0	56.0
0.0010	0.0	36.5	42.5

the line chokes of the filter and the d-c injection circuit does not introduce additional current loops or shunt paths for the r-f signals.

Tests can also be made to determine any faulty construction that would degrade the effectiveness of a shield. A portable sensitive radio receiver may be used about 10 feet from the shield. The radio-frequency spectrum

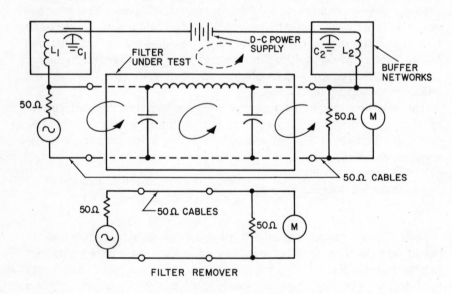

Fig. 7-9.   Insertion loss test method with rated load applied.

of interest should be scanned, and the location of the instrument and the frequency of the noise noted. If it is found that the noise field within one foot of the shield is considerably greater than elsewhere, the effectiveness of the interference suppressor is poor. The noise field near all openings, slits, etc., and near the joints of two shielding materials, should be investigated. The shielding should be improved at all places where the noise is found to be excessive.

A useful indicating device for locating leaks can easily be constructed using a tuned circuit consisting of a coil and variable condenser together with a 0-100 microammeter and crystal diode detector (1N34). Shielding may also be tested using a sample of the shielding material.

An excellent simplified technique was developed by the Naval Research Laboratory (NRL) for measuring shielding effectiveness, against both high- and low-impedance electromagnetic fields, of any desired material including such nonhomogeneous constructions as wire mesh and conducting coatings.

Small circular samples are cut to fit between two shield cans which are then fastened together. (See Fig. 7-10.) One of these cans contains a

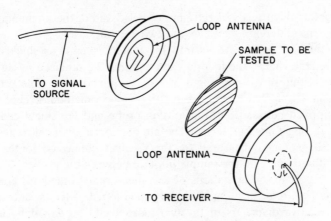

Fig. 7-10. Simple method for measuring shielding effectiveness.

small transmitting element; the other, a receiver element (loop or rod antennas). Attenuation of the material to be measured is determined by the ratio of the energies which reach the receiving element with and without the inserted sample. Both loops must be the same distance apart, with and without the material to be measured. This can be done by using a second sample of negligible attenuation, cut to exactly the same width of the sample being measured. This same distance must be maintained because the energy coupled between the samples varies with the cube of the distance between them. The measured values which are obtain by this method compare favorably with those predicted by calculation. In the NRL experiments, frequencies of 15 kc to 100 mc were used. Measurable attenuation was limited to about 110 db (due mainly to equipment sensitivies). In the opinion of NRL investigators, this procedure could be used for shielding measurements in the VHF and UHF regions using a waveguide technique.

In the equipment described above, one loop (the transmitter), is connected to a signal generator; the other to the field strength meter. After the current in the transmitting loop, the diameters of the two loops, and the distance of separation is determined, the field that the receiving loop should measure can be calculated. When cans made of 1/16-in. gauge copper are used, and they are fastened together by clamps, the fringing effect, i.e., energy coupling all the loops around the edges of the sample, can be neglected. If the initial meter reading is E_1, and the reading with the sample is E_2, the attenuation in decibels is given as:

$$\text{Attenuation} = 20 \log \frac{E_1}{E_2} \qquad (7\text{-}2)$$

If a meter which reads directly in decibels is used, the attenuation value is simply the difference between the two readings.

If attenuation values are desired for materials used as shields against high-impedance fields, the loop in each can may be replaced by an electric probe consisting of a 7-in. length of No. 12 tinned wire. The procedure, then, is similar to that employed in the two-loop method, except that the voltage applied between the transmitting probe and the shield can is kept constant during a measurement. The attenuation is then calculated as the ratio of the voltages measured on the receiver connected to the pickup probe, without and with the sample in place between the probes.

With respect to the limitations of this measurement method, apart from that of upper frequency limits already mentioned, NRL scientists found that the relative diameters of the two loops could be varied by as much as 2:1 without appreciably affecting the results. It was also found that no appreciable error in the measurements resulted from not having the loop coaxially spaced. At lower frequencies, the number of turns on either the transmitting or receiving loops can be increased for greater sensitivity.

As shown in Table 7-1, a number of instruments are commercially available for making r-f interference measurements. These are essentially refined and calibrated receivers. These devices usually use a loop antenna for measurements in frequencies above 18 megacycles, and a rod antenna below 18 megacycles. For pinpointing the frequencies of interfering sources, locating leaks, etc., many different devices are found to be useful. A very simple type of current probe using shielded inductive coupling is shown in Fig. 7-11. A 3-inch loop probe is a good device for measuring the magnetic component of an interfering field, but to be effective must be placed near the point of leakage. A rod antenna gives a good evaluation of the electrostatic component of an interfering field.

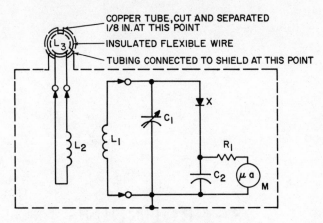

Fig. 7-11. R-f current probe.

Field experience in large systems has shown that the point at which single-end shield-grounding is no longer efficient is when cable lengths are up to about 20-30 feet. This magnitude of cable length will usually mean that for any interconnection cables, a single-ground point will be adequate.

8 – GROUNDING

8.1. Introduction

It has been shown that a great deal of unwanted r-f energy is brought into equipment by conduction, generally via connections that have to be made. The common connections that equipment have with a power supply are highly important and the chapter on filters has shown how interference from this source can be controlled. The common connection made between equipments through the grounding system, is of great importance, particularly since the grounding system not only connects equipments together but permits the equipments that make up an electric system to be connected to other, unrelated systems. It is for this reason, primarily, that the grounding system is so important.

To define grounding adequately is rather involved since the meaning is different in different fields of application. If one discusses circuitry, the ground merely means the actual connection to the power supply return bus. In radio transmission, ground means that portion of the radiated energy which travels through the earth, and is conditioned by the properties of the particular portion of the earth. In a prime power distribution system, the ground is the very important path through which the energy must pass to make it possible for protection devices to operate. But, despite these special meanings, a ground can be defined as the common connection of electrical circuits to a conducting medium that becomes a common reference plane. This conducting medium can be to the earth through ground rods, the hull of a ship, or the outer shell of an airplane. In addition to establishing this common reference plane, a ground system must also eliminate the possibility of any dangerous voltages from building up between the common reference plane and nonconducting portions of the equipment.

In electronic equipments, grounds are used extensively. There are circuit grounds, equipment grounds, and building grounds. Since circuits that are sometimes widely separated are joined electrically through the ground, potential differences are sometimes generated. It is for this reason that there must always be a very low impedance between ground connections. Furthermore, in electronic equipment, because of the increase of inherent capacitance between parts of the equipment as frequency increases, a common ground is necessary to assure that these capacitances are all referenced to one plane.

8.2. Earth Connection

The most important part of the grounding system is the connection to the earth itself. It is upon the adequacy of this connection that the required low resistance path to ground depends. If it were possible to make such a connection that would be electrically of zero resistance, an ideal situation would then prevail. Since, for obvious reasons, this is not possible to achieve in making the ground connection, the lowest practical resistance path to ground should be the goal. This lowest practical resistance path is based on a number of considerations and, even though it may be possible to obtain a resistance to ground of less than 1 ohm, other considerations must be kept in mind, such as the fact that this is also the path to ground for lightning discharges near the equipment and that the prime power fault current may travel over this path to ground.

Certain general specifications, that are useful in any application, can be used in considering a ground connection. If the ground connection is made by burying electrodes in the earth, these electrodes must be, in themselves, good conductors; they must not be subject to rapid corrosion when coming in contact with the earth; they must be mechanically strong to withstand damage by other objects in the earth, and they must have a very large surface area that will make good electrical contact with the earth, thereby assuring that the connection to the earth will meet the requirements of a low-resistance path. Once an earth connection is made with the electrodes, there must be a reasonable assurance that the resistance will not vary widely with changes in the earth surrounding the electrodes and that the stability of the low-resistance path will not be disturbed by a specific functional operation, e.g., several surges of lightning to ground through it.

In addition to satisfying the maximum electrical considerations, cost must be minimized if the optimum connection to earth is to be achieved. To optimize the connection of the grounding system to earth, the cost of each unit of conductance must be minimal. A further consideration in optimizing the earth connection is to consider the practical difficulties that may be encountered in material availability, environmental conditions, installation problems, criticalness of operation, etc.

From the system viewpoint, an earth conection may be resolved, chiefly by considering that the potential differences between parts of the system must be within a safe margin. To remove the physical problem which may be a cause of these potential differences, all parts of the system must be securely interconnected. To obviate the problem caused by the power system ground itself, it must be borne in mind that in calculation of fault currents from the power system ground to earth, it is necessary to consider the basic connection to earth. The effect resistance has on the magnitude of fault current depends on the ratio of the resistance of the basic connection to earth, to the total impedance of the system. Whether or not the magnitude of the ground resistance will make an appreciable change in the magnitude of the ground current, will, therefore, depend upon the type of system involved. In general, the higher the system voltage, the less will be the effect of ground resistance; whereas, the greater the short circuit kva, the greater will be the effect of system ground resistance.

Many problems develop when attempting to make an adequate ground connection. The resistance of the earth where the ground rods are placed, variation of this resistivity through different kinds of soil, varying environment conditions, etc., must be considered. All ground connections are made in either of two ways:

1. Connection to underground metallic piping, metal building frame-works, steel piping or any other metallic objects in good and intimate contact with the earth.
2. Connections to ground rods driven in the earth with the specific intention of making a ground connection.

Experience has shown that the first method is not as good as the second; in the first case, the range of values for the resistance of the path to earth is between 5 and 25 ohms, while, with ground rod electrodes, it is usually below 5 ohms.

8.3. Ground Calculations

There are many different forms that an electrode may take to make a ground connection. To facilitate the following analysis of earth resistivity, a metallic hemisphere with a radius A and buried, as shown in Fig. 8-1, will be considered. The resistance of such an earth connection will obviously be the resistance offered to the flow of the current into the immediately surrounding soil in contact with the hemisphere. (The resistance of the

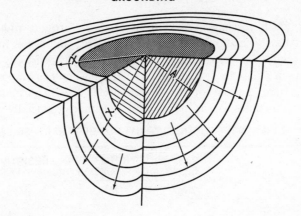

Fig. 8-1. Metallic hemisphere burned into earth with radius A. (From J. R. Eaton, "Grounding Electric Circuits Effectively," **General Electric Review**, June 1941)

hemisphere itself is neglected.) As noted, the resistance of a conductor of uniform cross-section is given by the expression:

$$R = \rho \; \frac{1}{A} \qquad (8\text{-}1)$$

where ρ is the specific resistivity of the conductor, ohm-in,
    1 is its length, in.,
    A is its cross-sectional area, in.^{2}

Equation 8-1 can be applied to this hemisphere, if the cross-sectional area of the conductor is considered to be the soil through which the current is flowing away from the hemisphere; this area increases with distance from the center of the hemisphere. At a distance x from this center, it becomes $2\pi x^2$. The value of R then may be obtained by the evaluation of the integral:

$$R = \rho \int_{A}^{\infty} \frac{dx}{2\pi x^2} = \frac{\rho}{2\pi A} \qquad (8\text{-}2)$$

From Eq. 8-2, it can readily be seen that the magnitude of the resistance of this earth connection is directly proportional to the earth resistivity at the place where an electrode is driven into the earth for a ground. Consequently, the importance of the knowledge of earth resistivity at the place where ground rods are driven cannot be overstressed. If this information is not available, earth resistivity measurements should be taken before the ground rods are driven. This is a good guide line, since experience has shown that there are many wide variations in earth resistivity and it is affected by many important factors.

The most general data on earth resistivity is that which only considers the type of soil and not environmental conditions. Such data—measured values of earth resistance of 5/8 in. x 5 ft. ground rods—has been assembled by the National Bureau of Standards and listed in Table 8-1.

It can readily be seen, from Table 8-1, that the resistivity of soil may vary as much as 50 to 1, depending on the particular composition of the soil. In certain sections of the United States these sharp differences in resistivity sometimes occur quite close together, especially in glaciered

TABLE 8-1.　THE RESISTIVITY OF DIFFERENT SOILS[1]

SOIL	RESISTANCE (OHMS) 5/8 IN. X 5 FT. RODS			RESISTIVITY (OHMS PER CM^3)		
	Avg.	Min.	Max.	Avg.	Min.	Max.
Fills Ashes, cinders, brine waste	14	3.5	41	2,370	590	7,000
Clay, shale, gumbo, loam	24	2	98	4,060	340	16,300
Same—with varying proportion of sand and gravel	93	6	800	15,800	1,020	135,000
Gravel, sand, stones, with little clay or loam	554	35	2,700	94,000	59,000	458,000

[1]Bureau of Standards. Technical Report No. 108.

areas. An example of this is given in Fig. 8-2 which shows the measured value of ground resistance at the base of transmission towers about 300 feet apart. This has posed a problem in some military installations, which are located in these regions.

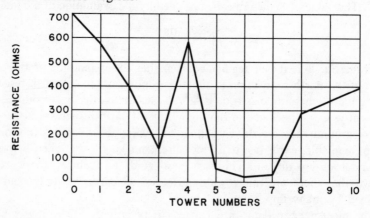

Fig. 8-2.　Measured values of resistance at base of towers. (From J. R. Eaton, **op cit.**)

Once a particular soil resistivity has been established, variations in this parameter, due to environmental changes, must be considered. Soil that is perfectly dry has so high a resistivity that it is practically a good insulator. The resistivity of loam as noted in Table 8-1, was given as a maximum value of 16,300 ohms/cm^3 (probably in loam with a moisture content of about 15 percent). Table 8-2 lists variations of soil resistivity together with varying moisture contents.

TABLE 8-2. THE EFFECT OF MOISTURE CONTENT ON THE RESISTIVITY OF SOIL[1]

MOISTURE CONTENT (PERCENT BY WEIGHT)	RESISTIVITY (OHMS PER CM CUBE)	
	TOP SOIL	SANDY LOAM
0	> 1,000 X 10^6	> 1,000 X 10^6
2.5	250,000	150,000
5	165,000	43,000
10	53,000	18,500
15	19,000	10,500
20	12,000	6,300
30	6,400	4,200

[1]P. J. Higgins. "An Investigation of Earthing Resistances," *IEE Journal,* Vol. 68, p. 136.

Variations of soil resistivity with moisture are very important since what might have been thought of as a very good low-impedance ground connection might become, due to fluctuations of the moisture content of the soil because of changing seasons, a very high resistance ground that would effectively compromise the ground system. It is for this reason that ground rod installations should be periodically inspected and monitored so that the quality of the grounding system will be maintained.

Another important environmental factor that influences soil resistivity is ambient temperature. For wide variations in temperature, the resistivity of the soil has shown wide variations in value. The effect of temperature on the resistivity of soil is listed in Table 8-3.

TABLE 8-3. THE EFFECT OF TEMPERATURE ON THE RESISTIVITY OF SOIL

	Sandy Loam: 15.2% Moisture	
Temperature		Resistivity
°C	°F	(Ohms/cm^3)
20	68	7,200
10	50	9,900
0 (water)	32	13,800
0 (ice)		30,000
− 5	23	79,000
−15	14	330,000

This effect is shown graphically in Fig. 8-3, but for a red clay soil with a moisture content of 18.6 percent. As the temperature approaches the melting point of water, the resistivity of the soil approaches zero asymptotically. Consequently, it would be suspected that soils with high moisture content are particularly troublesome if the ambient temperatures fall far below the freezing point of water.

The two variables—temperature and moisture—that have been considered so far are part of the seasonally changing environment. Further-

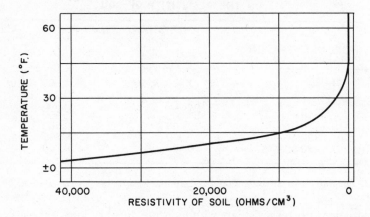

Fig. 8-3. "Lightning Arrester Grounds," Parts 1, 2, and 3. by H. M. Towne, **General Electric Review,** Vol. 35; pp. 173, 215, and 280; March, April, and May 1932.

more, their effects work simultaneously as the seasons change. This reaction is shown in Fig. 8-4. It will be well to note that the effects discussed are more important on the surface of the earth. If temperatures vary between 20°F and 100°F in a particular locality, according to the season, it is usually found that, approximately three feet below the surface, the swing is not nearly as wide. The resistivity of the soil varies at different depths below the surface because of the two variables (previously discussed) as well as the composition of soil in the various layers, and the physical position of the soil within the layers. Figures 8-5 and 8-6 show this variation of resistivity with depth. The conductance (reciprocal of resistance) is plotted to show a more meaningful relationship at the point at the lower end of the ground rod. It will be noted from these curves that the sharp increase in conductance, after 30 feet, is due to ambient climatic conditions no longer affecting this parameter in any way.

Since it has been established that areas of high resistivity exist in which ground rods must be driven for a particular installation, it will be shown that in certain situations it is practical to treat the soil around the ground

rods so that ground resistivity may be reduced. This treatment merely
consists of mixing the soil around the ground rods with fine common salt
(sodium chloride) before the soil is compacted into place. Data are available that show that for sandy loam with a moisture content of 15 percent

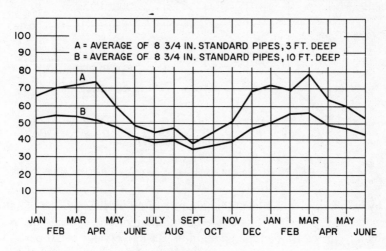

DATE OF TEST

Fig. 8-4. Variation in resistance of pipe grounds with seasons.

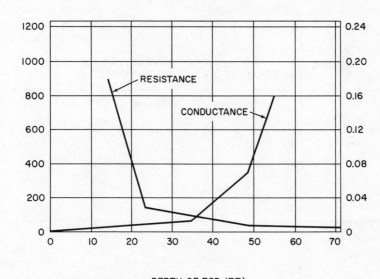

DEPTH OF ROD (FT.)

Fig. 8-5. Resistance and conductance curves as a function of rod depth.

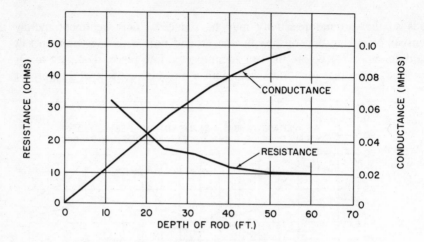

Fig. 8-6. Resistance and conductance curves as a function of rod depth.

by weight, and an ambient temperature of 40°F, the addition of salt to the value of 0.1 percent of the weight of the moisture reduces the resistivity by a factor of 10, and the addition of salt to the value of 20 percent of the weight of the moisture reduces the resistivity by a factor of 100. It has been pointed out that since the variation of resistivity with moisture content is sharply affected by the freezing of the moisture, it would naturally follow that the addition of salt will change the point at which the resistivity drops off sharply. Table 8-4 shows that the rise in resistivity, at temperatures below the freezing point, is not as great as that observed in untreated soil.

TABLE 8-4. THE EFFECT OF TEMPERATURE ON THE RESISTIVITY OF SOIL CONTAINING SALT[1]

Sandy Loam: 20% Moisture	
Temperature, °C	Resistivity (Ohms/cm^3)
20	110
10	142
0	190
− 5	312
−13	1440

[1]*Ibid.*

When salt is used to treat the soil around electrodes, it must be remembered that salt will be dissolved away. Figure 8-7 shows how the resistance varies as the salt content reduces over an interval of time. Resalting reduces the resistance again. Salting, to obtain a low ground resistance, therefore, requires periodic maintenance to assure that a low ground resistance is being kept.

8.4. Testing for Grounds

It has been shown that it is necessary to constantly monitor the low impedance path to ground (made by driving electrodes into the soil) because there are a number of factors which cause the value of the resistance to ground to change. If these ground rod connections are properly tested and maintained during the intended operating life of the system, a good ground connection will always be available. When the ground rods are installed, the resistance of the earth connection should be measured. This measurement should be followed by measurements taken as part of the periodic maintenance program associated with the ground system.

The earth resistance measurement, like all electrical measurements, has

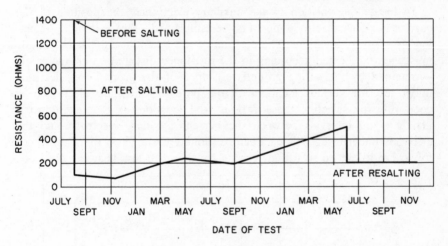

Fig. 8-7.   Changes in resistance of a ground connection in response to presence of salt over a considerable period.

many facets to consider. Even under the most favorable conditions, it has been found that the soil itself has an appreciable resistivity due to the contact resistance between the ground rods and the soil. The major problem is to be able to secure a reference point, on which to base these measurements, that is not influenced by any of the electrodes of the ground system, nor by the test electrodes themselves. From a practical viewpoint, the method of measurement used is a key consideration in evaluating the observed results. Whatever method of measurement is used, the key considerations are that the method must take into account the expected magnitude of the resistance being measured, its accuracy, the type of test equipment to be used, the power sources available for this test equipment, the installed circuit configuration, and the characteristics of the soil surrounding the electrode.

The three methods generally used to determine the resistance to ground of a ground rod electrode are:

1. Three-point
2. Fall-of-potential
3. Ratio

Each of these methods utilizes two independent auxiliary ground rod electrodes to be used in conjunction with the electrode under test. The location of these auxiliary electrodes is very important; they should be placed a sufficient distance away from the electrode under test and from each other so that any mutual interaction may be minimized.

To locate the position of the auxiliary electrodes, the position of the current auxiliary electrode must first be established. This is done by selecting an arbitrary location. The position of the potential auxiliary electrode must then be located according to the resistance distribution characteristic —obtained by measuring ground resistance of the ground rod electrode under test for various locations of the potential auxiliary electrode. A good rule for selecting these various trial locations is to pick approximately equal intervals between the current auxiliary electrode and the electrode under test. This data can be plotted as shown in Fig. 8-8. From this curve it can be seen that resistance values are low near the electrode

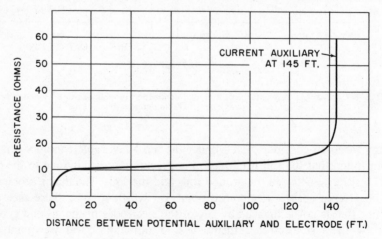

Fig. 8-8.   Resistance distribution characteristic.

under test and high near the current auxiliary electrode. At either end of
the curve, the measured resistances are influencd by interaction between
the potential auxiliary electrodes and other ground rods, while in the
middle positions, the interaction is less of a factor. A potential auxiliary
electrode in this middle region (between 20 to 100 feet) will give a good,
usable measurement of the resistance needed. If the current auxiliary electrode is too close to the electrode being tested, a constant middle region of
resistance values will not show up. In such a case the current auxiliary
electrode should be moved to another position and new readings taken.
Experience has given a good rule to follow: the potential auxiliary electrode
should be located at a distance, away from the ground electrode being
tested, that is more than half the distance between the test electrode and
the current auxiliary electrode. The current auxiliary electrode should be
at least 50, or, if possible, 100 feet away from the electrode being tested.
Consequently, the potential auxiliary electrode should then be between
25 to 50 feet away, depending on the distance chosen for the current auxiliary electrode. Another method for positioning the current and potential
auxiliary electrodes is to arrange them with the electrode under test as the
third electrode in each point of an equilateral triangle that has sides 50
feet, or more, in length.

It is sometimes possible in certain configurations, to find an equivalent
to these auxiliary electrodes by connecting them to an underground piping
system. Water supply systems are excellent for this purpose and it has
been found that resistances to ground of less than 0.5 ohm have been
measured for large water supply systems.

The three-point method of measuring ground resistance requires that
the resistances of the electrode being tested, x, and the auxiliary electrodes,
a and b, be measured two at a time. The value of x is then calculated as:

$$x = \frac{(x+a) + (x+b) - (a+b)}{2} \qquad (8\text{-}3)$$

The accuracy of the resulting magnitude of x is highly dependent on the
the value of the resistances of a and b being of the same magnitude as that
of x. These measurements may be made using either a bridge, or with a
voltmeter and ammeter. Either ac or dc may be used as a source of power.

The fall-of-potential method requires that a known magnitude of current
be passed through the electrode under test, and through one of the auxiliary
electrodes which has the other auxiliary electrode between it and the one
under test. The drop in potential between the electrode under test and
the "in-between" electrode is then measured. The ratio between this potential drop and the known value of current, is the value of the resistance
to ground. If a voltage measuring device, such as a null instrument is used,

the resistance of the electrode connected to the voltage measuring device will not appreciably affect the accuracy of the measurement. For this method, an ammeter and voltmeter may be used with either an a-c or d-c power source. Commercially available instruments such as a "megger" ground tester and a "ground-ohmer" may be used. These instruments have the advantage of giving direct readings of the resistance.

In the ratio method, the series resistance of the electrode being tested, as well as an auxiliary electrode, is measured by a Wheatstone bridge. A slide-wire potentiometer is shunted across the connections to the two electrodes and the detector is connected between the sliding contact and the second auxiliary electrode. The ratio of the unknown resistance to the total resistance of the two auxiliary electrodes, in series, is obtained. This ratio is then multiplied by the first series resistance measured, to obtain the required results. As noted, a Wheatstone bridge and a calibrated slide-wire potentiometer are needed to make these measurements. Commercial equipment, such as a "groundometer," combines these devices and gives direct readings, in ohms.

For making the measurements described, a Wheatstone bridge is a very important test instrument. Either alternating or direct current may be used when measuring ground resistances by means of a bridge, although certain precautions should be used with this apparatus. In the ordinary d-c bridge, possible errors from stray currents and contact voltages may be balanced by taking a number of readings and frequently reversing the battery polarity. With an a-c bridge, a buzzer and dry cell battery usually form the source of audible frequency with a telephone receiver as the detector. While the accuracy of this bridge will not be affected by stray ground current, the balance may be difficult to achieve if stray alternating currents are present. When a buzzer is used, the length of the leads to the auxiliary electrodes should be short enough so that errors will not result due to change of leads impedances at various frequencies.

Errors from stray currents can occur when using the voltmeter and ammeter in the measurement of resistances to ground unless the test current is large enough to render these errors negligible. Two sets of readings taken with reversed polarity will aid in minimizing the effects of stray currents.

The "megger" ground tester consists essentially of a current circuit and voltage circuit, so coupled, that a direct reading in ohms may be obtained. Current from a hand-driven, d-c generator, after passing through the current measuring coil, is commutated into low-frequency alternating current and carried into the ground connection under test, and returned by way of the current auxiliary electrode. The potential circuit is connected between the electrode being tested and the potential auxiliary electrode.

By virtue of another commutator, the potential drop is also reconverted into direct current before being applied to the potential measuring coil. This cancels the effects of any stray direct, as well as alternating, currents. Stray alternating currents will not affect the readings unless they are of the same frequency as the test current. The frequency of stray alternating currents can be varied by changing the speed of the crank. The megger ground tester is not the same instrument as the megger insulation tester (which is not suitable for testing ground connections).

The "ground ohmer" liker the megger, contains a hand-driven generator supplying alternating current to the ground electrode being measured. The method used is to balance the potential drop across the electrode being tested against the drop across a known resistance which is carrying an equal current, or multiple, of an equal current. The instrument gives a direct reading and requires only one adjustment. When balanced, the potential auxiliary draws no current so its resistance introduces no error. The effects of stray alternating currents may be limited by changing the speed of the generator until a positive reading is obtained. Stray direct currents of fairly steady character may be balanced out by adjusting the galvanometer to zero before starting the generator.

The "groundometer" is an instrument used in the ratio method. A battery and buzzer are used as the source of alternating current and a telephone receiver as the detector. After the ratio has been determined by means of a potentiometer, the circuit is converted into a Wheatstone bridge by throwing a key switch; the series resistance is then balanced against the potentiometer setting. Although this instrument affords direct reading in ohms, it requires two adjustments and is subject to the same errors as the a-c bridge.

8.5. Ground Rods

Ground rods driven into the soil may be rods or pipes, although rods are generally more economical. If soil conditions permit, a few long rods are usually more satisfactory than many short rods since the volume of soil affected increases directly with the length of the electrode below the surface. Soil resistivity generally decreases with depth due to increased moisture content. Furthermore, the deeper the ground rods, the more stability there is to the low impedance path to ground.

Driven ground rods are by far the most generally used type of ground electrodes. This is a result of the comparative ease of installation, and penetration through relatively great depths. Buried plates are used only in localities where conditions make it impractical to install driven rods. Grids of conductors are used in limited application in connection with substations. The choice of electrode metal for ground connections is not important *from the standpoint of resistance* since almost all voltage drop is in the surrounding earth.

In cases where soil conditions result in excessive corrosion of the connection, it may be desirable to use copper or zinc coated (galvanized) iron electrodes. Under ordinary conditions, iron or mild steel is the most economical material. Experience has shown that the use of dissimilar metals, at the solid soldered joint between the electrode and the ground lead (in the case of iron rods), causes no appreciable corrosion. Various chemicals, such as sodium chloride, used to reduce the resistance of ground connections, have a corrosive effect.

In direct-current installations, the electrolytic action causes serious corrosion and requires special attention. Rusting of ground rods has been shown to be of no importance. If electrodes are kept free of paint, grease, etc., and the earth is packed tightly around the electrodes so as to make good contact, the amount of contact resistance generally will be fairly stable. The formula for the approximate resistance to the flow of current away from a rod or pipe, driven vertically into the earth, will assist in the design of a ground rod layout.

$$R = \frac{100 \ \rho \ \log \dfrac{41}{D}}{2\pi 1} \quad \text{(in ohms)} \qquad (8\text{-}4)$$

where ρ is the resistivity of the surrounding soil in meter-ohms,
    1 is the length of the ground rod in centimeters,
    D is the diameter of the ground rod in centimeters.

Figures 8-9 and 8-10 show, graphically, the approximate results of Eq. 8-4.

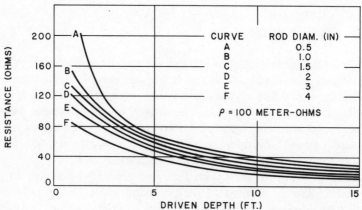

Fig. 8-9. Theoretical variation of resistance with depth for round electrodes of various diameters.

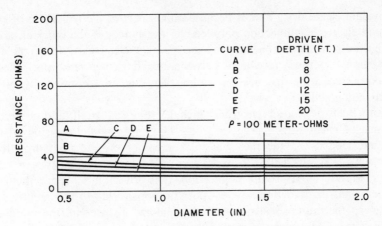

Fig. 8-10. Theoretical variation of resistance with diameter for round electrodes at various depths.

It can be noted from Fig. 8-10, that since an increase in the ground rod diameter does not have much effect on the resistance, and that thicker rods are harder to install, some other means must be used to reduce ground rod resistance if rods cannot be driven to greater depths. This can be done economically by installing additional electrodes. Parallel electrodes affords the lowest resistance to ground when their configuration is a straight line. The most desirable length of electrode is a balance between that which can be installed with the least amount of effort and that which will produce a resistance closest to the required value. Field observations, which showed the necessity for using long rods in certain locations, indicated that individual 5-foot rods had resistances to ground of from 2000 to 8000 ohms. These rods were driven into compact wet sand by using 40-foot pipes, long enough to go through the stratum of wet sand, to reach a stratum of low resistivity to ground connection resistances reduced to values ranging between 8 and 20 ohms.

Field experience has shown that a single ground rod of diameter 2a does not give as low a ground resistance measurement of that obtained by paralleling two rods each with a diameter of a. Since this is so, as long as the diameter of the rod enables it to take the punishment of being driven into the ground, larger diameters of ground rods should be avoided and parallel rods used. Sometimes, instead of solid metal rods, ordinary pipe is used for the ground electrode. These pipes pose special mechanical problems since the ends cannot be pointed to facilitate penetration into the soil and the threads must be protected from damage.

When several ground rods are connected together, their combined resistances may be higher than the calculated parallel resistances of the individual electrodes. This is because only a part of the resistance of each ground electrode connection parallels the resistances of the other electrode connections in close spacing between parallel electrodes; the remainder is common. Mutual resistance between two buried ground electrodes is proportional to the distance separating them and to the resistivity of the surrounding soil.

An effective ground electrode includes the rod itself and a certain volume of earth surrounding the rod. The shape and dimension of this volume depends on the fact that 90 percent of the potential drop from an electrode occurs within 6 to 10 feet of it. In paralleling two or more pipes or rods for a ground connection, it is advisable to space them far enough apart so the effective electrodes do not overlap to any great extent and keep the mutual resistance to a minimum. In general, the minimum spacing for 5-foot rods, in untreated soil, should be eight feet, however, between twelve and fifteen is preferable. For treated soil, the minimum should be twelve feet, but preferably between fifteen and twenty-five. The relationship between paralleling efficiency and spacing between rods is shown in Fig. 8-11, where the paralleling efficiency of a 5-foot rod is

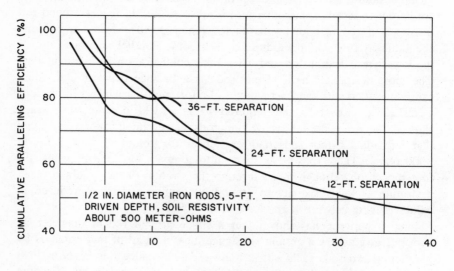

Fig. 8-11. Cumulative paralleling efficiencies of rod electrodes in untreated soils for various separations.

plotted against the number of rods for three spacings between rods. In localities where the presence of underlying rock makes it impractical to install driven rods with pipe, buried plates are sometimes used for electrodes. For designing plate electrodes, the approximate formula for the resistance to flow of current away from a circular plate buried into the earth at a considerable depth is:

$$R = \frac{110\rho}{4D} \text{ (in ohms)} \qquad (8\text{-}5)$$

where ρ is the resistivity of the surrounding soil, in meter-ohms,

D is the diameter of the circular plate, in centimeters.

The methods best suited for installing either a ground rod or a buried ground wire depends on the type of soil and the size of the grounding system. Ground rods, eight to ten feet long, are usually installed most economically by a sledge hammer. Sledging requires a minimum of driving equipment but may require considerable time per foot of rod. A modification of the sledging process has been developed consisting of a chuck and sliding hammer. Using this device has an advantage in that work may be carried on at a height convenient to workmen without a ladder or auxiliary platform. In addition, the blow is delivered to the rod at a point not far from the ground line. With this system, rods can be driven to considerable greater depths than would be possible by hand sledging. Jointed rods may be extended to considerable depths. If driving of grounds is to be undertaken on a comparatively large scale, it may be desirable to provide power-driving equipment. The gasoline hammer provides an effective tool for installing ground rods. A buried ground wire is usually installed by laying it in a trench that has been excavated by a trench digger, or by hand. Only if a very long length of ground wire has to be buried would it be considered practical, from a cost viewpoint, to utilize a wire and cable plough machine.

Table 8-5 shows formulas for calculation of resistances to ground for various types of ground rod and plate arrangements.

8.6. Grounding and Frequency

Grounding systems are inherently dependent upon the frequencies that are utilized in the grounded system. This frequency causes a change in the impedance-to-ground and, consequently, determines the effectiveness of the grounding system. At 60 cycles and low frequencies, the impedance is generally all resistive and, consequently, resistance to earth measurements are all that are necessary. As frequencies get higher, the reactive term becomes the important and controlling term. Even at higher frequencies, the resistance of an earth ground can be approximated and easily measured. It is more difficult to calculate reactance that goes to make up ground impedances for frequencies above 60 cycles. At fre-

TABLE 8.5 FORMULAS FOR THE CALCULATION OF RESISTANCE TO GROUND

	GEOMETRY	FORMULA
⌣	Hemisphere with radius, a.	$R = \dfrac{\rho}{2\pi a}$
o	One ground rod with length L, radius a.	$R = \dfrac{\rho}{2\pi L}\left(\ln\dfrac{4L}{a} - 1\right)$
o o	Two ground rods with length L, spacing S.	$R = \dfrac{\rho}{4\pi L}\left(\ln\dfrac{4L}{a} - 1\right) + \dfrac{\rho}{4\pi S}$ $\left(1 - \dfrac{L^2}{3S^3} + \dfrac{2L^4}{5S^4}\cdots\right)$
oo	Two ground rods with length L, spacing S.	$R = \dfrac{\rho}{4\pi L}\left(\ln\dfrac{4L}{a} + \ln\dfrac{4L}{S} - 2 + \right.$ $\left. \dfrac{S}{2L} - \dfrac{S^2}{16L^2} + \dfrac{S^4}{512L^4}\cdots\right)$
—	Buried horizontal wire with length 2L, depth S/2.	$R = \dfrac{\rho}{4\pi L}\left(\ln\dfrac{4L}{a} + \ln\dfrac{4L}{S} - 2 + \right.$ $\left. \dfrac{S}{2L} - \dfrac{S^2}{16L^2} + \dfrac{S^4}{512L^4}\right)$
L	Right-angle turn of wire with length of arm L, depth S/2.	$R = \dfrac{\rho}{4\pi L}\left(\ln\dfrac{2L}{a} + \ln\dfrac{2L}{S} - 0.2373\right.$ $+ 0.2146\dfrac{S}{L} + 0.1035\dfrac{S^2}{L^2} -$ $\left. 0.0424\,\dfrac{S^4}{L^4}\right)$
人	Three-point star length of arm L, depth S/2.	$R = \dfrac{\rho}{6\pi L}\left(\ln\dfrac{2L}{a} + \ln\dfrac{2L}{S}\right.$ $+ 1.071 - 0.209\,\dfrac{S}{L} + 0.238\dfrac{S^3}{L^3}$ $\left. - 0.054\dfrac{S^4}{L^4}\cdots\right)$
+	Four-point star length of arm L, depth S/2.	$R = \dfrac{\rho}{8\pi Lz}\left(\ln\dfrac{2L}{a} + \ln\dfrac{2L}{S}\right.$ $+ 2.912 - 1.071\dfrac{S}{L} + 0.645\dfrac{S^2}{L^3}$ $\left. - 0.145\dfrac{S^4}{L^4}\cdots\right)$
✳	Six- point star length of arm L, depth S/2.	$R = \dfrac{\rho}{12\pi L}\left(\ln\dfrac{2L}{a} + \ln\dfrac{2L}{S} + 6.851\right.$ $- 3.128\dfrac{S}{L} + 1.758\dfrac{S^2}{L^3} -$ $\left. 0.490\,\dfrac{S^4}{L^4}\right)$

TABLE 8-5. FORMULAS FOR CALCULATION OF RESISTANCE TO GROUND (CONT'D)

	GEOMETRY	FORMULA
✳	Eight-point star length of arm L, depth S/2.	$R = \dfrac{\rho}{16\pi L} \left(\ln \dfrac{2L}{a} + \ln \dfrac{2L}{S} + 10.98 - 5.51\,\dfrac{S}{L} + 3.26\,\dfrac{S^3}{L^3} - 1.17\,\dfrac{S^4}{L^4} \cdots \right)$
◯	Ring of wire with diameter of ring D, diameter of wire d, and depth S/2.	$R = \dfrac{\rho}{2\pi^2 D} \left(\ln \dfrac{8D}{d} + \ln \dfrac{4D}{S} \right)$
▬	Buried horizontal strip with length 2L, section a by b, depth S/2, b = a/8.	$R = \dfrac{\rho}{4\pi L} \left(\ln \dfrac{4L}{a} + \dfrac{a^2 - \pi ab}{2(a+b)^2} + \ln \dfrac{4L}{S} - 1 + \dfrac{S}{2L} - \dfrac{S^2}{16L^2} + \dfrac{S^4}{512L^4} \cdots \right)$
◍	Burned horizontal round plate with radius a, depth S/2.	$R = \dfrac{\rho}{9a} + \dfrac{\rho}{4\pi S} \left(1 - \dfrac{7a^2}{12S^2} + \dfrac{33a^4}{40S^4} \cdots \right)$
	Burned vertical round plate with radius a, depth S/2.	$R = \dfrac{\rho}{4\pi L} \left(\ln \dfrac{4L}{a} + \dfrac{a^2 - \pi ab}{2(a+b)^2} + \ln \dfrac{4L}{S} - 1 + \dfrac{S}{2L} - \dfrac{S^2}{16L^2} + \dfrac{S^4}{512L^4} + \cdots \right)$

NOTE: Approximate formulas including effects of images. Dimensions must be in centimeters to give resistance in ohms. Specific resistance of earth in ohms per cm³.

quencies below 5 kc, capacitance will exist inherently between the buried ground electrode and the surrounding soil. If alternating current is impressed on a buried ground electrode, the resultant entering current will have a "leading" component which will not be important at low frequencies (power frequencies) but important at high frequencies. The "leading" component of current, since it is capacitive, will increase as the capacitance between the buried electrode and the surrounding soil increase; this capacitance is a function of the surface area of the buried ground electrode and the resistivity of the surrounding soil. Figures 8-12, 13, and 14 show the variation of impedance with frequency. In each of these figures, it will be observed that there is an inverse proportionality between impedance and frequency and, in some cases, show, after certain frequencies, that the slope is almost flat, and that there is no further decrease in impedance as the frequency goes higher. For increased lengths of ground electrodes, the decrease in impedance was not so sharp; treated soil around the electrode also had the same effect in that there was a reduced percentage

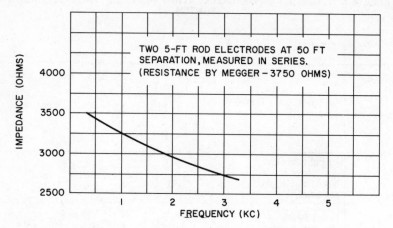

Fig. 8-12.   Impedance to ground versus frequency.

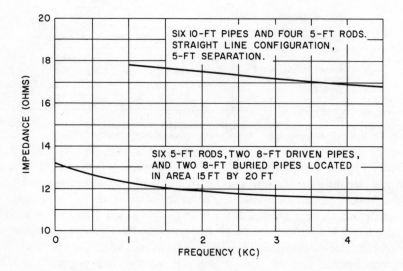

Fig. 8-13.   Relation between impedance to ground and frequency for two multiple rod
connections.

decrease in impedance. The depth of the wavefront of the impressed
voltage does not appear to make much difference. The greatest difference
between a 60-cycle sine wave and a high impulse impedance was noted
for higher resistance ground connections which had higher voltage drops.
These differences were less dependent upon voltage than upon the ground
rod configuration and the surrounding soil characteristics. A reason for

impedance reduction during the high impulses was thought to be the presence of high resistance contacts between the more conductive particles of soil at, or near, the surface of the electrode. With higher voltage, these high resistance contacts will arc over.

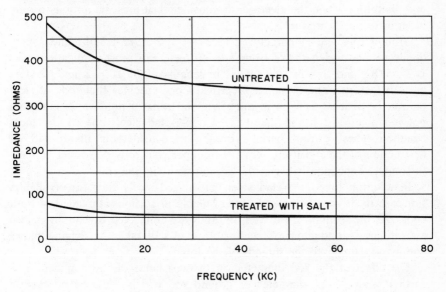

FREQUENCY (KC)

Fig. 8-14.   Relation between impedance to ground and frequency for a one-inch pipe electrode. Driven depth: 21.5 feet.

8.7.   Grounding Configurations

From the experience that has been accumulated on the current loading capacity of various ground connections, it has been found that the chemical treatment of ground rod electrodes improves the current carrying capacity of the electrodes and also makes the contact resistance problem easier to overcome. As ground current flows through the ground rod electrode, heat is generated that follows the well known I^2R heat-loss pattern. This heating effect causes the temperature of the soil surrounding the electrode to rise, driving out moisture. In normal, untreated soil, the loss of moisture causes the electrode contact resistance to rise and consequently there is a reduction in the current dissipation rating of the connection. Chemically treated soil which surrounds the ground connection overcomes this difficulty since the chemical treatment usually introduces a negative temperature coefficient of resistance so that ground currents can then be carried off with the resistance of the ground connection increasing.

When selecting a particular ground electrode configuration, it is most important to obtain as low a contact resistance as the cost factors will permit. This low resistance must be traded against as high a loading capacity as possible. For ground currents that will flow for a relatively long period of time, soil conditions alone control the current capacity and, therefore, when the electrode is considered, it must be appraised only in terms of the desired resistance.

Ground rods are manufactured in 3/8-, 1/2-, 5/8-, 3/4-, and 1-inch diameters and in lengths of from 5 to 40 feet. For most applications, the 1/2-, 5/8-, and 3/4-in. diameters, in lengths of 8, 10, 12 and 16 feet are satisfactory. The National Electrical Code specifies that rods of steel or iron be at least 5/8 in. in diameter, and rods of nonferrous materials not less than 1/2 in. in diameter. Copper-clad steel, one of the most common types of rod, permits driving to considerable depth without destruction of the rod itself, while the copper coat provides direct copper-to-copper connection between the ground wire and the rod.

In addition to copper-clad steel, galvanized steels rods are available. For ease in driving, some rods are available in sections, threaded at both ends. As the sections are driven, the rods are connected by couplings into a continuous conductor. A removable stud will take the driving blows and avoid damage to the threads of the joint.

The effect of the rod diameter on the resistance of the connection to earth is small. The diameter of ground rod will be determined mainly by the mechanical rigidity required for driving. It is advantageous to select the smallest diameter rod that meets the driving requirements. Average soil conditions will permit use of the 1/2-in. rod. The 5/8-in. rod can be driven in nearly all types of soil, and the 3/4-in. diameter rod may be reserved for exceptionally hard conditions, or for deep-driven rods.

For ordinary soil conditions, the 10-foot length has become fairly well established as a minimum standard length to meet the code requirement of a minimum of eight buried feet.

Since all ground connections described up to now had their limitations pin-pointed, it would appear that there must be some sort of an ideal grounding system. An ideal system would not, of course, be practical to install, but would show the qualities that must be stressed in a practical situation. The ideal system would consist of a single, sufficiently large, electrically homogeneous conducting plate covering the entire system to be grounded and connected to the earth at an infinite number of points. The cost of such a configuration would be excessive. The qualities of an ideal grounding system, taking due notice of the cost, can be approached by installing a suitable ground grid surrounding the installation. This ground grid would be a continuous copper cable buried beneath the surface of the earth and connected to buried ground rods, plates, or a water system. The size of the grid cable would depend on the magnitude of the currents it would have to carry, but for practical purposes, should not be less than 4/0 AWG copper cable and as large as 1,000,000 circular mils for large systems. If the cable were laid in a grid pattern, electrically, it will begin to look like an ideal system.

Grid systems usually extend over entire system installations, and may also extend some distance beyond. They consist of conductors buried a minimum of six inches in the ground, or stone fill, to form a network of squares. The sizes of the squares will vary with the particular installation, but cable spacings of 10 to 12 feet are commonly used. All cable crossings should be securely bonded and the system connected to the normal ground system as well as all equipment and structural steel work. In rocky ground, where driven electrodes are impractical, it is sometimes more economical and desirable to use a grid system in place of buried strips. In this case, the cables are usually buried at a depth of one or two feet.

Where bedrock is near the surface, or where sand is encountered, the soil may be very dry and of high resistivity; therefore, it is necessary to have an earth connection of considerable extent. Under such conditions buried metal strips, wires, or cables offer the most economical solution. Since the effectiveness of this type of electrode for lightning discharges is a function of its inductance, the use of a number of well spaced, shorted strips, in parallel, is preferable to one or more long strips. The depth at which the strips are buried is not critical. Tests by the Bureau of Standards have shown that the decrease in resistance from the minimum depth to the practicable maximum (about 18 to 36 inches) is approximately 5 percent (based on uniform soil resistivity). Similarly, the effect of conductor size is extremely small.

Because of the wide variety of shapes and combinations that can be made into a grid, it is rather difficult to treat this ground grid question analytically. If the form of the grid is complex, only a high-powered, theoretical analysis would even begin to approach an expression of the boundary conditions for the equipotential surface of the ground conductors in analytical terms. Probably the biggest stumbling block in such analytical calculations is the vaguely defined soil-resistivity measurements. These measurements change drastically for varying reasons—variations with seasons, strata, etc.—that even if an accurate solution could be reached for the geometric design of the particular grid, these variations would probably compromise the measurements.

From a practical engineering viewpoint, then, a strict analytical approach would have to be replaced with an approximate method whose strongest recommendation is that it gives results that have proven practical.

An example of a grounding grid is shown in Fig. 8-15. The resistance to infinite ground of such a network can be written as:

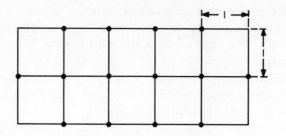

Fig. 8-15. Example of a grounding grid.

$$R = \frac{\rho}{\pi l} \left(\log \frac{2l}{a'} + K_1 \frac{1}{\sqrt{A}} - K_2 \right) \qquad (8\text{-}6)$$

Where ρ is the soil resistivity, in ohm-centimeters,

    l is the total length of all connected conductors, in cm,

    a' is $\sqrt{a \times Z}$ for conductors buried at a depth of Z cm ($a' =$ a for conductors on the earth's surface),

    A   is the area covered by conductors in cm²,

    K_1 and K_2 are constants.

Curve A in Fig. 8-16 shows the plotted coefficient K_1 for square and rectangular plates at earth surface; curves B and C show the coefficient K_1 for plates buried at different depths. These are based on tests which provide data for plates of length-to-width ratios up to 1:4. Curves B and

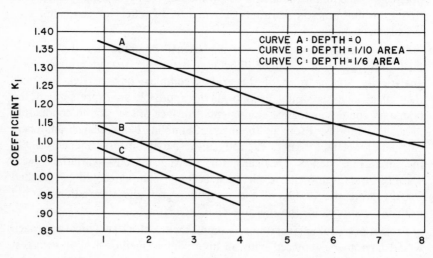

Fig. 8-16. Values of coefficient K₁ as a function of length to width ratio X of Area.

C are presented here primarily for comparison. In most practical cases, grids or rod beds are buried to a sufficient depth so the coefficients K_1, for the surface level, hold with sufficient accuracy. At worst they may produce values that are somewhat high, and, thus, are on the safe side. Coefficients K_2 shown in Fig. 8-17, have been calculated for loops encircling areas of the same shape and depth. For other configurations

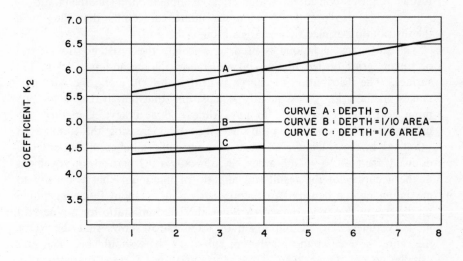

Fig. 8-17. Values of coefficient K_2 corresponding to coefficients K_1 in Fig. 8-16.

and depths, the corresponding coefficients, K_1 and K_2, may be developed accordingly. For areas other than square or 1:2 rectangles, similar results can be obtained for different ratio rectangles, or even irregular areas.

It would not be practical, from a cost viewpoint, to attach ground rods to the ground grid simply to obtain a lower resistance to earth. However, ground rods assist in other ways that make them useful. Under certain climatic changes, the soil resistivity around the grid may increase beyond the stated limit. If ground rods are attached to the grid, contact is with the deeper layer of strata that is probably not affected by such climatic changes.

8.8. Calculating Ground Resistance

To calculate the resistance to ground of a grounding grid is the same as calculating the capacitance of the grid to what is known as its "image" below the surface of the ground. The depth of this image is dependent on the resistivity of the soil surrounding the grid. Once this capacitance between the grid and its image is known, one can deduce, by a simple relationship, the resistance to ground. So that the capacitance of the grid to its image may be calculated, a technique has been developed, known as the method of sub-areas, which is applicable to a symmetrical body. Fairly accurate results can be obtained with this technique although to get such results requires considerable numerical manpulation. The technique of sub-areas is also useful for obtaining numerical results that illuminate the distribution of electrical charges around the grid.

The sub-areas technique is used to calculate the resistance to ground of square grids buried in the soil to shallow depths and parallel to the surface. The distribution of charge is nearly uniform along the wire that makes up the grid. Consequently, calculations that obtain results for one mesh grid can be expected to have slide rule accuracy. Generally, no improvement is obtained in this accuracy by increasing the number of sub-areas in the calculations. Actually, when the number of sub-areas is doubled, from 48 to 96 sub-areas, there is only a 0.2 percent improvement in the accuracy of the results. The ratio of minimum charge density to maximum charge density, for a four-mesh grid, is about 0.65 depending on the size of the area covered by the grid. The same ratio for a nine-grid mesh becomes 0.58. Comparison of these ratios shows that the lower the ratio, the greater the number of sub-areas there should be. The grid usually covers a relatively large area and the average variations in resistivity are apparent at the buried grid depth. For these reasons, high accuracy is obtainable by resistance-to-ground calculations.

The resistance of the grounding grid varies inversely with the size of the area enclosed, the diameter of the wire, and the depth to which it is buried. If the buried depth of the grid is in the same order of magnitude as the diameter of the grid wire, the resistance is high. However, if the depth is increased, the resistance diminishes rapidly until a depth is reached where the lowered resistance decreases less rapidly.

In the design of a grounding grid, the following criteria should be used:

1. The area enclosed by the grid should be as large as possible. If further decrease in resistance is desired, criss-cross conductors should be added; however, the number of meshes need not exceed sixteen in an economical design.

2. The diameter of the wire is determined by thermal rather than electrical considerations. Tubing may be used advantageously instead of wire.

3. The depth to which the grid is buried is determined by the nature of the soil. The grid should be buried as deeply as possible without involving too much expense in excavation.

The most economical method of installation for a grounding grid depends upon local soil conditions and upon how much grid must be buried. For small installations, the hand-trenching method is most widely used. For larger installations, the use of power machinery is desirable. Machines of different types that can plow wire into the ground to a depth of 20 to 30 inches are now on the market. These machines are built sturdily and must be pulled by heavy caterpillar-type tractors. The speed used depends on the type of soil into which the wire is being placed, and also on the number of roots, rocks and any other obstructions. Under favorable conditions it is possible to plow in several miles of cable per day.

The resistivity of different types of soils varies considerably in any particular area. This is due primarily to the chemical composition of the soil. Besides this chemistry dependence, the resistivity varies rather widely because of variations in ambient conditions of moisture and temperature. To perform analytical calculations to determine what the ground resistance will be at each required point is a formidable test for any arrangement of ground electrodes except the most elementary arrangement. As a matter of fact, even for a simple arrangement, assumptions have to be made, for example, that the surrounding soil has uniform resistivity. Actually, soil composition varies widely from one point to another, sometimes changing considerably in several thousand feet. It must be recalled that soil moisture content and temperature varies widely at different depths.

For these reasons, complete dependence on calculated ground resistance would be foolhardy; it can never be a substitute for direct field measurements. These measurements have become so simplified since the industry has developed direct reading, self-contained instruments, that there is no real need to make the approximations and assumptions that any calculation would require. Because these direct measurements can be used, it is very easy to determine the effectiveness of the ground system at the time of its installation, and to constantly monitor the ground system to assure that the system continues to operate without any degradation of performance. The manufacturers of such test equipment have advanced this knowledge of measurement to such a degree that provisions have been made for the most specialized types of measurements that may have to be taken on various occasions.[1]

8.9.   *Corrosion and Protection*

If large quantities of bare copper wire and plates are buried in the moist soil, good grounds can always be achieved. Such an approach makes a grounding system with excellent properties of conductivity and will last for

---

[1] J. G. Biddle Company of Philadelphia.

many years. However, if there are other buried structures—underground pipe, buried cable, steel footings—a penalty is paid for this good ground by the problems that these structures create. If a steel pipe is buried in the earth, it will gradually develop a potential of approximately 0.7 volt negative with respect to a buried bare copper ground cable. If the pipe happens to be a galvanized one, the potential difference will be 1.1 volt. This difference in potential naturally causes a current to flow from the higher to the lower points. Such current is associated with the galvanic corrosion at the steel pipe, in this case, the anodic surface. Effects at the copper ground wire tend to protect it against corrosion and various salts may be precipitated out of the soil; this reaction is cathodic.

Corrosive action can be prevented in almost any situation, but the principal limiting factor is the cost. Measures proven to be the cost useful are:

1. Insulation of buried steel from the copper ground wires.
2. Replacement of copper ground electrodes with galvanized steel ground rods.
3. Installation of sacrificial anodes to provide drainage of current, and, thereby prevent damage to buried structures.

The first of these methods (insulation of buried steel) is only a practical method for such uses as on power transmission lines. The second method has been used successfully and is discussed in detail for a particular installation. A description of the design and installation of the grounding systems at Fairless Works, U. S. Steel Corporation, presents a typical case of cathodic protection of grounding systems.[1] The terrain and geological formation at the location of the plant site at a bend of the Delaware River consists of a top strain of soil, sand and gravel, a lower strata of gravel, rubble and silt. Samples of soil were tested in the research and development laboratory. These readings varied from 10,000 to 90,000 ohms-cm. Field tests were made by driving test rods to various depths; these checked closely with the laboratory tests. Based on this resistivity data, an excessive number of twenty-foot rod electrodes would have been required, so forty-foot rods were driven deeper into the earth.

A formula was developed whereby groundbeds of any desired resistance could be obtained by installing a plurality of rods and anodes with a ratio of two rods to one anode. The steel rods were 40-feet long by 1-1/4-in. in diameter. The anodes were 10-feet long, 1-in. in diameter. The rods and anodes were spaced to twelve feet apart to give optimum resistance per minimum number of electrodes.

The rods were all connected, in parallel, by 250,000-cm. neoprene-

[1]W. E. Coleman and H. G. Frostick. "Electrical Grounding and Cathodic Protection at the Fairless Works," *Applications and Industry*, AIEE paper 55-110 (March 1955).

jacketed copper cable terminated at a test plate; the anodes were connected the same way. The test plate facilitates separation of the two elements for checking resistivity and current-voltage characteristics. The test plates also permit separation of equipment ground cables for measuring insulation to ground. Building structure ground cables were also terminated on test plates.

The connecting cables of the grid were 250,000-cm. neoprene-jacketed copper which was welded to the tops of the rod and anode electrodes; then taped with neoprene tape to eliminate galvanic action between copper and steel. The grid connection cables were supported on crushed rock and covered with rock for mechanical protection and drainage. The rods were driven with equipment similar to a pile driver. The anodes were placed in a 8-in. diameter well, bored to a depth of 15 feet; then back-filled with bentonite, sodium sulphate, and gypsum for magnesium-to-earth contact. After the grounds were completed, tests were made for resistivity, voltage and current characteristics. Table 8-6 lists the readings obtained.

TABLE 8-6. EARTH RESISTIVITY (OHMS) FOR DIFFERENT GROUND ROD MATERIALS

Location	Magnesium	Steel	Magnesium and Steel	Number of Rods	Number of Anodes
No. 1	4.2	3.3	3.0	13	6
No. 2	5.8	3.3	3.1	13	6
No. 3	2.8	2.0	2.0	13	6
No. 4	6.25	3.0	2.8	13	6

Test data have been prepared for recording periodic tests. Arrangements have been made to secure this data, and, thereby, enable control of necessary maintenance of the ground systems as well as furnish valuable data for future reference.

The third method (sacrificial anodes for cathodic protection) has provided sufficient potential and current to protect the steel ground rods as well as for building substructures within the environment of the anodes. In addition, grid system resistance has been lowered by the anodes being connected in parallel with the rods. Based on data of previous experiments, the steel ground rods with cathodic protection should last indefinitely and assure adequate ground protection. Magnesium anodes will deteriorate, but with replacement, not for 20 years or more.

The cathodic protected grounding systems described, not only provide the necessary low resistance to earth, but offer cathodic protection to adjacent metallic substructures.

A highly satisfactory solution to the cathodic protection problem for new electric cable installations includes the following:

1. Use of recognized high resistance coatings on the sheath.
2. Insulation of the sheath from external grounds, etc.
3. Provision of special heavy-duty and reliable cross-bond grounding connections to the sheaths at selected locations.
4. Provision of a special generating device (or devices) to provide adequate cathodic protection.
5. Provision of special grounding devices that will not appreciably increase or adversely interfere with the cathodic protection scheme.

Necessary connections that have to be made to ground electrodes are best accomplished by use of the exothermic process—widely known as the Cadweld process, and available from a number of manufacturers. This process has been used successfully in recent years, because it has represented great savings in time and cost. It eliminates contact resistance, provides a permanent connection, is relatively corrosion free, and has great flexibility and versatility. Its principal disadvantage is its permanency: it requires separate disconnecting means, such as an above-ground, bolted joint for monitoring of the ground system by resistance measurements. Other methods of joining, such as brazing or welding, are satisfactory depending on the quality of the finished joint which is not as easy to control as a joint formed by an exothermic process. Joining to pipe presents several problems. Clamp-type fittings are relatively expensive, since they must obviously accommodate large pipe, in addition to a relatively small conductor. Welding or brazing to the pipe will cause localized stress which may impair the function of the pipe, particularly if it contains fluid under high pressure. The exothermic process can also be used on pipes.

9 – GROUNDING OF STRUCTURES AND BUILDINGS

9.1. Introduction

In the last chapter, a low resistance connection to the earth was obtained —the largest equipotential plane possible—to which all ground installations must be referenced. The hull of a ship and the fuselage of a plane are other comparable reference planes to which all grounds are ultimately referenced. In this chapter, a more detailed study of the grounding system will be made, establishing criteria for grounding connections made to the earth ground. We will be primarily concerned with the control of conducted interference through common ground connections, and the use interference reduction of equipment, in terms of its smallest black box, to connect with the earth ground.

A distinction must be drawn between the two types of grounds that are referenced to earth ground:

1. Grounding of the current-carrying parts of a system.
2. Grounding of noncurrent-carrying parts.

The first includes the ground returns of electronic circuitry within the equipment, ground returns of the power supplies for the equipment, and grounding of the prime power systems, especially those using the ground return for carrying fault currents. Each of these ground returns will be treated in detail—the grounding of prime power systems being treated separately in Chapter 11. Grounding of noncurrent-carrying parts of a system includes grounding of all noncurrent-carrying parts of equipment, buildings and structural steel, noncurrent-carrying parts of substations (where prime power is brought in), the fences, lightning arrestors, and enclosures.

Typical grounding systems for substations and buildings that house electrical or electronic equipment are shown in Figs. 9-1, 9-2, 9-3 and 9-4. Figure 9-1 shows the grounding installation at a substation where the prime power will be brought into an installation. Figure 9-2 is a cutaway section of a building and shows, primarily, a heavy electrical instal-

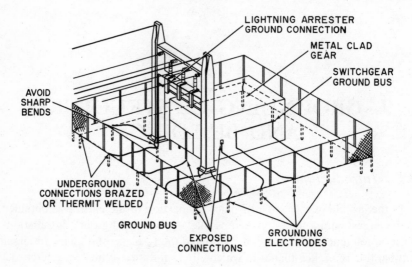

Fig. 9-1. Typical grounding system for an outdoor substation. (From L. J. Carpenter, "Equipment Grounding for Industrial Plants," **Electrical Engineering,** March 1954)

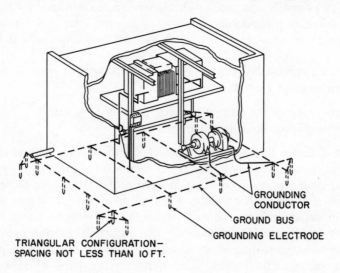

Fig. 9-2. Typical grounding system for a building and heavy electric apparatus in the building. (From L. J. Carpenter, **op. cit.**)

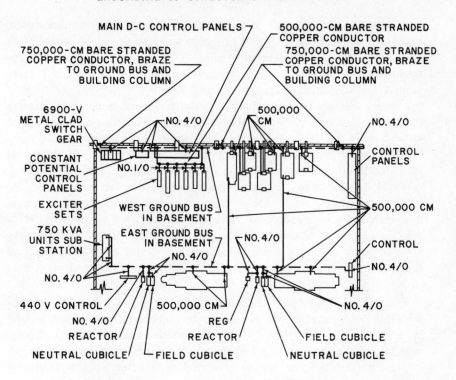

Fig. 9-3. Typical grounding system for a large motor room. (From L. J. Carpenter, op. cit.)

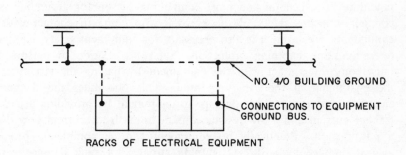

RACKS OF ELECTRICAL EQUIPMENT

Fig. 9-4. Typical grounding for an electronic equipment installation.

lation that might be seen at a radar site where a large antenna might be rotated. Figure 9-3 shows a typical large area grounding within a building, including a variety of equipment. Figure 9-4 depicts a typical grounding for an electronic equipment installation.

In substation grounding (Fig. 9-1), attention must be given to the relationship of the grounding of the noncurrent-carrying part to the power distribution system ground. Coordination is of the utmost importance, because if a line-to-ground fault in the power system should occur (when one of the conductors of a three-phase power system is grounded unintentionally), such large fault currents would flow through the earth around the substation that large potentials may be set up, resulting in dangerous voltages being established between various noncurrent-carrying parts of the system. It will be shown in a later chapter that an adequate ground mass must be available. Additional coordination is necessary between the prime power system, lightning-arrestor ground subsystem and the ground subsystem for the noncurrent-carrying parts. Usually a common ground mass, for the prime power protective system and the lightning arrestors, solves this problem. The utilization of such common masses reduces impedances to the earth and between subsystems. This goes a long way toward reducing any potential differences that may arise between the earth connection and the various conducting parts of the system. This is most important if the substation is located in an area of high earth resistivity.

The structural steel and steel plate floors (if any) of a building containing electrical equipment should always be considered part of the ground system and be connected to it at as many points as practical. Steel fences, especially those located around prime power equipment, must be grounded. It must be remembered that any building or structure, unless extremely small and containing little equipment, represents a relatively complex problem to effectively maintain it at, or as close as is practical to, earth potential. The general and most compelling reason for grounding is, of course, to insure safety of the persons who come in contact with the equipment. However, it is also necessary for equipment safety, equipment operation, and lightning protection. Safety is assured to persons who must come in contact with the equipment by having the structure and the equipment at the same potential. This eliminates the dangers of electric shock and possible damage to equipment by providing a path for leakage current and a low resistance path to earth for current flow during a power fault. Practically no equipment can be completely protected against damage by a direct lightning stroke, but such damage can be minimized if a low resistance path to the earth is provided for the lightning current. A very dangerous situation exists when an equipment installation is housed in a building that does not provide a low resistance path, because then the lightning stroke is permitted to seek its own low resistance path —perhaps through equipment that might be completely destroyed by the passage of such current.

The first requirement of a building, or structure ground system, is to ensure the safety of persons who come in contact with accessible noncurrent-carrying metallic parts of equipment that is supposedly electrically de-energized, but which has become temporarily energized from the power circuit. Energizing may be caused by failure of the insulation, breakage or displacement of a conductor by induced voltage from an adjoining circuit, or by an arc jumping from a power circuit.

A second requirement is that arrestor grounds be provided for a low impedance path to earth for lightning discharges, and for high voltages from high frequency circuits to lightning arrestors so that discharges may be quickly dissipated to protect electrical equipment from damage or destruction.

A third requirement is that grounds be provided to properly operate the prime power system. This requires the grounding of some point in the electrical circuit, such as the neutral of rotating machines, power transformers and instrument transformers. These grounds may carry heavy power and fault currents and must be capable of doing so without injury to the ground system or causing a potential gradient that might endanger personnel or equipment.

The most general requirement for all ground connections is that they remain intact, ready to perform at all times. There are three other general requirments:

1. A conductor must be of sufficient size that it will not fuse, or burn open, under the most severe operating or fault conditions. The maximum current and length of time required to allow a fault to clear determines this size.

2. Serious corrosion of the conductor must be prevented. Corrosion usually occurs at the junction of dissimilar metals. To eliminate corrosion, all buried joints should be of similar metals, if practical. However, if it is necessary to use joints of dissimilar metals, they should be readily accessible for inspection to determine that corrosion has not developed.

3. Ground wires must be given reasonable mechanical protection in their installed configurations. Usually, conductors are mounted in places where danger of mechanical damage is least likely.

All grounding systems are ultimately dependent upon the adequacy of their earth connection. This connection may be obtained either by an electrode system being installed specifically for grounding purposes, or, by an underground metallic water pipe system. The National Electrical Code specifies an adequate ground as a continuous underground water, or gas pipe system, with a resistance to earth of less than 3 ohms; metal building, structural members, local metallic underground piping system, metal well casings, etc., and, generally with a resistance substantially less than 25 ohms.

It is interesting to note that public utility companies, who provide electrical energy and have always had a deep concern for the grounding problem, specify the following requirements: that resistance for various installation, when measured alone, disconnected from transmission line ground wires, etc., should not exceed certain quanties, as those listed in Table 9-1.

TABLE 9-1.

Generating stations	1 ohm
66 kv and higher voltage substations	1 ohm
Substations of lower voltages than 66 kv (except those listed below)	5 ohms
34.5-4kv and 13.2-2.4kv outdoor unit substations made up of transformer banks which are not larger than 2000kva each.	15 ohms

A good general rule, however, widely accepted and with successful operating experience behind it, is that building and structure grounds be within a 5- to 15-ohm range.

An important factor in reducing the resistance of an installation, is the quality of the connection between the individual structural members and the structure and ground connection. Careful attention must be given to the size and type of the particular bond installed. These will be discussed more fully in connection with specific equipment.

The minimum requirement for a ground system within a building is that it consist of a bare, copper ground conductor at least No. 4/0 AWG in size. This ground conductor must be installed around the periphery of the building with enough cross-grid conductors so that all ground connections to equipment can be made easily. The conductor may be buried in the concrete slab under the equipment with pigtail conductors protruding above the concrete for equipment grounds, or it may run along the walls of the building or be carried in a cable tray, etc. This ground conductor should also connect to all outside building steel columns and, on larger buildings, include a fair number of inside steel columns; if steel floor plating is used, the ground connection should be made to it.

Grounding requirements of a structure can be based on engineering approximations, which in turn, are based on experience, or upon an exact analytical approach depending upon the magnitudes of current that will flow in the ground systems under different conditions of operation. Obviously, the analytical solution is the most exact, but unfortunately, it requires a great deal of data that is oftentimes not available to the design engineer.

An approximation of the grounding requirements can be made with relative ease if the design engineer knows where the structure is located, architectural and structural details and, of course, the various equipments that will be installed in the structure. An analytical solution requires that calculations be made that will determine the magnitude of potential gradients occurring at various times during operation of the equipment. Particular attention must be paid to gradients (that will occur when faults exist in the prime power system), since they may render the installation dangerous to persons coming in contact with equipment because of the voltage that may exist between grounded equipment and the actual earth.

Unfortunately, accurate precalculation of these gradients and potentials is seldom practical, and it is emphasized, a low station ground is no guarantee of safety. There is no simple relation between the resistance of the entire ground system and maximum shock potential. A station of relatively low ground resistance may be dangerous under some circumstances, while some stations with high resistances are, or can be, made safe by careful design. In addition to the magnitude of local gradients, other factors enter the safety problem, including duration of shock, body resistance, physical condition of the individual, and probability of contact. The misconception that any grounded object can be safely touched has resulted in many tragic accidents. While it is true that the achievement of safety from ground fault gradients may never become an exact science, considerable valuable information is available. Application of this knowledge could reduce the "ignorance factors."

Tolerable potential differences between any two points of contact can be calculated in terms of the circuit constants and allowable body current. According to Thevenin's theorem, the body current between these two points will be equal to the flow through the body resistance, in series, caused by pre-existing voltage, with the external network connecting the points of contact. However, a simplified approach is adequate. Since it is necessary to limit the body current to some value in milliamperes, and, since the fault currents concerned are expressed in hundreds, or, possibly, thousands of amperes, the change in pre-existing voltage, by current diverted through the body, can be neglected. It can be assumed that the full potential difference existing prior to contact will still be present to force current through the body. Due to fault gradients, some electrical power companies establish arbitrary voltage limits, such as 150 volts, for step-and-touch potentials.

9.2. Mechanical Items

The National Electrical Code specifies that exposed conductive materials enclosing electric equipment, or forming a part of such equipment, should be grounded to prevent a potential above ground on the equipment; this equipment may be cabinets, junction boxes, outlet boxes, controllers, cable trays, conduit, couplings, fittings, cable armor, lead sheath, grill work, switch-gear, transformers, switchboard frames, motors, generators, elevators, frames and tracks of cranes, and portable equipment.

Because of the great number of conductor enclosure items that are part of this subject, all cannot be described in detail, but general principles should be mentioned. Metal boxes, cabinets and fittings, or noncurrent-carrying metal parts of other fixed equipment, if metallically connected to grounded cable armor or metal raceway, are considered grounded by such connections. Where the metal enclosure of a wiring system is used as part of the protective grounding, the electrical continuity of the enclosure should be assured, with special attention given to obtaining secure fastenings by the proper installation of bonding straps.

For conduit, armored cable, or metal raceways, the ground connection should be as near as possible to the point where the conductors in the raceway system receive their power supply.

The lead sheaths, shields, and armor of three-conductor and small single-conductor (less than 500,000 circular mils) power cables should be grounded at both ends. Communication cables should also be grounded at both ends. In long cables, it is sometimes desirable that sheaths be grounded at several intermediate points.

The lead sheath, shield, and armor of large, single-conductor cables (500,000 circular mils and above) should only be grounded at one end to prevent circulating currents. The sheath, shield, and armor of such a cable should be insulated from the ground throughout its length, unless the cable is excessively long; then, insulating joints must be provided to permit grounding at a sufficient number of points to keep the sheath voltage down to desirable limits. For example, the mutual reactance to neutral (X_m) for a 500,000 circular mils, standard strand cable (varnish-cambric insulated), lead sheathed (approximate outside diameter 1.5 inches), with equivalent spacing between cables of 3 inches, is approximately 0.0525 ohm per 1000 feet. Assuming a current (I_c) of 400 amperes in the conductor, the induced voltage to neutral per 1000 feet can be calculated from the formula:

$$e_3 = I_c\, X_m \qquad\qquad (9\text{-}1)$$
$$= 400 \times 0.0525 = 21 \text{ volts}$$

The sheath voltage of lead-sheathed cable should be limited to from 12 to 15 volts. For jacket cable, sheath voltages of 40 to 50 volts may be permitted because the jacket acts as an insulator. The minimum size ground conductor for lead-cable sheaths should be No. 1/0 copper.

If conduits, coupling, or fittings with protective coatings of nonconducting material, such as enamel, are used, such coatings should be entirely removed from the threads of both couplings and conduit and fitting surfaces (where the conduit or ground clamps are secured), to obtain the required good electric connection. Grounded pipes should be free from scale, rust, etc., at the place of attachment of ground clamps. In installations where a great deal of moisture is present, conduits, attached to metal cabinets, cutout, pull, or junction boxes by locknuts and bushings should be bonded.

The grounding conductor should be attached to the grounding electrode by means of the following:

1. Suitable bolted clamp of cast bronze, brass, or cast iron (malleable or plain).
2. Pipe fitting, plug, or other suitable device, screwed into pipe or into the fitting.
3. Brazing, welding, or the equivalent. (Soldered connections should not be used.)

Where practicable, the point of attachment should be accessible.

Ground clamps, for use on copper water tubing, and copper, brass, or lead piping should preferably be copper, while those for use on galvanized or iron piping should be cast iron or similar material.

In any good ground system, buses and conductors should be made of copper, except where impractical. If the ground conductor is not copper, its current carrying capacity should not be less than the allowable copper conductor for such a purpose. All joints in the ground bus should be brazed or welded, except in specific situations. The sizes of the ground buses should be the minimum sizes as listed in Table 9-2. Current values are root-mean-square symmetrical values for short-circuit currents.

TABLE 9-2.

Condition	Minimum Standard Cable	Copper Size Bar Copper
Current up to 15,000 amps	No. 4/0 cable	1 in. × 1/4 in.
15,000 to 20,000 amps	350,000 cm	1 in. × 1/4 in.
20,000 to 35,000 amps	500,000 cm	2 in. × 1/4 in.
35,000 to 45,000 amps	750,000 cm	2 in. × 1/4 in.
45,000 to 50,000 amps	750,000 cm	3 in. × 1/4 in.
Above 50,000 amps		

9.3. Effects of Power Systems on Communication Systems

In structures and buildings where it is necessary to run power and communication systems in close proximity, a coupling problem generally exists between them. This coupling generally leads to unwanted voltages being induced into the communication system, whose magnitude is dependent upon a number of factors including the physical separation of the systems, the magnitude of the harmonics in the power system, the length of the affected cables, etc. Any communication circuit that is close to a power circuit will have unequal voltages induced in the inductors located in positions of different field strengths.

Capacitive coupling exists because of the close proximity of communication circuits to the electrostatic field of the conductor. And, of course, direct coupling exists because of the common ground system between the power and communication circuits, causing interference due to the potential difference arising from changing ground currents and random power line noise. These currents and noise can be reduced considerably by the use of neutral impedance devices and by careful selection of a grounding point. This grounding point can be moved so that its ultimate location can materially assist in reducing the effect of fault currents and even eliminate the total effect of a certain percentage of faults. Neutral impedance devices provide an important and effective method for controlling low-frequency coupling, particularly where the exposures are relatively close to the ground point.

The theoretical treatment of this coupling problem has been treated at great length in a number of texts, but design criteria have generally come out of direct experience on operating systems. A good set of criteria can be developed from the design experience of large military systems where it has been necessary to transmit communication signals over distances several hundred feet (within a structure) and running parallel to necessary power circuits.

Voltages induced in a communication circuit wire by a single-phase power circuit can be calculated from[1]:

$$e_{induced} = 7.42 j\omega \left(\log \frac{r_1}{r_2} \right) li(10^{-4}) \text{ volts} \qquad (9\text{-}2)$$

where ω is $2\pi f$,

   r_1 is the distance between the communication conductor and one power conductor,

   r_2 is the distance between the communication conductor and the second power conductor,

   l is the length of the parallel exposure (in miles),,

   i is the current in the power system.

A simplified approximation of Eq. 9-2 is:

[1]H. G. Schwarz, "Design of a Wire Communication System in a Shielded Passageway of the BMEWS Radar System," *Proceedings of the Fifth Conference on Radio Interference,* Armour Research Foundation (October 1959).

$$e_{induced} = 3.835\frac{fdi}{r}(10^{-4}) \text{ volts per 1000 ft} \qquad (9\text{-}3)$$

where f is frequency (60 cycles per second),

      r is the separation between the power and communication wire (11 ft.)

      d is the separation between the power wires (1.25 in.),

      i is the power current (5,775 amps).

These equations can be used to develop criteria for a working installation where it is necessary to run power and communication cables side by side. It has been reported that on a recently completed military installation it was necessary to run power and communication cables parallel to each other through a long underground tunnel approximately 4000 feet in length. The size of the structure was such that a minimum separation of 11 feet was possible. The power system was a 60-cycle, three-phase system delta, connected at the load end, and with a grounded wye connection on the source end. Utilizing Eq. 9-3, $e_{induced}$ is calculated to be 5.0 volts for the 4000 feet of exposure. However, this result has to be qualified because of the actual conditions that existed. In a three-phase system, power was carried by 25 cables, and induced voltage was affected by the shielding of cable armors, trays, etc. The following correction factors were selected and are considered sound (Table 9-3.):

TABLE 9-3.

CONDITION	ATTENUATION
3-phase system	−6db
Random addition of 25 cables (90 percent probability)	−10db
Shielding by armor, etc.	−6db
Twisting of power cables	−26db
	−48db

With such an attenuation, $e_{induced}$ becomes 20 millivolts. If, finally the factor is introduced by which the communication cables are made up of balanced twisted pairs, a balanced-to-unbalanced ratio of -80 db can then be assumed at 60 cps. This, then, gives the estimated induced voltage appearing on the balanced line as 2 microvolts.

The calculated figure of 2 microvolts is considerably below the tolerable interference levels for wire and data communication circuits. Consequently, the following criteria can be set down as a design guide:

1. Utilize the maximum permissible separation of power and communication circuits.

2. Take full advantage of the inherent shielding effectiveness of the installed cable trays, structures, etc.
3. Twist the power cables within practical limitations.
4. Always use twisted balanced pairs for the communication circuits.

These criteria have been used effectively to minimize the effect of power cables on communication circuits within buildings and structures. These same criteria apply for special conditions of the power system, such as when a fault current is present.

10 – GROUNDING OF EQUIPMENT

10.1. Introduction

The most general, and, ultimately, the most important reason for the grounding of any type of equipment is to make sure that no dangerous voltages are present on accessible parts of equipment that will endanger the safety of persons who come in contact with it. Under this general reason, there are many and varied special reasons for specific types of equipment installation; one of the most important is, of course, the reduction of interference. On large military installations, because of the critical function of some operations, a criterion has to be arbitrarily established that places the importance of proper operation of the equipment on the same level as the safety of personnel. Needless to say, no one will suggest that a human life can be declared expendable simply to be assured that a military defense system will function. So a criterion should be established whereby safety of personnel and operating in the intended manner conditions can be met.

Equipment grounding generally is designed to provide maximum safety for operators and other persons who must intentionally, or accidentally, come in contact with the equipment. All parts of the steel structures, motors and generator frames, control equipment enclosures, switchgear, cable armor, conduit, portable electrical equipment, and all metallic bodies near a conducting portion of an electrical circuit, should be at ground potential. The National Electrical Code gives rules for grounding which have the widest commercial application. Generally, these same rules, with more detailed information added, apply equally to all types of installation, civilian or military.

If external contact is made between an electric circuit and any metallic body, the metallic body will assume a potential above ground, equal to the

173

same potential above ground of the electrical circuit. If the case on an equipment that uses 28-V d-c power comes in contact with this power, it will assume a potential of 28-V dc. If the metallic body does not have a good ground connection, there will be no way in which this potential difference can be conducted away. This is the case even if there is a direct contact to ground, however through a high resistance contact. This high resistance contact may be several *thousand* ohms rather than several ohms as would be expected in a good ground. If the potential differences between the conducting portion and ground are similar to those found in most installations, the conducting portion will be at a potential above ground and there will be a flow of current to ground, through the leakage paths, which may cause undesired effects.

In the event of an accident to insulation, the actual grounding of the conducting body allows sufficient current flow to ensure positive operation of ground detecting devices and the operation of fuses and circuit breakers. It also prevents the potential, between a conducting body and ground, from rising to a dangerous value. Thus, it is essential that the impedance of the return path for ground fault currents be as low as possible, and that the grounding conductors be large enough to carry the maximum ground current, for a reasonable time, without burning off.

The 60-cycle reactance of a ground return circuit, remote from the outgoing circuit conductor, will probably be high compared to its resistance, and limit the magnitude of ground return current which it will carry. When circuit conductors are enclosed in a metallic enclosure, such as a conduit, wire way, bus enclosure or armor, the metallic enclosure will carry a major portion of the return fault current. Failure to provide a continuous path in the enclosure will result in arcing and heating at breaks and joints. If an additional current carrying capacity is required in the return circuit, it should be added by means of additional conductors (green wire) inside the conduit or metallic enclosure. The following types of equipment should always be grounded:

1. Conductor enclosure, conduit, trays, etc.
2. All motors and their associated control devices.
3. Fixed equipment constructed of conducting materials, such as tanks, compressors, etc.
4. All portable electrical equipment.
5. Communication equipment and all racks, enclosures, chassis, frames.

An effective equipment grounding system should maintain a low potential difference between machine frames, equipment enclosures, and metallic parts to avoid electric shock to persons and unwanted circulating currents to other equipments; it must consist of a sufficiently large mass of conducting material to carry away maximum currents that might be presented to the grounding conductors without causing any damage or degradation to these conductors.

10.2. Detailed Requirements

The grounding of electrical equipment has many details that have to be considered in coming up with a good design. Any item of conducting material that encloses, or is in close proximity to, an electrical circuit should be at ground potential at all times. A low-impedance path must be provided intentionally, otherwise, the item may become isolated from ground and be connected to earth through a poor conductor of many-ohms resistance.

There are three general conditions which govern the adequacy of equipment grounding:

1. The condition of extremely high resistance isolation from ground; the equipment assumes the potential of the circuit with which it has come in contact and becomes a hazard to persons who may come in contact with it.
2. The condition of several thousand ohms resistance to ground through a poor conducting path; the equipment structure again assumes the potential of the circuit with which it has come in contact, and again becomes a hazard to persons. Also, the moderate resistance path or leakage path to ground allows enough current flow to cause heating and the ignition of any combustible material present.
3. The condition of proper ground connections with a minimum resistance and adequate ground conductor size to carry the maximum ground current for a short time. In this case, the equipment potential does not rise high enough above ground to be dangerous to persons and the current flow does not cause heating. Actually the ground current flow is only of such magnitude as to actuate protective devices. This is the design objective that should be pursued.

In grounding of electrical equipment, detailed criteria should be worked out for each installation. These should be based on the general criteria which follows.

The grounding conductor should be a system neutral or a current carrying conductor. The enclosing cases, mounting frames, etc., of all switches, circuit breakers, control panels, motors and other electrical, or electrically operated, equipment should be grounded by running a grounding conductor from a ground (established at the source of supply) to the equipment to be grounded. The grounding conductor (preferably bare or green wire) should be run inside the conduit, or wiring channel, enclosing the power conductors that supply the equipment, or as in the case of a multiconductor cable, be located inside the sheath of the cable. In the case of a lead-sheathed power cable, the lead sheath may be used as the grounding conductor and must be connected to ground at both ends. The farther away the ground return is physically from the supply conductor, the higher its inductive reactance.

All metallic conduits, wiring channels, and armor of cables should be connected at each end of the grounding conductor, or firmly attached, with a good electrical contact to a properly grounded connection box. All ground connections should be connected to the grounding conductor which in turn should be run through the connection box.

Where circuits consist of two or more power conductors in a conduit, or wiring channel, the grounding conductor may be one standard wire size smaller than the power conductor, but in no case smaller than No. 12 AWG or larger than No. 4/0 AWG. The grounding conductor should be a bare, solid conductor, or stranded, and covered with green flamenal (type TW) jacket up to No. 2 AWG. Larger sizes may be bare or stranded. If green is not available, the grounding conductor should be clearly and permanently identified at all terminating points by use of green adhesive marking tape code markers, or other similar identifying means.

In multiconductor cables, the green conductor should be used as the grounding conductor and the white as the system neutral.

In interlocked armor, use the two or three grounding conductors located in the interstices between the larger current-carrying power and neutral conductors. Due to corrosive action causing increased resistance with age, the sheath of the interlocked armor does not make a satisfactory ground. The combined sizes of the grounding conductors furnished with this type of interlocked armor cable equals about 50 percent of the size of one power conductor.

If a machine frame switchgear enclosure, control panel, etc., is located within six feet of a metallic ground (such as building steel, metal pipes, or other machine frames), and is not interconnected, mechanically, by structural steel, pipes, conduits, etc., whose circuit lengths are less than 100 feet, a bare copper conductor of a size previously discussed should be used to directly interconnect the two items.

Lighting fixtures, whether incandescent, mercury, or fluorescent, should be grounded in accordance with the practices previously outlined for equipment. A continuous row of fixtures may be considered as one fixture if the mechanical connections between fixtures are such that electrical continuity is assured.

Static electricity discharge arcs have caused a considerable number of accidents to personnel, and have often caused explosions resulting in fires causing loss of life and property by discharging in an explosive atmosphere. Application of the best known building ground techniques is not always an adequate solution. Each installation in a hazardous location should be studied separately to determine the necessity and means of safely removing static charges.

Static electricity is produced by the action of contact and separation of dissimilar substances (one of which is an insulator), such as a rapidly moving belt and pulley, liquid flowing rapidly through a pipe, or gas escaping from a nozzle. The result is two substances with positive and negative charges. There is no one cure-all for all electrostatic charges. The best preventive measures are to ground, properly, all equipment, structures, containers, and metallic items in the area, and to provide a means of removing charges as they are produced. This can be accomplished using conducting belts or belt dressing on all belt drives, grounded conducting floors, conducting shoes, and, possibly, nonstatic-producing clothing for employees in the area.

All portable equipment, i.e., any equipment not permanently installed, but used as part of the normal operation of an installation at various places in the installation, should be adequately grounded; these include such equipment as portable tools, extension lights, arc welders, etc., which are used in installation maintenance. Grounding of portable devices may be accomplished by three methods:

1. Utilization of the metal enclosure housing the power conductors to the portable equipment, and an approved plug with a third pin to connect the metal enclosure to ground.
2. Using a separate grounding conductor in the portable power cord, and an approved three-prong plug (whose third pin makes good electrical contact to the grounding conductor in the power system).
3. Use of a clamp-type terminal dangling from the plug end that is fastened to a close-at-hand, readily available, ground connection.

Of these three methods, the first two have had rather wide acceptance and have been used successfully because they incorporate into their design an automatic ground connection, as it were. The third method, which requires a special attention on the part of the user and actual special equipment in a readily accessible ground terminal, has not proven too successful and should be used with a great deal of caution.

10.3. Ground Conductor Sizes

The size of the ground conductor is determined primarily by the size of the conductor supplying power to the equipment. Data for determining these sizes are given in Table 10-1.

TABLE 10-1.

Size of Largest Power Conductor or Equivalent for Multiple Conductors (AWG No.)	Size of Copper Grounding Conductor (AWG No.)
2 or smaller	8
1 or 1/0	6
2/0 or 3/0	4
over 3/0 up to 350,000 cm	2
over 350,000 cm up to 600,000 cm	1/0
over 600,000 cm up to 1,100,000 cm	2/0
over 1,100,000 cm	3/0

If the wiring system is not grounded at the installation, the size of a grounding conductor for a raceway, the metal sheath or armor of a service cable, and service equipment should not be less than is given in Table 10-2.

TABLE 10-2.

Size of Largest Power Conductor or Equivalent for Multiple Conductors (AWG No.)	Size of Grounding Conductor		
	Copper Wire (AWG. No.)	Conduit or Pipe Trade Size (inches)	Metallic Tubing Trade Size (inches)
2 or smaller	8	1/2	1/2
1 or 1/0	6	1/2	1
2/0 or 3/0	4	3/4	1-1/4
over 3/0 up to 350,000 cm	2	3/4	2
over 350,000 cm up to 600,000 cm	1/0	1	2
over 600,000 cm up to 1,1000,000 cm	2/0	1	2
over 1,100,000 cm	3/0	1	2

The size of the grounding conductor is determined by the rating of the overcurrent protective device used with the power circuits as part of the equipment to be grounded. This data is shown in Table 10-3.

To avoid higher electrical resistance within the grounding system, all grounding conductors must be adequately bonded. Bonding should provide substantial and reliable mechanical connections and assure good electrical conductivity. Bonds should be mechanically strong and not affected adversely by electrolysis. For small size conductors, AWG Nos. 14 to 4, a good bond can be achieved with terminal screw sizes listed in Table 10-4.

For larger size conductors, bonding can be accomplished using the exothermic process. Details of this will be discussed later in connection with problems associated with electronic equipment.

TABLE 10-3.

Rating Amperes	Size of Grounding Conductor		
	Copper Wire (AWG No.)	Conduit or Pipe (inches)	Electrical Metallic Tubing (inches)
20	16	1/2	1/2
30	14	1/2	1/2
40	12	1/2	1/2
60	10	1/2	1/2
100	8	1/2	1/2
200	6	1/2	1
400	4	3/4	1-1/4
600	2	3/4	1-1/4
800	1/0	1	2
1000	2/0	1	2
1200	3/0	1	2

TABLE 10-4.

AWG Size of Conductor	Minimum Size of Screw
14-8[1]	No. 10
6	1/4 inch
4	5/16 inch

[1]The common form of wire-binding screw is not recognized for securing wire larger than No. 8 AWG solid, or No. 10 AWG stranded.

So that good electrical conductivity may be preserved, surface coatings, such as preservatives, enamels, etc., should be removed prior to bonding a ground connection. When such a coating is removed, it should be refinished to return it to its original state. A clear finish, conforming to military specification MIL-L-6806, is good to use in such cases.

10.4. Special Items

Specific rules for grounding can be given for many kinds of electrical equipment commonly used in many installations. Equipment frames and bedplates for generators, motors, and other rotating apparatus, should be grounded according to the specifications listed in Table 10-5.

TABLE 10-5.

Equipment	Ground Connection for Equipment Located in Oily, Wet or Hazardous Locations	Ground Connection for Equipment Not Located in Oily, Wet or Hazardous Locations
Motors, generators and rotating equipment above 300v, except fractional HP Motors.	Equal in cross-section to size of machine supply leads, but not greater than ground bus.	Equal in cross-section to size of machine supply leads but not greater than ground bus.
Integral HP motors of 300v and less.	Equal in cross-section to size of machine supply leads but not greater than 1 in. x 1/4 in.	Equal in cross-section to size of machine supply leads but not greater than 1 in. x 1/4 in. (See Note)
Fractional HP motors above 300v.	Equal in cross-section to size of machine supply leads but not greater than 1 in. x 1/4 in.	Equal in cross-section to size of machine supply leads but not greater than 1 in. x 1/4 in.
Fractional Horsepower motors of 300v and less.	Equal in cross-section to size of machine supply leads but not greater than 1 in. x 1/4 in.	No ground connection required.
Portable motors above 150 v.	Frame must be grounded by separate conductor in supply cable of same size as main leads.	Frame must be grounded by separate conductor in supply cable of same size as main leads.
Portable motors 150v and below.	Frame must be grounded by separate conductor in supply cable of same size as main leads.	Frame must be grounded by separate conductor in supply cable of same size as main leads.

NOTE: No additional ground is required if the motor is mounted on grounded metal structures or attached to grounded metal conduit or the sheath of metallic cable. Shielding tape on nonmetallic cable should not be used for this purpose.

Power transformers, or grounding transformers, should have tanks or cases grounded with a connection equal in cross-section to the maximum lead size connected to the transformer, but not larger than the main ground conductor in the installation. The tanks or cases of potential transformers should be grounded except where mounted on grounded steel structure or the primary voltage is less than 150 volts to ground. The ground connector, if practical should be equal to, or larger than, the primary connection. The metal cases, or cores, of current transformers, if exposed, should be grounded, except where mounted on a grounded steel structure or the primary voltage is less than 150 volts to ground. The ground connection should be equal in cross-section to the primary leads, however, if impractical, 1 in. $\times$ 1/4 in. copper, or the equivalent, may be used. On suspension-mounted current transformers, the ground connection should be flexible.

For circuit breakers and other current-interrupting devices that have all three phases mounted on a common, metal framework, grounding can be accomplished by connecting the framework to the ground bus with copper bus. In the case of separate mounting (when the different phases are mounted separately), each shall be connected to ground.

All conduit systems, or metal sheaths, for control and power cables should be connected to the main ground bus by any one, or a combination of the following:

1. Metallic conduit between boxes should be grounded, by means of bushings and locknuts, to boxes which are mounted on grounded building steel.
2. Metallic conduits that do not terminate at boxes should be provided with a copper tie to the ground bus unless mounted on grounded steel structure.

All cable trays should be installed with all trays and tray sections bonded together. Each tray should form a continuous electrical circuit. Sections of each tray should be welded, brazed, or bonded to each succeeding section. Tray construction, utilizing slip pins, should not be relied upon to form part of the electrical connection between tray sections. Non-metallic cable trays, if used, will not supplement the cable shielding when reducing interference coupling between circuitry. Care must be exercised in providing physical isolation between high and low signal-level cables, and control and instrumentation circuits where switching transients, or high-level pulse signals, may appear on control circuits. Expanded metal trays may be used instead of solid sheet metal except when primary power leads must be carried in them. Location of these power trays should be at a maximum distance from instrumentation and control cable trays. Metal shielding over power cables, protective covers, and all trays or conduits should be bonded to the ground system at least at one end.

10.5. Kinds of Grounds

As noted, when considering electronic equipment grounding, especially that used for military purposes, a two-fold grounding philosophy becomes important: safety, and the minimizing of interference through the common ground. Therefore, since safety is always a consideration and applies equally to all kinds of equipment, when discussing the grounding of electronic equipment, emphasis will be placed on the interference problem rather than safety considerations.

The very use of the word "ground" is rather confusing when discussing electronic equipment. While all the uses of the term ultimately refer to a common reference plane, the relationship of the various connotations of the word is not always apparent. If a piece of electronic equipment is thought of as a rack, containing perhaps eight drawers; or a chassis, containing perhaps thirty modules; or cards, which, in turn, contain the electronic circuitry, a frame of reference may then be established for distinguishing the various types of grounds. There are what can be referred to as the "electrical grounds": the ground return of the electronic circuitry that may, or may not, eventually be bonded to the building ground, depending on the particular grounding system chosen. There exists what can be referred to as the mechanical or hardware ground— the bonding of the chassis to the equipment ground bus, which in turn is usually bonded to the building ground. A distinction between the grounds is as follows (Table 10-6.):

TABLE 10-6. TYPES OF GROUNDS

Mechanical or Hardware	Electrical
Structure	Prime Power
Buildings	Equipment Power Supply
Electrical Equipment	Electronic Circuits
(Noncurrent-carrying parts)	
Electronic Equipment	
(Noncurrent-carrying parts)	

There are three known systems which can be used for grounding electronic equipment:

1. Multi-point system
2. Floating system
3. Single-point system

The multi-point ground system requires the existence of an equipotential ground plane for the system. Such an equipotential plane exists in a building with a heavy steel floor, shell, and building columns, all electrically bonded together, or in a building with a concrete floor with a heavy ground grid connected to the columns. Equipment cabinets are then connected to either the building steel or the grounding grid. Chassis are connected to the equipment cabinets, and all components, signal return leads, etc., are connected to the chassis. The ground plane will be truly equipotential, and of good quality, only if the grounding system has virtually no resistance, or the currents in it are held to low values.

A good example of this type of grounding system, used, in conjunction with an extended electronic equipment system, is the shipboard installation, where the hull of the ship is used as the equipotential surface. All equipment is strapped to the structure of the ship, with low-impedance grounds at all mounting points. Cable shields are "grounded" by galvanized or white metal-plated straps (as are cable hangers) at intervals not exceeding 24 in., and within 12 in. of all bulkheads penetrated by the cable. All cables are armored with galvanized or plated-steel wire; this armor is used as the shield. Field fixes, for interference reduction, are handled by increasing the bonding to the hull to reduce the impedance of the ground. The system works well if grounding is complete and maintained; however grounding is difficult to maintain because corrosion, vibration, and mechanical damage continually reduce the effectiveness of the ground bonds.

The floating ground system is completely insulated from the building or from any wiring that may be a source of circulating currents. How effective floating ground systems are depends on their true isolation. In large systems it is difficult to provide sufficiently good insulation to maintain a true floating ground. Insulation breakdowns occur easily because static changes, fault potentials, and lightning potentials may accumulate between the floating ground and other accessible grounds (water pipes, external power line neutrals, etc.).

In the single-point ground system, all equipment is referenced to a single point; this reference ground is connected to the building ground. In a cabinet, all electronic circuits are tied to a ground which is insulated from the cabinet and building, and are then tied to the one reference point. This, of course, isolates the cabinet and prevents any conducted, circulating currents in the building ground from producing potential drops within the equipment. Conversely, no conducted circulating currents are introduced into the building ground from the cabinets. However, ground currents can circulate and produce voltage drops within the cabinet or subsystem which can be a source of interference, although, because of the generally small magnitude, are not enough to cause the signal-to-noise ratio to become intolerable.

In a single-point ground system, the stress on ground insulation is low, since a copper path exists in parallel with the insulation. However, as systems become larger, the paths of copper that connect to the single reference point become longer and begin to generate appreciable ground loops, consequently, increasing noise magnitude. The effectiveness of this type of system must then be traded against the other possible solutions.

In most large systems, the architectural or building ground provides the most used and readily available source of equipotential planes. The key requirement is that all connections to it are made with low-resistance leads. A number of important facts may be deduced by considering typical grounding connections for electronic equipment as shown in Fig. 10-1. If the prime power system is adequately grounded (by methods to be described later), and the ground of the system is returned by a copper path to the power source, the copper should not introduce currents into the building ground. The only currents that would be introduced by the copper path would be those due to coupling or leakage, neither of which should be of appreciable magnitude. An exception to this will occur when there is a fault in the power system during which large currents may flow; this is effectively a failure on the part of the power system and should be treated as such because the power system is not operating in the intended manner. The electronic circuit returns are usually connected to the cabinet ground bus through the individual equipment chassis. The

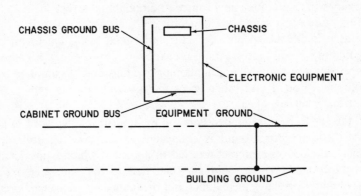

Fig. 10-1. Typical grounding connections for electronic equipment.

cabinet ground buses are connected to the equipment ground which is bonded to the building ground. The electronic circuit ground returns, however, are d-c and can practically be eliminated by isolating the d-c power return from the equipment ground. The return circuits will be a problem whether they are ac, dc, high frequency, low frequency, etc., and will cause an appreciable current to flow in the building ground if grounded unbalanced lines are used for the transmission of signals. Balanced lines will correct this problem. The total effect of three major sources of ground currents (coupling, leakage, and faults) can, therefore, cause relatively large currents to flow in the building ground.

The single-point system is usually most effective in large extended systems; ground current and current flow in the building ground is minimized. In most parts of large systems, when not using the single-point ground system, it is usually necessary to use heavy ground connections within and between racks of equipment to minimize voltage gradients.

The magnitude of noise, introduced by the grounding system, that can be tolerated on an input signal received by an equipment, depends on the nature of the signal. For analog signals, a noise level of 0.1 volt can be tolerated; for digital signals at least twice this amount can be tolerated. This is one of the more important reasons for the wide use of digital data transmission systems.

10.6. Frequency and Power Supplies

Since electronic circuit grounds are the first important consideration in the grounding of electronic equipment, the importance of frequency must be stressed. If the electronic ground had low impedance at all frequencies, there would be, practically speaking, no problem. Low impedance means that there will *not* be a potential difference of a magnitude sufficient to cause interference with desired signals. The smaller the system, the more easily low impedance is achieved. This goal is usually achieved in a common broadcast receiver, but becomes more elusive, because of the difficulty of implementation, on large radar and digital data transmission systems. As systems grow in size, the inherent inductances and capacitances of the grounding conductors become more important, even at relatively low frequencies. Because of this, the impedance of the grounding conductors must be reduced to a level that it makes it impossible to be implemented. Therefore, it can generally be expected, in any large system, that some potential differences will exist between the various parts of the system. The magnitude of these potential differences should be considered as parameters when the ambient noise level of the system is defined and the expected signal-to-noise ratio is determined. Figure 10-2 shows, schematically, the relationship of a grounding network to a typical circuit network that runs between a receiver and transmitter. The inter-

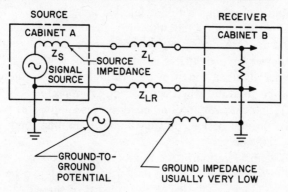

Fig. 10-2. Schematic diagram illustrating a potential difference between the same ground in a system.

ference effect is due to a common impedance by conductor coupling; this occurs between the interfering and interfered-with circuits. Instances of conductive coupling are present almost "across the board" in electronic equipment systems because of the common use of power supplies and the common return paths through ground. Needless to say, if these common paths were eliminated, the problem would disappear.

However, engineering solutions always have to consider the economic aspects of a particular design; advanced technical expertise has to be tempered by down-to-earth consideration of cost. The high additional costs of eliminating common paths *would* arise, since it would be necessary to use a large number of relatively costly power supplies which would add to the overall physical bulk of the equipment as well as figuratively increasing its electrical bulk, in the sense that power consumption would be less efficient. Isolation of ground return circuitry from each other would pose similar problems of cost, bulk, etc. Finally, a host of peripheral problems would be introduced—noise generated by isolation components, reduced reliability because of the added number of components, difficult installation problems, etc.

If the question of power supplies were treated as an abstract problem, the ideal solution could lead to an individual power supply for each electronic circuit. All circuits would be a closed loop in themselves and no interference could be conducted from one path into another by the common conducting paths. No one, however, could afford, let alone use, equipment that was designed to such criteria. The interference problem would become unimportant, but, as noted, interference is only a problem for equipment that is operable in the first place. Consequently, a resolution of this problem of interference caused by power supplies can be achieved at the expense of three parameters:

1. Grouping of circuits within a feasible arrangement. The first is the logical placement of circuits in a particular power supply; e.g., circuits that are susceptible to interference can be grouped together on a power supply. If this is not practical, voltage regulators (such as Zener diodes) can provide decoupling. The following criteria should be followed when considering grouping:
   (a) Standardization of as many power supplies as possible.
   (b) Basing design on maximum operating and maintenance efficiency.
   (c) Consideration of the number of voltage types and levels; the degree of voltage regulation required should be thought out.
2. Economic factors. Basically, this consists of shrewd "horse trading": how can the best value be obtained for the least cost. Very little has been done to approach this rigorously.

3. Physical location. The goal of this consideration is to have all the circuits associated with a particular power supply located together.

In all three considerations, reduction of interference is necessary. However, interference reduction also has to be approached with economic and physical location viewpoints in mind. Consider the hypothetical coupling case illustrated in Fig. 10-3, in which it is necessary to connect points X and Y of an electronic circuit return path. For comparison, two cases

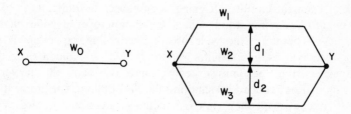

Fig. 10-3. Different paths between X and Y a circuit can take.

are treated: (1) with a single conductor, W_o connecting the two parts; (2) with three conductors, W_1, W_2 and W_3 connecting the two points, with the added condition that d_1 and d_2 are very much larger than the diameters of W_1, W_2 and W_3. If L_o is the inductance of W_o, and this parameter is independent or the area of W_o, three wires can be used to replace it, each with an inductance of L_1, L_2 and L_3, respectively. Since W_1, W_2 and W_3 are physically far apart, the effect of mutual inductance is minimized. In practical cases, the three wires may not be physically far apart enough to allow this to work out so neatly, but, the total current would be divided into three paths, creating lower values of circulating currents. If it is decided to use more wiring, cost trading, for economic and physical considerations must then be pursued.

Another technique that is useful for decoupling power supply leads is the decoupling capacitor illustrated in Figure 10-4. This is used frequently

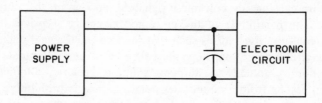

Fig. 10-4. Method useful in decoupling power supply leads.

in digital data circuits because large current pulses that are generated make sudden demands on power supplies. If the leads to the power supply are sufficiently long, inductance may be large enough to increase the charging time constant or L/R constant of the lines. If this happens, the power supply cannot supply the energy fast enough to allow for the fast-rise time pulse that is needed and, as a consequence, output pulse characteristics will be different that the intended pulse. The decoupling capacitor improves the pulse characteristics at the risk or developing "ringing," which occurs when the parameters of the capacitors and the lines form parallel resonant circuits. Ringing is an especially difficult problem when the circuitry requires good voltage regulation over a wide band of frequencies. Therefore, the wide use of decoupling capacitors is generally recommended. Large capacitor ratings should be avoided since the initial charging current becomes excessive and overloads the power supply. Ringing can be reduced by shunting the decoupling capacitor with a small high-frequency capacitor, since inductance, inherent in large capacitors causes resonances at relatively low frequencies.

Isolation of circuits is the next important consideration. It can be seen from Fig. 10-5 that noise may be introduced into the electronic circuits if there is a potential difference between the grounds of the electronic circuit in cabinet A and in the electronic circuit of cabinet B. An additional genera-

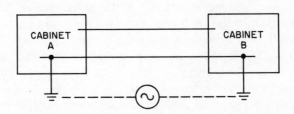

Fig. 10-5.   A potential difference exists between the two cabinets which may introduce interference in the form of noise.

tor has been effectively introduced by the potential gradient existing between the two cabinets and can be considered as an added voltage generator, causing an unwanted signal to appear at the output of the circuit. The magnitude of the unwanted signal is of prime importance. If the signal-to-noise ratio is such that the unwanted signal is large enough to effect circuit operation, steps must then be taken to eliminate the signal. Elimination is actually a stop-gap solution because, although it gives excellent results from a circuit viewpoint, its cost is prohibitive. It should only be used after all efforts to remove the cause of ground noise have been exhausted.

One method of cancelling the effects of ground noise, which gives excellent results from a circuit standpoint but not from a cost standpoint, is isolation of the two circuits. As shown in Fig. 10-6, an isolation transformer is inserted in the wires connecting the two circuits. This method,

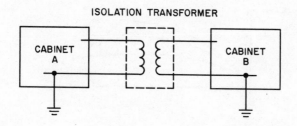

Fig. 10-6. Isolation transformer is used to eliminate noise.

useful at audio and low frequencies, is ineffective at higher frequencies because of the development of more coupling paths.

Another method used to isolate circuits uses the electronically-coupled circuit. Generally, all parts of the grounding system are electrically connected, and, although potential differences may exist between the various areas, impedance is relatively low. Thus ground noise can be considered as a low impedance generator in series with the signal-return circuit. A typical electronically-coupled circuit is shown in Fig. 10-7 with a phantom generator shown for the ground system noise. Due to the plate characteristics of the pentode, a change of plate voltage has little effect on the plate current. Characteristic curves of such a pentode is shown in Fig. 10-8. Consequently, any noise that is coupled to the circuit via R_K does not have much effect on the circuit.

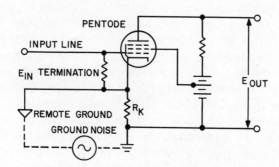

Fig. 10-7. Pentode used to eliminate noise.

Bandpass filters are another means of isolating circuits. Bandpass filters reduce the effects of noise when the frequencies of the interference energy is outside of the frequency band of the desired signal. The bandpass filter rejects the noise signal across the load, preventing voltage drop at

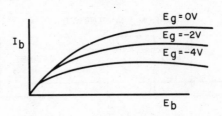

Fig. 10-8. Typical characteristic curves for a pentode.

the load. When bandpass filters are used, care must be taken to insure that "ringing" is not initiated by the noise signal.

In digital pulse circuits, regeneration can be used to reduce the effects of interference. In a synchronous system, gating can eliminate the effects of noise when clock pulse is not present. Pulses can be clipped and the top of the pulse used. In both gating and clipping, the signal may then be regenerated to obtain the proper waveform.

10.7. Relays

Many large electronic systems use great numbers of relays to perform switching functions. These relays represent a large problem area because of the need for arc suppression associated with them (previously discussed in Chapter 8), and because of the power supply problem. A typical relay system in electronic equipment utilizes a 28-volt d-c power supply which represents a compromise between low voltage (with its attendant disadvantage of requiring large amounts of copper to handle the relatively large currents) and high voltage (with its arc suppression problems).

The power system used to supply relay circuitry is rarely used to supply power to other electronic circuitry, because it would create an extremely "noisy" circuit for the other circuits. It is more common for relay power supplies to supply power for indicator lights, small motors, etc., because these devices would not be adversely affected by relay operation and are, in themselves, sources of interference.

As has been noted, the principal interference problem associated with relays develops when they are de-energized. As the circuit opens, the collapsing magnetic field of the relay coil induces a large opposing voltage across the coil. This opposing voltage develops an arc across the opening contacts. It is this arc which is the source of interference since it contains a wide band of frequencies that cause conducted and radiated interference. Although arc suppression reduces interference, a certain amount cannot be eliminated completely and this residue is conducted or radiated away. Another residual amount of interference is caused by changes in the magnitude of current flowing in the relay power supply bus due to constantly changing demands of relay circuit operation. This is another reason for the necessity of isolating relay circuits. It may be necessary sometimes to insert filters in relay circuits which are exposed to a high level of ambient noise, so that their circuitry will not pick up this interference and conduct it to another part of the equipment. Generally, to accomplish isolation of relay circuits and to preclude the possibility of a floating ground system that may develop dangerously high voltages, the relay systems should use single-point grounding; the ground point should be at the power supply.

If a single-point ground system is used, difficulties may develop because of the effects of an unintentional ground on the ground return of a relay. Since the total current in the relay circuit return is relatively large, potential differences may exist on it. If an unintentional ground occurs, due to insulation failure, the potential difference may cause enough current to flow in the return lead to rupture it. The only preventive measure that can be used to preclude such an occurrence is to make sure that relay return circuits are adequately insulated, or make the return wire of sufficient size to limit the current.

For relay systems that develop large currents, it is necessary to consider the voltage drops in the conductors, as well as their current carrying capacities. The fact that low voltages are involved does not make this consideration academic as long as large currents exist. Generation of changing magnetic fields (because of changing relay demand currents) is a situation that develops and which can be corrected by running the supply and return leads close together to reduce the loop areas of the relay circuits.

The grounding technique for low impedance pulse circuits has rather special considerations connected with it. Since the input and output impedances of transistorized pulse circuits are relatively low, these circuits are particularly susceptible to interfering low impedance fields. An important parameter in this susceptibility to low impedance fields is the loop area of the circuits. By reducing the loop areas a good portion of the interference problem can be eliminated.

10.8. Mechanical Considerations

For equipment (used on military systems) made up of racks consisting of chassis, which, in turn, are made up of modules, this ground loop area of circuits can be minimized by mounting the modules on a sheet of good conducting material and connecting this sheet directly to ground. Any wiring between modules should be run as close to this conducting sheet as practical; this reduces the loop area, but has the detrimental effect of increasing the capacitive coupling of the circuits. The capacitive coupling does not increase rapidly enough to become a serious problem, but its overall effects should be considered.

When grounding the noncurrent-carrying parts of electronic equipment, careful attention should be given to various mechanical factors which greatly influence its efficiency. Mating surface finishes must be chosen so that good electrical connections between mechanical parts of the equipment are achieved, not only at the time of installation, but also during the operating life of the equipment. Joints in copper bus bars used in the grounding system must be sweat soldered, brazed or connected using an exothermic (Cadweld) process so that formation of copper oxides inside the joint does not increase resistance or result in rectification and mixing of a-c signals developed on the ground bus. Removable portions of shields must be connected to mating surfaces by the use of straps, contact between "clean" surfaces, or electrical weather stripping. Ground straps to cabinets must be fastened securely to points free of paint or other insulating finish. In a single-point system, ground wires and metal parts must be carefully insulated from undesirable grounds. A bare ground wire rubbing against a chassis or wireway can cause a considerable amount of noise in a system.

The problem of connecting the mechanical or hardware ground is best discussed by considering a common piece of electronic equipment as shown in Fig. 10-9A. In the cabinet shown, the chassis are mounted on the standard rack-type door. Each of the chassis contains a group of modules and provides for their physical support as well as plug-in connectors and the necessary hardware for ground connections. A group of these cabinets may be placed side by side and back to back. Their ground bus is connected to a main ground bus of 0.250 in. $\times$ 2 in. copper, 12-feet longs, and Chromate Brite dipped to assure a clean surface. These 12-ft. sections are joined together to make a continuous bus.

There are a number of methods that make statisfactory electrical and mechanical connections. The quality of the electrical connection is of the utmost importance because a potential point of high resistance exists wherever a joint occurs. The ground bus should have a uniform value of resistance throughout its entire length as close to the resistance of the copper of which it is made.

Bolting two pieces of bus bar together, followed by a brazed joint of high quality makes a satisfactory electrical connection.

An exothermic (Cadweld) process is still another good method. It consists of clamping a preformed graphite mold around the two pieces to be connected; then igniting a measured amount of powder inside the

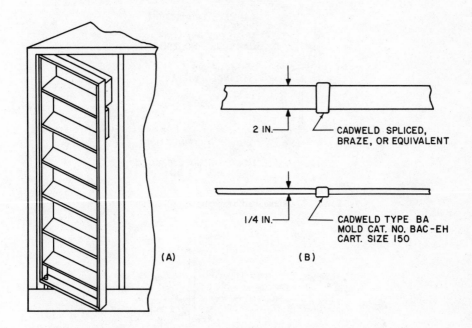

Fig. 10-9.   (A) A common piece of electronic equipment.   (B) Recommended bus bar splice.

mold. The powder, composed of copper oxide and powdered aluminum, when ignited, throws off a great quantity of heat, raising the temperature to 4200°F. At this temperature, the aluminum oxidizes, resulting in a large deposit of metallic copper connecting the two pieces. The joint that is formed is electrically continuous with the bars. Two bus bars, 1/4 in. × 2 in., can be joined in this manner within two minutes. The Cadweld process is especially recommended because of its low cost and simplicity of installation. A bus bar joined in this manner is shown in Fig. 10-9B.

A third method of connecting bus bars is by bolting two solder-coated bus bars, and applying heat to make a continuous connection.

A fourth method makes use of silver or tin plate at the ends of the bus bars, and bolting the sections together. The last two methods are not as effective as the first two.

The system ground bus is then mounted throughout the building (in which the equipment is installed) by hanging supports to the overhead steel beams as shown in Figs. 10-10 and 10-11. This type of installation is far superior to that of a bolted hanger, which sometimes causes arcing

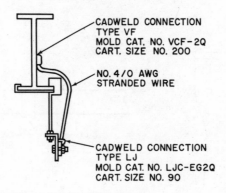

CADWELD CONNECTION
TYPE VF
MOLD CAT. NO. VCF-2Q
CART. SIZE NO. 200

NO. 4/0 AWG
STRANDED WIRE

CADWELD CONNECTION
TYPE LJ
MOLD CAT. NO. LJC-EG2Q
CART. SIZE NO. 90

Fig. 10-10.   Recommended beam support for ground bus.

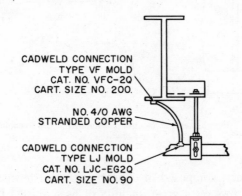

CADWELD CONNECTION
TYPE VF MOLD
CAT. NO. VFC-2Q
CART. SIZE NO. 200.

NO. 4/0 AWG
STRANDED COPPER

CADWELD CONNECTION
TYPE LJ MOLD
CAT. NO. LJC-EG2Q
CART. SIZE NO. 90

Fig. 10-11.   Recommended typical hanger installation.

or high resistance joints. A typical terminal connection is shown in Fig. 10-12. The connection of a ground bus to a structural column is detailed in Fig. 10-13. Figure 10-14 shows the detailed connection to the end of a bus bar; Fig. 10-15 shows the details for connection to a console cabinet.

The system ground bus is typically connected to the equipment cabinet ground (1 in. $\times$ 1/4 in. bus bar) with a No. 4/0 solid copper wire. The

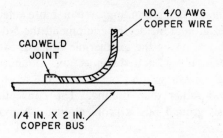

Fig. 10-12. Recommended terminal connection.

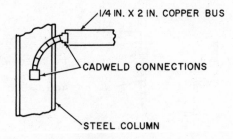

Fig. 10-13. Preferred column connection.

cabinet ground bus can be connected to the chassis ground bus (a copper bar with connectors mounted on it) with a No. 4/0 solid copper wire. On the chassis, a stand-off terminal is connected to the highest numbered pin in each connector; this pin carries a No. 16 AWG wire that becomes a part of the cable harness. The cabinet bus also has a No. 4/0 wire connected to it which, in turn, connects it to the swing-out door frame. No attempt should be made to either insulate or bond the door to the chassis bus.

In the procedure described above, a number of modifications can be

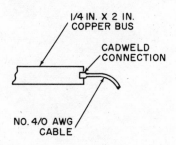

Fig. 10-14. Preferred connection of bus bar to the end of a bus bar.

incorporated to make the grounding system more effective. When connecting the cabinet ground bus to the equipment, the No. 4/0 cable should be joined to the buses, using the exothermic process, to eliminate possible high impedance and "noisy" bolted connection. Connection of the cabinet ground bus to the chassis ground bus should be accomplished using the exothermic process rather than bolting. The connection of the chassis itself to the chassis ground bus is problematical. A more suitable means

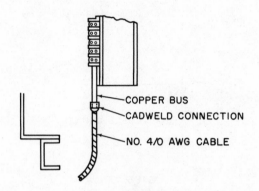

Fig. 10-15.   Preferred connection of a bus bar to a console.

should be contrived to connect the chassis to its ground bus without having to resort to the potentially troublesome procedure described. Direct bonding of the chassis to the chassis ground bus appears to be the soundest approach. This would eliminate potential noisy connection points at the connectors and at the connectors on the chassis ground bus, as well as any potential problems which could be created by running the No. 16 ground wire in the harness. Some work has been done in contriving means of bonding the chassis to the chassis ground bus.

11 – GROUNDING OF POWER SYSTEMS

11.1. Introduction

In previous chapters we have examined connecting of the secondary power systems to ground, and connecting of electrical circuits to ground. In this chapter, guide lines will be provided for the third link in this chain —grounding of the prime power system. Since all of these are grounded to a common conducting medium, interference in any one of the parts will be reflected into the electronic system.

Grounding of the prime power system is, strictly speaking, the concern of the power engineer. However, advances in technology have resulted in prime power systems as a minimal source of conducted interference.

In this chapter, the guide lines that are developed will enable the electronics engineer to analyze and make suitable recommendations to eliminate sources of interference.

To adequately select a method of grounding a power system is difficult because of the number of variables that must be considered. Grounding of power systems has followed almost a stereotyped procedure:

1. No grounding.
2. Resistance grounding.
3. Solid, or effective grounding.

Experience has proven that the best power system is a grounded one, no matter what its characteristics of voltage and physical configurations may be. This is generally true since a grounded power system results in reduced operating and maintenance costs, improved reliability, ease in locating and reducing the number of faults, greater protection from lightning and equipment damage, and finally, greater safety for operating personnel. Table 11-1 summarizes the advantages of a typical 480-volt grounded system as compared to the ungrounded system.

TABLE 11-1. ADVANTAGES OF THE GROUNDED-NEUTRAL
480-VOLT SYSTEM[1]

	Grounded Neutral System	Ungrounded System
Safety	Safest—Only 277 volts to ground at any time (assume good ground and 480-volts maximum line-to-line).	Normally 277 volts to ground when no ground on system. When one phase is grounded 480 volts to ground on two conductors.
	Safest—Voltage on system limited to about 277 volts when primary to secondary failure occurs in transformer supplying system.	Voltage on secondary system may be as high as primary and secondary transformer windings.
	Safest—Ground fault in control wiring can only put 58% line voltage on line-to-line connected contactor closing coils.	Control circuit ground fault likely to put full voltage on contactor closing coils.
Service reliability	Highest—Ground faults are readily located and repaired, no removal of system to find ground faults.	Part of all of system must be taken out of service to find ground faults.
	Highest—Ground faults are localized and trip circuit breakers.	Ground faults, if not removed, may, upon occurrence of a second ground fault, cause two circuits to go out at once thus losing twice as much production equipment.
	Highest—Floating grounds very unlikely.	Floating or arcing grounds are likely.
Maintenance cost	Lowest—Ground faults easily located.	Time must be spent hunting ground faults.
First cost	About same as delta-connected substation and ground detector.	
High-voltage fluorescent lighting	Provides 277 volts for direct operation of lamps; result in cost saving by elimination of lighting transformers and reduction in copper.	Must use step-down transformers of 480 to 277 volts or lower.

[1]Neutral Grounding of the Industrial Power System. General Electric Company, GET-1181D.

11.2. Need for Grounded Systems

As the magnitude of operating voltages in power systems grows and becomes more physically extended, the need for system-grounding becomes more acute. Larger voltages mean larger currents to ground when a line-to-ground fault occurs; transient grounds are no longer self-clearing, and arcing grounds (caused by alternately clearing and restriking of a ground with its attendant high surges), become an important consideration. Ungrounded systems produce higher voltages during faults and in switching operations, and generally cause hazardous operating conditions for equipments.

A logical step toward limiting the high overvoltages is to limit the current flow by inserting a suitable resistor in the ground connection. The rating of the resistor that is suitable can be approximated by examining the length of the conductors, charging current to ground, etc. Another approach has led to other types of grounding such as reactance grounded systems and solidly grounded systems.

A grounded system is far superior over an ungrounded system. For example, although a line-to-ground fault is unlikely to cause an immediate failure, it is likely to produce a second and uninitentional ground. This second ground will, in time, cause an operating failure. In a grounded system, any failures or faults will immediately be isolated and cleared. In general, better service and a minimum number of critical failures are obtained with a grounded system.

Danger to operating personnel is minimized on grounded systems, but are maximized on ungrounded systems. If contact is made between a phase to ground in the ungrounded system, the full line-to-line voltage would be felt. In a grounded system, the line-to-ground voltage would be felt which is considerably less than the line-to-line voltage.

Most prime power systems are effectively shielded against direct lightning strokes. Lightning arrestors, applied at the incoming line, limit, within the installation, the surge of voltages, resulting from strokes to exposed lines. When an installation is supplied from a substation, stepping down from some higher voltage, lightning arrestors may be required on the low side of the transformer to protect equipment from surges past the high-side arrestors being reflected to the transformers.

Normal switching operations, due to changing loads in the prime power system, can cause overvoltage usually more than three times normal voltage, and of short duration.

Neutral grounding is not likely to reduce the total magnitude of overvoltage produced by lightning or switching surges, but it can distribute the voltage between phases and reduce the possibility of excessive voltage stress on the phase-ground insulation of a particular phase.

Overvoltage, due to buildup of static charges, is not too much of a problem in most installations because of usually adequate grounding on the metal noncurrent-carrying enclosures around most equipment. Even static charges, caused by moving belts on motor driven equipment, can be drained off by a good ground to the motor frame. Overvoltage, due to mechanical failure, that causes a high voltage line to come in to direct contact with and energize a low voltage line, is more serious if the system is ungrounded. An ungrounded system will permit this high voltage to remain until the low voltage causes an insulation failure on the low-voltage system. Line-to-ground faults are more serious in an ungrounded system because they subject the phase wire insulation to a 73 percent overvoltage. Several other considerations, such as resonant overvoltage and restriking ground faults, cause an ungrounded system to respond less adequately than a grounded system.

TABLE 11-2. SYSTEM CHARACTERISTICS WITH VARIOUS GROUNDING METHODS

	Ungrounded	Essentially Solid Grounding		Reactance Grounding	Ground-fault Neutralizer	Resistance Grounding
		Solid	Low Value Reactor	High Value Reactor		Resistance
Current for phase-to-ground fault in percent of three-phase fault current	Less than 1%	Varies, may be 100% or greater	Usually designed to produce 25%-100%	5- to 25%	Nearly zero fault current	5- to 20%
Transient overvoltages	Very high	Not excessive	Not excessive	Very high	Not excessive	Not excessive
Automatic segregation of faulty zone	No	Yes	Yes	Yes	No	Yes
Lightning arrestors	Ungrouded neutral type	Grounded neutral type	Grounded neutral type if current 60% or greater	Ungrounded neutral type	Ungrounded neutral type	Ungrounded neutral type
Remarks	Not recommended due to overvoltage and nonsegregation of fault	Generally used on systems 600 volts and below and over 15 kv		Not used due to excessive overvoltages	Best suited for high-voltag overhead lines where faults may be self-healing	Generally used on industrial systems of 2.4 kv to 15 kv

11.3. Obtaining a Neutral

The key consideration when grounding a power distribution system, is to obtain a system neutral. With a source that is wye-connected, the system neutral is readily available. The only requirement is careful specification of a wye-connected secondary by the design engineer. If it is necessary to establish a neutral with a delta-connected secondary, grounding transformers are used to form a neutral solidly connected to ground. Grounding transformers may be either a zig-zag or wye-delta type. In higher voltage system (up to 15 kv), neutral resistors can be added.

Having once obtained a system neutral, a variety of methods can be used to ground this neutral, as shown in Fig. 11-1. Characteristics of the various methods are summarized in Table 11-2.

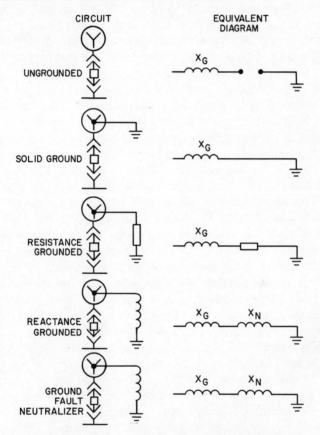

Fig. 11-1. System-neutral circuits and methods of grounding.

In a simple ungrounded neutral system, line conductors have capacitances between one another and to ground. In a perfect transposed line, each phase conductor will have the same capacitance to ground for the balanced three-phase voltage applied to the line. Current in each of the equivalent capacitances will be equal and displaced 120 degrees from each other; voltages across each branch will be equal and displaced 120 degrees from each other. Consequently, there will be no potential difference between the neutral points of the supply and that of the capacitances if these magnitudes are compared by a vector diagram. Since the neutral of the capacitance is at ground potential, the neutral of the supply is also at ground. The system may be considered capacitance grounded.

Should one conductor become faulted to ground, difference of potential will no longer exist since no current will flow in the capacity branch between the phase and ground. However, the voltage across the other two capacity branches will increase because this voltage rises to phase-to-phase voltage. Also, the voltages to ground are now 60 degrees out of phase, rather than 120°. The sum of the current is then no longer 0, but three times the original current to neutral.

In a resistance-grounded power system, the resistance generally has a higher value than the system reactance; consequently, the line-to-ground fault current is limited by the resistor itself. The capacitive current is usually small, as compared to the resistive current, and of no importance. In resistance-grounded systems the power loss in the resistor during line-to-ground faults is of some magnitude. The value of the grounding resistor required will vary widely depending upon circuit voltages and system capacity. This effect is shown in Fig. 11-2 (arbitrarily assuming that the ground fault current is to be limited to 1/4 of the full load system current). It has been found practical that small variations from the resistor rating as shown in Fig. 11-2, have proved satisfactorily.

The term "effectively grounded" is more meaningful than "solidly grounded." A system is solidly grounded when impedance exists between the neutral and earth; however, solidly grounded systems may have too small a transformer capacity (in comparison to the size of the system), to be effective in stabilizing the voltages from phase to ground when ground faults occur. This is particularly the case when small grounding transformers are used to provide a source of ground current for relaying. The term solidly grounded is not a good one for use in describing a grounding procedure that varies so widely. A definition that requires a knowledge of symmetrical components is more exact and is quoted from the American Institute of Electrical Engineers Standard: "a system or portion of a system can be said to be effectively grounded when for all points from the system or specified portion thereof, the ratio of zero sequence reactance to positive sequence reactance is not greater than 3 and the ratio of zero sequence resistance to positive sequence reactance is not greater than 1 for any condition of operation and for any amount of generator capacity."[1]

---

[1]*Electrical Transmission and Distribution Reference Book.* Westinghouse Electric Corporation, p. 646.

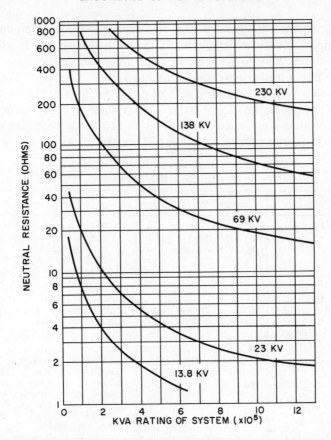

Fig. 11-2. Effect of system size and operating voltage on size of neutral resistor to limit ground fault current to one-quarter full-load system current. (From **Westinghouse Electrical Transmission and Distribution Reference Book,** Westinghouse Electric Corporation.)

A reactance-grounded system is one in which a reactance is inserted in the connection to ground. It is not a solidly grounded system, and, may or may not be effectively grounded according to the AIEE definition. A reactance ground means simply that the grounding element is principally reactive. A ground fault neutralizer is an especially selected reactor which, during a fault, has an inductive current flowing through it that neutralizes (by being 180 degrees out of phase) the capacitive component of current caused by the fault. The neutralizer effectively limits the number of operations of fault-clearing devices and reduces failure. Its principal use is on higher voltage systems.

The most common method used for grounding prime power systems that have voltages over 13 kv is to use a solid or effective grounding. This method is most economical in cost and requires the least amount of physical space. Resistance grounding is the method most widely used on voltages between 2 kv to 13 kv, and solid grounding on voltages below 2 kv. The various methods are summarized in Tables 11-3 and 4. For common utilization voltages (supplied as part of the facilities at the electronic equipment installation site), 208 Y/120-volt systems are most commonly used and are always grounded. These 208 Y/120-volt systems are widely used because of their great flexibilities. Power equipment can be con-

TABLE 11-3. HOW TO GROUND THE SYSTEM
Low-voltage systems-typical voltages: 208, 240, 480, 600.

Condition	Grounding Method	Remarks
If wye-connected generators on system.	Ground generator neutral through low-value reactance.	1. Total capacity of generators should be adequate for grounding. 2. Grounding reactance should pass through currents equal to at least 25% of 3-phase value.
If low-voltage system is supplied by transformer with wye-connected secondaries.	Ground transformer neutrals solidly.	Total capacity of transformers should be adequate for grounding.
No wye-connected generators or transformer secondaries on system.	Use grounding transformer solidly grounded.	Grounding transformer should pass ground-fault currents equal to at least 25% of 3-phase value. Check adequacy of this fault current for tripping circuit breakers and any fuses on system.

nected to such a system if it runs on 208 volts, and motors, up to at least 25 hp, can readily be accommodated; lightning can be accommodated on its 120-volts portion, and power to electronic equipment can be drawn from this portion. Such a system should obviously be grounded since it is wye-connected. When 480-volt systems were used, the grounding of neutrals was impractical because most of the systems were delta-connected and a ground was not readily available. Standard wye-connected equipment is now available at this voltage. In systems under 600 volts, a relatively high magnitude of ground-fault current is required to actuate the usual protective devices, and solidly grounded, low-voltage systems assure that sufficient fault current will be drawn to operate the protective devices.

To be able to calculate the magnitude of ground fault currents, it is usually necessary to know the reactance of the system and the resistance and reactance of the ground return path, including any intentional grounding resistance or reactance.

TABLE 11-4. HOW TO GROUND THE SYSTEM

Medium-voltage systems-typical voltages: 2400, 4160, 4800, 6900, 11,00, 13,800.

Condition	Grounding Method	Remarks
If wye-connected generators on system.	Use resistance grounding. Grounding resistor. Do not ground solidly.	1. Generators used for grounding should be of adequate size. 2. When severe lightning exposure is present, generator may be grounded through low-value reactance to permit use of grounded-neutral type of lightning arrest. 3. Small systems, where the resulting ground-fault current would not be excessive, may be reactance-grounded, if desired, in the interest of economy.
If wye-connected transformers on system (use transformers which supply power to the system; avoid transformers which are loads on the system).	Use resistance grounding. Resistor.	1. Capacity of transformers used for grounding should be of adequate size. 2. Small systems, where the resulting ground-fault current would not be excessive, may be solidly grounded, if desired, in the interest of economy.
If no wye-conducted generators or transformers on system.	Use one or more grounding transformers with resistors.	In small systems, where the resulting ground-fault current would not be excessive, the grounding transformer may be solidly grounded in the interest of economy.
Solidly ground neutrals of all systems above 15kv (no. rotating equipment assumed operating directly at these voltages).		

When a single line-to-ground fault occurs in a resistance-grounded system, a voltage appears across the resistor nearly equal to the normal line-to-neutral voltage of the system. The resistor current, equal to the fault currents will have an ampere rating equal to that current produced when a line-to-neutral voltage is applied to the resistor. Thus a maximum fault current of approximately 2000 amps will be obtained on a system using a resistor of suitable rating. This is a simple method of obtaining the ground-fault current, but is only suitable when that current is small when compared to the three-phase fault current.

The method just outlined, however, does not apply if the fault is internal to rotating machines or transformers, in which case ground fault will be less.

In a reactance-grounded system with a single line-to-ground fault, the ground fault current may be computed from the formula:

$$I_G = \frac{3E}{X_1 + X_2 + X_0 + 3X_N} \qquad (11\text{-}1)$$

where $X_1 =$ system positive sequence reactance, ohms per phase,

$X_2 =$ system negative sequence reactance, ohms per phase,

$X_0 =$ system zero sequence reactance, ohms per phase,

$X_N =$ reactance of neutral grounding reactor, ohms,

$E =$ line-to-neutral voltage, volts,

$I_G =$ ground-fault current, amperes.

Resistance is usually neglected.

In a system with solid neutral connections to ground, the ground-fault current for a single line-to-ground fault may be calculated from the formula:

$$I_G = \frac{3E}{X_1 + X_2 + X_0} \qquad (11\text{-}2)$$

where X_1, X_2 and X_0 have the values as described.

11.4. Grounded vs. Ungrounded Systems

Since there is no ideal method of system grounding, the method decided on will, essentially, be a trade-off of advantages against disadvantages. Data for making such a choice is listed in Table 11-5. As noted, an ungrounded system does clear ground faults quickly if the power lines are relatively short. Lightning arrestors applied to such lines must be sized on the basis of full line-to-line voltage; this makes them relatively expensive and of limited effectiveness. Because selective relaying cannot be used, detection and isolation of faults on such lines is quite difficult. Probably the most important associated difficulty is the hazard to life that ungrounded systems presents. From an interference viewpoint, ungrounded systems have low valued fault currents, and it is not usual for them to cause high voltages to be induced into adjacent communications systems. This advantage is a mixed one, since communication systems are also affected by the persistency and harmonics of ground currents, and because such currents can flow, undetected, for a long interval of time in ungrounded systems, communication systems are vulnerable to this. From an overall viewpoint, ungrounded systems are considered less desirable than grounded systems, because of the more important induced interferences resulting from them.

TABLE 11-5.

	Ungrounded	Effectively Grounded	Reactance Grounded	Resistance Grounded	Resonant Grounded
Apparatus insulation	Fully Insulated	Lowest	Partially Graded	Partially Graded	Partially Graded
Fault-to-ground current	Usually low	Maximum value rarely higher than three-phase short circuit current.	Cannot satisfactorily be reduced below one-half or one-third of values for solid grounding.	Low	Negligible except when Petersen coil is short circuited for relay purposes when it may compare with solidly-grounded systems.
Safety from voltage gradient consideration	Usually good, but not fully dependable because of possibility of simultaneous fault on another phase.	Gives greatest gradients, but not usually a problem where continuous ground wires are used.	Slightly better than effective grounding.	Better than effective or reactance grounded.	Least gradient normally, but may approach effective grounding values when necessary to shunt ground-fault neutralizer to isolate faulty circuit by relaying.
Stability	Usually unimportant.	Lower than with other methods but can be made satisfactory by use of high speed relays and circuit breakers.	Improved over solid grounding, particularly if used at receiving end of system.	Improved over effective grounding particularly if used at sending end of system.	Is eliminated from consideration during single line-to-ground faults unless neutralizer is short circuited to isolate fault by relays.
Relaying	Difficult	Satisfactory	Satisfactory	Satisfactory	Requires special provisions but can be made satisfactory.
Arcing grounds	Likely	Unlikely	Possible if reactance is excessive.	Unlikely	Unlikely

TABLE 11-5. (CONT'D)

	Ungrounded	Effectively Grounded	Reactance Grounded	Resistance Grounded	Resonant Grounded
Localizing faults	Effect of fault transmitted as excess voltage on sound phases to all parts of conductivity connected network.	Effect of faults localized to system or part of system where they occur.	Effect of faults localized to system or part of system where they occur unless reactance is quite high.	Effective of faults transmitted as excess voltage on sound phases to all parts of conductivity connected network.	Eeffct of faults transmitted as excess voltage on sound phases to all parts of conductivity connected network.
Double faults	Likely	Unlikely	Unlikely unless reactance is quite high and insulation weak.	Unlikely unless resistance is quite high and insulation weak.	Seem to be more likely but conclusive information not available.
Lightning protection	Ungrounded neutral service arrestors must be applied at sacrifice in cost and efficiency.	Highest efficiency and lowest cost.	If reactance is very high arrestors for ungrounded neutral service must be applied at sacrifice in cost and efficiency.	Arrestors for ungrounded, neutral service usually must be applied at sacrifice in cost and efficiency.	Ungrounded neutral service arrestors must be applied at sacrifice in cost and efficiency.
Inductive coordination	Will usually be low except in cases of double faults or electrostatic induction with neutral displaced; duration may be great.	Will be greatest in magnitude due to higher fault currents but can be quickly cleared particularly with high-speed breakers.	Will be reduced from solidly-grounded values.	Will be reduced from solidly-grounded values.	Will be low in magnitude except in case of double faults or series resonance at harmonic frequencies; duration may be great.
Radio influence	May be quite high during faults or when neutral is displaced.	Minimum	Greater than for solidly grounded when faults occur.	Greater than for solidly grounded when faults occur.	May be high during faults.
Line availability	Will inherently clear themselves if total length of interconnected line is low and require isolation from system in increasing percentages as length increases.	Must be isolated for each fault.	Must be isolated for each fault.	Must be isolated for each fault.	Need not be isolated but will inherently clear itself in about 60 to 80% of faults.

TABLE 11-5. (CONT'D)

	Ungrounded	Effectively Grounded	Reactance Grounded	Resistance Grounded	Resonant Grounded
Adaptability to interconnection	Cannot be interconnected unless interconnecting system is ungrounded or isolating transformers are used.	Satisfactory indefinitely with reactance-grounded systems.	Satisfactory indefinitely with solidly-grounded systems.	Satisfactory with solidly or reactance-grounded systems with proper attention to relaying.	Cannot be interconnected unless interconnected system is resonant-grounded, or isolating transformers used. Requires coordination between interconnected systems in neutralizer settings.
Circuit breakers	Interrupting capacity determined by three-phase fault conditions.	Same interrupting capacity as required for three-phase short circuit will practically always be satisfactory.	Interrupting capacity determined by three-phase fault conditions.	Interrupting capacity determined by three-phase fault conditions.	Interrupting capacity determined by three-phase fault conditions.
Operating procedure	Ordinarily simple but possibility of double faults introduces complication in times of trouble	Simple	Simple	Simple	Taps on neutralizer must be changed when major system switching is performed; difficulty may arise in interconnected systems. Difficult to tell where faults are located.
Total cost	High, unless conditions are such that arc tends to extinguish itself when duplicate circuits may be eliminated reducing total cost.	Lowest	Intermediate	Intermediate	Highest unless arc suppressing characteristic is relied on to eliminate double circuits when it may be lowest for the particular type of service.

Resistance-grounded systems, due to the ground current limiting feature, will have fewer interference effects on adjacent communication systems. Effectively grounded systems have some disadvantages associated with them that are positively detrimental to communication systems; the ground fault currents are high and generally cause interference problems. Reactance-grounded systems are better than effectively grounded systems, but not quite as good as resonant-grounded systems (which use ground fault neutralizers). The effectiveness of the reactance-grounded system depends on the ratio of its zero-sequence to its positive-sequence impedances. If this ratio is less than 3, the fault currents will be the same as for the effectively grounded system; if the ratio is more than 3, the fault currents will be lower. In a resonant-grounded system, the ground fault neutralizer will decrease the number of faults approximately 30 percent, bringing less of a chance of such a system causing interference to adjacent communication systems.

According to the National Electrical Code, the neutral points of high-voltage systems should be grounded as a means of "fixing" the potential on the other parts of the systems to protect them from abnormal rises of potential resulting in damage to the equipment. Three-phase systems normally operate with the neutral point at one potential. When such neutrals are well grounded at the source of supply, no current flows on the normal operation. Other grounds then burn themselves clear, or open circuit breakers so that excessive pressure cannot be continuously impressed on other parts of the system as happens in an ungrounded system.

In larger systems with grounded neutrals, it is well known that an accidental phase ground becomes a short circuit which, in turn, is likely to necessitate use of a current-limiting device in neutral circuits. This is, of course, a resistance. Secondary distributing mains are grounded for the protection of both cable and equipment. Failure of a transformer (or a cross between primary and secondary wires) may cause fatal shocks or become a source of fire when secondary wires are not grounded. Grounds, however, should not be made of only one point. In such an instance, it is desirable that the neutral conductor of the secondary mains be grounded as often as possible to insure dependable ground.

Secondary distribution systems should be grounded at the neutral conductor if the maximum voltage to ground does not exceed 150 volts; they may also be grounded if maximum voltage is above 150, but does not exceed 300 volts. Grounding guards against imposition of dangerously high voltages should breakdown occur in the transformer of a cross of secondary wire. Service neutral should be grounded at the point of entrance before any disconnecting equipment and should consist of a copper wire or bus not smaller than indicated in Table 11-6.

TABLE 11-6.

Size of Largest Service Conductor	AWG No. of Copper Grounding Conductor
No. 2 or smaller	8
No. 1 or 0	6
00 or 000	4
over 000 to 250,000cm	2
over 350,000 to 600,000cm	1/0
over 600,000 to 1,100,000cm	2/0
over 1,100,000cm	3/0

APPENDIX 1 – GLOSSARY

The following are definitions of terms related to interference suppression, and grounding. These definitions are from the Institute of Electrical and Electronic Engineers and from the American Standards Association.

Absorption: Absorption is the loss of energy in the transmission of waves over radio or wire paths due to conversion into heat or other forms of energy. In wire transmission, the term is usually applied only to loss of energy in extraneous media.

Attenuation: Attenuation is a general term used to denote a decrease in magnitude in transmission from one point to another. It may be expressed as a ratio or, by extension of the term in decibels.

Balanced: In communication practice, the term balanced signifies (1) electrically alike and symmetrical with respect to ground or (2) arranged to provide conjugacy between certain sets of terminals.

Balanced Wire Circuit: A balanced wire circuit is one whose two sides are electrically alike and symmetrical with respect to ground and other conductors. The term is commonly used to indicate a circuit whose two sides differ only by chance.

Band-Elimination Filter (Bandstop Filter): A band-elimination filter is a wave filter which has a single attenuation band, neither of the cut-off frequencies being zero or infinite.

Bandpass Filter: A bandpass filter is a wave filter which has a single transmission band, neither of the cut-off frequencies being zero or infinite.

Bandwidth (of a Device): The range of frequencies within which performance, with respect to some characteristic, falls within specific limits.

Bandwidth (of a Wave): The least frequency interval outside of which the power spectrum of a time-varying quantity is everywhere less than some specified fraction of its value at a reference frequency. (This definition permits the spectrum to be less than the specified fraction within the interval unless otherwise stated; the reference frequency is that at which the spectrum has its maximum value).

Bonded: Electrically connected by means of welding, brazing, compressing or other mechanical means not likely to be affected by heat or corrosion and which will give a good low-impedance electrical path.

Brazing or Welding: These terms are used in the usual sense and also intended to include the Cadweld process.

Cable: A cable is an assembly of one or more conductors, usually within an enveloping protective sheath, in such structural arrangement of the individual conductors as will permit of their use separately or in groups.

Capacitive Coupling: Capacitive coupling is the association of two or more circuits with one another by means of capacitance mutual to the circuits.

Characteristic Impedance (Surge Impedance): The characteristic impedance of a transmission line is the (driving-point) impedance which the line would have if it were of infinite length. Note: It is recommended that this term be applied only to lines having approximate electrical uniformity. For other lines or structures the corresponding term is "iterative impedance".

Co-Channel Interference: Interference between two signals of the same type in the same radio channel.

Coaxial Transmission Line: A transmission line consisting of two coaxial cylindrical conductors.

Coupling: Coupling is the association of two or more circuits or systems in such a way that power may be transferred from one to another.

Crosstalk: Crosstalk is the unwanted sound reproduced by an electro-acoustic receiver associated with a given transmission channel resulting from cross coupling to another transmission channel carrying sound-controlled electric waves or, by extension, the electric waves in the disturbed channel which result in such sound.

Decibel (db): The decibel is a dimensionless unit for expressing the ratio of two values of power, the number of decibels being 10 times the logarithm to the base 10 of the power ratio. The abbreviation db is commonly used.

With P_1 and P_2 designating two values of power and n the number of decibels denoting their ratio:

$$n = 10 \log_{10} (P_1/P_2) \text{ db}$$

When the conditions are such that scalar ratios of currents or voltages (or analogous quantities in other fields) are the square roots of the corresponding power ratios, the number of decibels by which the corresponding powers differ may be expressed by the following formulas:

$$n = 20 \log_{10} (I_1/I_2) \text{ db}$$
$$n = 20 \log_{10} (V_1/V_2) \text{ db}$$

where I_1/I_2 and V_1/V_2 are the given current and voltage ratios, respectively.

By extension, these relations between numbers of decibels and scalar ratios of currents or voltages are sometimes applied where these ratios are not the square roots of the corresponding power ratios; to avoid confusion, such usage should be accompanied by a specific statement of this application.

The decibel is commonly used for exressing transmission gains, losses, levels and similar quantities. It was formerly called a "transmission unit."

The decibel was originaly defined as one-tenth of a "bel," the number of bels being equal to the logarithm to base 10 of the power ratio. However, the term bel is not in common use.

Direct Coupling: Direct coupling is the association of two or more circuits by means of a self-inductance, capacitance, resistance or a combination of these which is common to the circuits.

Electric (Magnetic) Field Strength: The magnitude of the electric (magnetic) field vector.

Ground: A conducting connection, whether intentional or accidental, between an electric circuit (or equipment) and earth, or to some other conducting body which serves in place of the earth.

Ground Bus: A bus used to connect the number of ground conductors to one or more ground electrodes.

Ground Cable Bond: A cable bond used for grounding the armor and/or sheaths of cables.

Ground Clamp: A clamp used in connecting a grounding conductor to a grounding electrode (or to a thing grounded).

Ground Current: A current flowing in the earth or some other body serving in its place.

Grounded Circuit: A circuit in which one conductor or point (usually the middle wire or neutral point of transformer or generator windings) is intentionally grounded.

Grounded Conductor: A conductor used to connect an equipment, device, solidly or through a current-limiting device.

Grounded Parts: Parts which are so connected that they are intentionally grounded.

Grounded System: A system of conductors in which at least one conductor or point (usually the middle wire or neutral point of transformer or generator windings) is intentionally grounded, either solidly or through a current-limiting device.

Ground Indication: An indication of the presence of a ground on one or more of the normally ungrounded conductors of a system.

Grounding Conductor: A conductor used to connect an equipment, device, or wiring system to a grounding electrode.

Grounding Connection: A connection (used in establishing a ground) and consisting of a grounding conductor, a grounding electrode, and the earth (soil) which surrounds the electrodes.

Grounding Electrode: A conductor imbedded in the earth used for maintaining ground potential on conductors connected to it and for dissipating into the earth current conducted to it.

Ground Lug: A lug used in connecting a grounding conductor to a grounding electrode (or to a thing grounded).

Ground Plate: A plate of conducting material buried in the earth to serve as a grounding electrode.

Ground-Return Circuit: A ground-return circuit is a circuit which has a conductor (or two or more in parallel) between two points and which is completed through the ground or earth.

Harmonic Distortion: Nonlinear distortion characterized by the appearance in the output of harmonics other than the fundamental component when the input wave is sinusoidal.

Highpass Filter: A highpass filter is a wave filter having a single transmission band extending from some critical or cut-off frequency, not zero, up to infinite frequency.

Inductive Coupling: In communication circuits, inductive coupling is the association of two or more circuits with one another by means of inductance mutual to the circuits.

Insertion Gain: The insertion gain resulting from the insertion of a transducer in a transmission system is the ratio of the power delivered to that part of the system following the transducer to the power delivered to that same part before insertion. Note: If more than one component is involved in the input or output, the particular components used must be specified. This ratio is usually expressed in decibels.

Insertion Loss: The insertion loss resulting from the insertion of a transducer in a transmission system is the ratio of the power delivered before the insertion to that part of the system following the transducer to the power delivered to that same part after the insertion. Note: If more than one component is involved in the input or output, the particular components used must be specified. This ratio is usually expressed in decibels.

Interference: In a signal transmission system, either extraneous power which tends to interefere with the reception of the desired signals, or the disturbance of signals which results.

Lowpass Filter: A lowpass filter is a wave filter having a single transmission band extending from zero frequency up to some cut-off frequency, not infinite.

Matched Transmission Line: A transmission line is said to be matched at any transverse section if there is no wave reflection at that section.

Pair: Pair is a term applied in electrical transmission to two like conductors employed to form an electric circuit.

Pickup: (1) A device that converts a sound, scene, or other form of intelligence into corresponding electrical signals. (2) Interference from a nearby circuit or system.

Radio Receiver: A device for converting radio waves into perceptible signals.

Reflection Loss: The reflection loss for a given frequency at the junction of a source of power and a load is given by the formula

$$20 \log_{10} \left| \frac{Z_1 + Z_2}{4 \ Z_1 Z_2} \right| \text{ (db)}$$

where Z_1 is the impedance of the source of power and Z_2 is the impedance of the load. Physically, the reflection loss is the ratio, expressed in db, of the scalar values of the volt-amperes delivered to the load to a load of the same impedance as the source. The reflection loss is equal to the number of decibels which corresponds to the scalar value of the reciprocal of the reflection factor. Note: When the two impedances have opposite phases and appropriate magnitudes, a reflection gain may be obtained.

Resistive Coupling: Resistive coupling is the association of two or more circuits with one another by means of resistance mutual to the circuits.

Selectivity (of a Receiver): That characteristic which determines the extent to which the receiver is capable of differentiating between the desired signals and disturbances of other frequencies.

Sensitivity: The least signal input capable of causing an output signal having desired characteristics.

Shield: A shield is a housing, screen, or other object, usually conducting, which substantially reduces the effect of electric or magnetic fields on one side thereof upon devices or circuits on the other side.

Sidebands: (1) The frequency bands on both sides of a carrier frequency within which fall the frequencies of the wave produced by the process of modulation. (2) The wave components lying within such bands.

Signal-to-Noise Ratio: The signal-to-noise ratio is the ratio of the magnitude of the signal to that of the noise. This ratio is often expressed in decibels. Note: This ratio is expressed in many different ways, for example, in terms of peak values in the case of impulse noise and in terms of root-mean-square values in the case of random noise, the signal being assumed sinusoidal. In special cases other measures of signal and noise may be used if clearly stated.

Transmission System: In communication practice, a transmission system is an assembly of elements capable of functioning together to transmit signal waves.

Unbalanced: Unbalanced means lacking the conditions for balance. Frequently it is used to mean having one side grounded.

Unbalanced Wire Circuit: An unbalanced wire circuit is one whose two sides are inherently electrically unlike.

Wave Impedance: The wave impedance of a transmission line, at any specified plane, is the complex ratio, at every point in that plane, of the transverse component of the electric field to the transverse component of the magnetic field. Note: Both incident and reflected waves may be present.

Voltage To Ground: The voltage between any live conductor of a circuit and earth (or common reference plane).

APPENDIX 2 – FORMULAS AND
CABLE CHARACTERISTICS

These formulas and characteristics are useful for resistance and imped-ance calculations for electrical conductors and coaxial cable.

A. Length and Weight

Weight (lb./1000 ft.)

$$= d^2 \times \delta \times 0.34049 \times 10^{-3}$$

Length (ft./lb.)

$$= \frac{1}{d^2} \times \frac{1}{\delta} \times 2.9369 \times 10^6$$

d = diameter of wire, mils
δ = density of the wire material

B. Total Resistance

$$R = \frac{K \times l}{CM}$$

R = resistance, ohms,
l = length of wire, ft.,
CM = circular mil area,
K = resistance of one mil-ft., ohms

C. Density

$$\delta = \frac{W_a \times d}{W_a - W_1}$$

δ = density, grams/cc.,
W_a = weight in air, grams,
W_1 = weight in liquid, grams,
d = density, grams/cc.

D. Temperature Correction

$$R_1 = R_0 \, [\, 1 + \alpha \, (t - t_0) \,]$$

$R_1 =$ resistance at operating temperature,
$R_0 =$ resistance at a known temperature,
$t =$ operating temperature,
$t_0 =$ temperature for a known resistance,
$\alpha =$ temperature coefficient of resistance at t_0
          (0.00393/degree C at 29° C.).

E. Areas

Area, circular mils $= d^2$
Area, square mils $=$ Thickness $\times$ Width (in mils)
Convert circular mils to square mils: $d^2 \times 0.7854$
Convert square mils to circular mils: Sq. Mils $\times 1.2732$

F. Transmission Line Characteristic Impedance (Z_0):

Single Coax Line

$$Z_0 = \frac{138}{\sqrt{\epsilon}} \log_{10} \frac{D}{d}$$

$\epsilon =$ dielectric constant,
$D =$ inner diameter of outer conductor,
$d =$ outer diameter of inner conductor.

Balanced Shielded Line

$$Z_0 = \frac{276}{\sqrt{\epsilon}} \log_{10} \left[\, 2v \, \frac{1 - \delta^2}{1 + \delta^2} \,\right]$$

$$= \frac{120}{\sqrt{\epsilon}} \ln \left[\, 2v \, \frac{1 - \delta^2}{1 + \delta^2} \,\right]$$

$$\delta = \frac{h}{D}; \; v = \frac{h}{d}$$

$D =$ inner diameter of outer conductor
$d =$ outer diameter of inner conductor
$h =$ distance between two inner conductor centers

G. Open Two-Wire Line in Air

$$Z_0 = 120 \cosh^{-1} \frac{D}{d}$$

$$= 276 \log_{10} \frac{2D}{d}$$

$$= 120 \ln \frac{2D}{d}$$

$d =$ outer diameter of conductors
$D =$ distance between conductor centers

H. Capacitance of Coax Cable

$$C = \frac{7.36\epsilon}{\log_{10}\dfrac{D}{d}}$$

C = capacitance, $\mu\mu f$/ft.,
ϵ = dielectric constant,
D = inner diameter of outer conductor,
d = outer diameter of inner conductor.

I. Attenuation for Copper Coax Line

$$R_t = 0.1 \left(\frac{1}{d} + \frac{1}{D}\right) \sqrt{f}$$

$$A = 4.35 \frac{R_t}{R_o} + 2.78 \sqrt{\epsilon} \ (pf) \ f$$

R_t = total line resistance in ohms per 100 ft.
R_o = characteristic impedance of coax
D = inner diameter of outer conductor in inches
d = outer diameter of inner conductor in inches
ϵ = dielectric constant
A = attenuation in db per 100 ft.
(pf) = power factor of dielectric medium
f = frequency in megacycles

Note: Pages 222 to 227 lists characteristics of representative AWG sizes and coaxial cables.

TABLE A2-1. CHARACTERISTICS OF REPRESENTATIVE AWG SIZES

Size	Diameter	Area	Area	Weight	Tensile Strength Maximum	Breaking Strength Maximum	Maximum D-C Resistance At 68°F.
AWG	In.	Cir. mils	Sq. in.	lbs. per 1000 ft.	psi	lbs.	ohms per 1000 ft.
10	0.1019	10,380	0.008155	31.43	38,500	314.0	0.9989
12	0.0808	6,530	0.00513	19.77	38,500	197.5	1.588
16	0.0508	2,580	0.00203	7.818	38,500	78.10	4.016
21	0.0285	812.0	0.000638	2.452	38,500	24.50	12.80
22	0.0253	640.0	0.000503	1.945	38,500	19.43	16.14

Diameter Tolerances:

(a) Soft or annealed (ASTM Spec B3) ± 1%.

(b) Medium hard (ASTM Spec B2) or hard drawn (ASTM Spec B1):

For wires .100 mils in diameter or larger ± 1%.

For wires less than .100 mils in diameter ± .001.

TABLE A2-1 CHARACTERISTICS OF REPRESENTATIVE AWG SIZES (CONT'D)

Size	Medium Hard					Hard Drawn		
	Tensile Strength		Breaking Strength		Maximum D-C Resistance At 68°F.	Tensile Strength Minimum	Breaking Strength Minimum	Maximum DC Resistance At 68°F.
AWG	Maximum psi	Minimum psi	Maximum lbs.	Minimum lbs.	ohms per 1000 ft.	psi	lbs.	ohms per 1000 ft.
10	57,330	50,330	467.5	410.4	1.033	64,900	529.2	1.039
12	58,000	51,000	297.5	261.6	1.643	65,700	336.9	1.652
16	59,330	52,330	120.3	106.2	4.154	66,600	135.1	4.176
21	61,000	54,000	38.81	34.36	13.24	67,700	43.07	13.31
22	61,300	54,300	30.94	27.41	16.70	67,900	34.26	16.79

Resistances of copper wires in above table are maximum values for nominal diameters based on ASTM specifications. There are no ASTM specifications for wire No. 18 AWG or smaller and the resistances shown are based on 96.666% conductivity for medium hard and 96.16% conductivity for hard-drawn wire. Breaking strengths are based on tensile requirements of ASTM Spec. B3 (soft or annealed) for No. 20 AWG and larger and on B2 (medium hard) and B1 (hard drawn) for No. 18 AWG and larger. ASTM B2 (medium hard) or B1 (hard drawn) does not list tensile strength requirements for wire sizes smaller than No. 18 AWG. ASTM Spec. B3 (soft or annealed) does not list tensile strength requirements for wire sizes smaller than No. 20 AWG.

TABLE A2-2. CHARACTERISTICS OF REPRESENTATIVE COAXIAL CABLES

RG/U Type	Inner Conductor	Dielectric Material	Nominal Diameter Of Dielectric (in.)	Number And Type Of Shielding Braids	Protective Covering	Nominal Over-All Diameter (in.)	Nominal Impedance (ohms)	Nominal Capacitance (μμf/ft.)	Engineering Data	Nominal Attenuation in db/100 ft. Freq. (mc)	Atten.	Maximum Operating Voltage (volts rms)
8	7/0.0285 in. Copper	A-1	0.285	Copper, single braid	1	0.405	52.0	29.5		100	2.1	4000
* 8A	7/0.0285 in. Copper	A-1	0.285	Copper, single braid	11A	0.405	52.0	29.5	Now designated as RG-213/U	100 1000	2.1 9.0	5000
9	7/0.0285 in. Silvered Copper	A-1	0.280	Double braids; inner, silver coated copper; outer, copper	11	0.420	51.0	30.0		100 1000	2.0 8.5	4000
9A	7/0.0285 in. Silvered Copper	A-1	0.280	Silver coated copper, double braid	11	0.420	51.0	30.0		100 1000 10000	2.3 8.6 42.0	4000
9B	7/0.0285 in. Silvered Copper	A-1	0.280	Silver coated copper, double braid	11A	0.420	50.0	30.0	Now designated as RG-214/U	100 1000 10000	2.3 8.6 41.0	5000
13	7/0.0159 in. Tinned Copper	A-1	0.280	Copper, double braid	1	0.420	74.0	20.5		100 1000	2.1 7.8	4000
*13A	7/0.0159 in. Tinned Copper	A-1	0.280	Copper, double braid	11A	0.420	74.0	20.5	Now designated as RG-216/U	100 1000	2.1 7.8	5000
14	0.102 in. Copper	A-1	0.370	Copper, double braid	11	0.545	52.0	29.5		100 1000	1.4 6.2	5500
*14A	0.102 in. Copper	A-1	0.370	Copper, double braid	11A	0.545	52.0	29.5	Now designated as RG-217/U	100 1000	1.4 6.2	7000

TABLE A2-2. CHARACTERISTICS OF REPRESENTATIVE COAXIAL CABLES (CONT'D)

RG/U Type	Inner Conductor	Dielectric Material	Nominal Diameter Of Dielectric (in.)	Number And Type Of Shielding Braids	Protective Covering	Nominal Over-All Diameter (inch)	Nominal Impedance (ohms)	Nominal Capacitance (μμf/ft.)	Engineering Data	Nominal Attenuation in db/100 ft. Freq. (mc)	Atten.	Maximum Operating Voltage (volts rms)
22	2-conductor, 7/0.0152 Copper	A-1	0.285	Tinned copper, single braid	1	0.405	95.0	16.0		30 200	1.7 5.3	1000
22A	2-conductor 7/0.0152	A-1	0.285	Tinned copper, double braid	11	0.420	95.0	16.0		400		1000
22B	2-conductor 7/0.0152 inch copper	A-1	0.285	Tinned copper, double braid	11A	0.420	95.0	16.0	Dual coaxial balanced cable Twisted conductors	400	10.5 max.	1000
55	20 AWG Copper	A-1	0.116	Tinned copper, double braid	111A	0.206 (max)	53.5	28.5		10 100 1000	1.0 4.2 16.0	1900
55A	1/0.035 Silver covered copper	A-1	0.116	Silver-covered copper, double braid	11A	0.216 (max)	50	29.0		400	11.7 max.	1900
55B	0.0320 inch silver covered copper	A-1	0.116	Tinned copper, double braid	111A	0.206 (max)	53.0			400	11.7 max.	1900
58	20 AWG Copper	A-1	0.116	Tinned copper, single braid	1	0.195	53.5	28.5		10 100 1000	1.0 4.2 16.0	1900
58A	19/0.0071 Tinned copper	A-1	0.116	Tinned copper, single braid	1	0.195	52	28.5		10 100 1000	1.3 5.3 22.0	1900

TABLE A2-2. CHARACTERISTICS OF REPRESENTATIVE COAXIAL CABLES (CONT'D)

RG/U Type	Inner Conductor	Dielectric Material	Nominal Diameter Of Dielectric (in.)	Number And Type Of Shielding Braids	Protective Covering	Nominal Over-All Diameter (inch)	Nominal Impedance (ohms)	Nominal Capacitance (μμf/ft.)	Engineering Data	Nominal Attenuation in db/100 ft. Freq. (mc)	Atten.	Maximum Operating Voltage (volts rms)
58B	20 AWG Copper	A-1	0.116	Tinned copper, single braid	11A	0.195	53.5	28.5		10 100 1000	1.0 4.2 16.0	1900
58C	19/0.0071 inch tinned copper	A-1	0.116	Tinned copper, single braid	11A	0.195	50.0	28.5		10 100 1000	1.3 5.3 22.0	1900
59	22 AWG copperweld	A-1	0.146	Copper, single braid	1	0.242	73.0	21.0		10 100 1000	1.0 3.8 14.0	2300
59A	1/0.0230 copperweld	A-1	0.146	Copper, single braid	11A	0.242	75.0	21.5		400	9.0 max.	2300
59B	0.0230 inch copper-covered steel wire	A-1	0.146	Copper, single braid	11A	0.242	75.0	21.0		400	9.0 max.	2300

TABLE A2-2 CHARACTERISTICS OF REPRESENTATIVE COAXIAL CABLES (CONT'D)

RG/U Type	Inner Conductor	Dielectric Material	Nominal Diameter Of Dielectric (in.)	Number And Type Of Shielding Braids	Protective Covering	Nominal Over-All Diameter (inch)	Nominal Impedance (ohms)	Nominal Capacitance (μμf/ft.)	Engineering Data	Nominal Attenuation in db/100 ft. Freq. (mc) Atten.	Maximum Operating Voltage (volts rms)
161	7/38 AWG silver plated cadmium bronze	F-1	0.057	Single silvered copper	Extruded black nylon	0.090	70.0	20.0	Miniature		1000

* Covered by Specification MIL-C-17B

Dielectric materials:

A-1: Solid polyethylene
A-2: Air-spaced polyethylene
B: Polyisobutylene mixture
C: Synthetic-rubber compounds
D: Layer of synthetic-rubber dielectric between thin layers of conducting rubber
E: Layer of conducting rubber plus two layers of synthetic-rubber dielectric
F-1: Solid tetrafluorethylene (teflon)
F-2: Taped tetrafluorethylene (teflon)
F-3: Air-spaced tetrafluorethylene (teflon)

Dielectric consists of solid polyethylene with semi-conducting layers. Nominal diameter of dielectric is value over outer semi-conducting layer.

Jacket materials:

I: Low temperature black polyvinylchloride, contaminating type plasticizers
II: Grey polyvinylchloride, non-contaminating plasticizers
IIA: Low temperature black polyvinylchloride, non-contaminating plasticizers
IIIA: High molecular weight black polyethylene
IV: Black synthetic rubber
V: High temperature lacquer impregnated fiberglass braid, usually with Teflon tape between shield & jacket
VI: Polyester fibre impregnated with high temperature lacquer over wrapped or extruded silicone rubber over silicone impregnated fiberglass

APPENDIX 3 – BIBLIOGRAPHY

In the following bibliography, no attempt has been made to list all the published material in the electrical interference field. All the items listed would be of interest to anyone seeking to broaden his understanding of a specific area. It is for this reason that items have been listed according to subject matter. A complete bibliography has been published by the Professional Technical Group on Electromagnetic Compatibility of the Institute of Electrical and Electronics Engineers.

RADIO INTERFERENCE

REDUCTION

1. Albin, A. L. and Sachs, H. M. "The Reduction of Radio Interference in Aeronautical Communications Systems," *Transactions of the IRE,* Vol. CS-4, No. 2 (May 1956).

2. Arnold, P., Metzger, H., and Jeter, I. "Suppression of R-F Interference in Primary Navigation Systems," Sperry-Gyroscope Company, Report No. 5298-2493-6, ASTIA No. AD-117684, December 1956.

3. Ball, A. H. and Nethercot, W. "Ignition Interference with Television Reception," *Proceedings of IEE,* Vol. 100, Part 1 (September 1953), p. 299-300.

4. Blanks, B. L., and Free, W. R. "Investigation and Study of Communication Interference Reduction Techniques," Georgia Institute of Technology Engineering Experiment Station, Atlanta, Report No. RADC-TR-58-104, December 1956; ASTIA No. AD-148844, January 1958.

5. Bond, F. E., Meyer, H. F., "The Effect of Fading on Communication Circuits Subject To Interference," Army Signal Research and Development Laboratory, Fort Monmouth, N. J., ASTIA No. AD-150397, June 1951, February 1953.

6. Church, H., and Tooke, F. A. E. "Classified Bibliography of Man-Made Radio Interference and Associated Measurements," British Electrical and Allied Industries Research Association, Technical Report M/T22, 1954.

7. Cooney, J. D., "How To Suppress Radio Interference," *Electric Manufacturing,* Vol. 54 (1954).

8. Davidson, R. "Interference Suppression," *Electrical Review,* Vol. 157 (October 1955).

9. *Design Techniques for Interference Free Operation of Airborne Electronics.* U. S. Department of Commerce, PB111051.

10. *Determination of Interference Levels.* U. S. Department of Commerce, PB120438.

11. Eastman, A. V., and Cozine, O. D. "The Investigation of Interference Radiated From Coaxial Transmission Lines," Bureau of Ships, Electronics Division, Index No. NE 120810, 3 Reports, 1952-1956.

12. Emerson, C. D. "R. F. I., A Problem of Automatic Machine Control," *American Machinist* (November 1955).

13. Engels, R., and Augustine, J. "VHF Interference," Armour Research Foundation, March 1956.

14. "Final Radio Interference Research Report," Bureau of Ships, Electronics Division, Index No. NE 120828, Vol. III — Radar.

15. Hale, A. P. *Electrical Interference.* New York: Philosophical Library, Inc., 1956.

16. "Harmonic Suppression for High Power Transmitters," General Electric Company, Report No. RADC TR-57-112, ASTIA No. AD-131-159, 1956.

17. Haviland, R. P. "The Prevention and Elimination of Certain Electrical Interference in Missiles," U. S. Army Ordnance Corps, Report No. R53A0511, ASTIA No. AD-19117, June 1953.

18. Hunter, A. "Suppression of Electrical Interference to High Frequency Apparatus in Naval Vessels," *Journal of IEE,* Vol. 96, Part III, March 1949, p. 159-165.

19. Hylas, A. E. "Radiation Suppression of Radar Pulses," *Sperry Engineering Review,* Vol. 10 (January, February 1957).

20. "Interference Suppression," *Electrical Review,* (September 1955).

21. Klingaman, G. W. "Reduction of Interference From Radio-Frequency Heating Equipment," *Transactions of the AIEE,* Vol. 68 (1949).

22. McFee, Richard, and Mayer, Thomas M. "Effect of Surface Reflections on Rain Cancellation of Circularly-Polarized Radars," Syracuse University Research Institute, Report No. EE 492-5711T2 (RADC-TN-58-51), ASTIA No. AD-148601, November 1957.

23. Neuman, M. M. "Impulsive Radio Interferene and Reduction Methods, Vol. 6, April 1951.

24. Newcomb, R. R. "Radio Interference Suppression System," U. S. Army Signal Research and Development Laboratory, Fort Monmouth, N. J., Report No. 1953, ASTIA No. AD-200315, April 1958.

25. Paananen, Roy A. "A Receiver Design for Rejecting Interference," Research Laboratory of Electronics, Massachusetts Institute of Technology, Technical Report No. 245, ASTIA No. AD-28467.

26. Pearce, S. F. "Radio Interference from High Voltage Distribution Systems," British Electrical and Allied Industries Research Association, Technical Report M/T22, 1954.

27. *Proceedings of Conference on Radio Interference Reduction.* Armour Research Foundation, ASTIA No. AD-76686 (1955).

28. ————, ibid. Second Conference, March 1956; Third, 1957; Fourth, 1958; Fifth, 1959; Sixth, 1960; Seventh, 1961.

29. "Radio Interference Suppression Techniques: A Guide for Manufacturers," Coles Signal Laboratory, Signal Corps Engineering Laboratories, Fort Monmouth, N. J., ASTIA No. AD-21192, November 1953.

30. "Radio Interference Studies," Burroughs Corporation, ASTIA No. AD-35200, June 1951, February 1953.

31. Rheingold, Irving, and Carter, John L. "The Duplexer As A Means of Eliminating Interference from Nearby High-Power Radar Systems," Evans Signal Laboratory, U. S. Army Signal Engineering Laboratories, Belmar, N. J., Technical Memorandum No. M-1872, ASTIA No. AD-129787, April 1957.

32. Rounds, P. W., and Lakin, G. L. "Equalization of Cables For Local Television Transmission," *Bell System Technical Journal,* Vol. 34, 1955.

33. Ruzgis, Albert. "Radio Interference Suppression System Design Considerations for Electrical Office Machines," U. S. Army Signal Corps Engineering Laboratories, Fort Monmouth, N. J., Technical Memorandom No. M-1877, ASTIA No. AD-132952, April 1957.

34. Seaman, Floyd D. "Radio Interference Minimization Design Techniques: Fractional Horsepower D-C Motors," Burroughs Corporation, ASTIA No. AD-35286, January 1954.

35. Schelkunoff, S. A. "Methods of Electromagnetic Field Analysis," *Bell System Technical Journal,* Vol. 27 (1948).

36. ————. "Some Equivalence Theorems of Electromagnets and Their Application to Radiation Problems," *Bell Laboratory Record,* Vol. 15. (1936).

37. ————. "The Impedance Concept and Its Application To Problems

of Reflection, Refraction, Shielding and Power Absorption," *Bell System Technical Journal,* Vol. 17 (January 1938).

38. Stephens, G. L. "Radio Interference Suppression," *Wireless World,* Vol. XLV (1939).

39. ————. *Radio Interference Suppression.* Iliffe and Sons.

40. "Study and Investigation of Interference Specification," Electro-Mechanics Company, Report No. RADC TN-57-97, ASTIA No. AD-114389, October 1956, February 1957.

41. "Suppression of Radio Interference," *Electronic Engineering,* Vol. 22 (September 1950).

42. "Suppression of Radio Interference," *Electrical Review,* Vol. 159 (August 1956).

43. Thomas, L. "Handling Radio Interference," *BuShips Journal,* NavShips 250-200, Vol. 1:10 (February 1953), p. 31-34.

44. ————. "Radio Interference On a Modern Parkway," *ibid,* Vol. 4, No. 6, (October 1955), p. 29-31.

45. Weaver, Donald K. "Electrical Interference Problems", Stanford Research Institute, SRI Project No. 336, Interim Report No. 2.

46. Weiss, G. "Troubleshooting In Advance By Proper Wiring Design," *Control Engineering,* Vol. 1. (September 1954).

47. Wright, W. W. "Communication Interference Reduction Study," Georgia Institute of Technology Engineering Experiment Station, Atlanta, Report No. RADC TN-57-426, ASTIA No. AD-148529, July, September, and October 1957.

SOURCES

1. Adams, G. W. "The Calculation of the Radio Interference Level of Transmission Lines Caused by Corona Discharges," *Transactions of the AIEE,* Vol. 75 (1956).

2. ————, "An Analysis of Radio Interference Characteristics of Bundled Conductors," *ibid.*

3. Brown, G. H. "Interference from Radio Frequency Heating Equipment,' *Transactions of the AIEE,* Vol. 67, (1948).

4. Newell, H. H. and Warburton, F. W. "Variations in Radio and Television Interference From Transmission Lines, *Transactions of the AIEE,* Vol. 75. (1956), AIEE 56-223.

5. Motter, D. P. "Commutation of D-C Machines and Its Influence On Radio Interference Voltage Generation, *Transactions of the AIEE,* Vol. 68, (1949).

6. Pope, R. "Interference From Forced Drainage, *"Bell System Technical Publications,* Monograph 1775, ASTIA No. U-14713.

7. Schatz, E. R., Taylor, M. E., Robl, R. F., and Konnerth, K. L. *"Leakage Radiation From A Braided Coaxial Cable,"* *IRE Convention Record,* Part 5 (1956).

8. Schelkunoff, S. A. "Electromagnetic Theory of Coaxial Transmission Lines and Cylindrical Shields," *Bell System Technical Publications,* Monograph B-816 (1934).

9. "Television Interference Problems," *Electric Light and Power,* Vol. 32, No. 2 (February 1954).

10. Underwood, W. Bruce, and O'Bryhim, Donald H. "Electronics Interference Survey," International Electronics Engineering, Inc., Report No. 2-514-1-53, ASTIA No. AD-108658, November 1953.

11. Weiss, G. "Wiring Design to Avoid Pickup," *Product Engineering,* Product Design Digest Issue, Vol. 26, No. 11. (October 1955).

12. Wilmotte, R. W. "Interference Caused By More Than One Signal," *Proceedings of the IRE,* Vol. 38, No. 10 (October 1950).

MEASUREMENT

1. Adair, G. P. "TV/FM Field Intensity Measurements," *Communications,* Vol. 29, No. 5. (May 1949).

2. Aggers, C. V., Foster, D. E., and Young, C. S. "Instruments and Methods of Measuring Radio Noise," *Transactions of the AIEE,* Vol. 59 (March 1940), p. 178-192.

3. Bennett, W. R. "Techniques for Measuring Noise," *Electronics,* Vol. 29, No. 5 (May 1956).

4. Burrill, C. M. "An Evaluation of Radio Noise Meter Performance In Terms of Listening Experience," *Proceedings of the IRE,* Vol. 30, (October 1942).

5. Deleeuw, A. M. "Research on Staggered Lay For Shipboard Telephone Cables," Material Laboratory, New York Naval Shipyard, Report No. NS 672-100, ASTIA No. AD-145795, October 1957.

6. Dinger, H. "Factors Affecting the Accuracy of Radio Noise Meters," *Proceedings of the IRE* (January 1947).

7. ————. "Measurements On Noise Radiation From High Voltage Transmissions Lines," U. S. Civil Aeronautics Administration, Technical Development Note No. 46, May 1947.

8. Dreyer, J. F. "Technique For TV Field Survey," *Electronics,* Vol. 22, No. 10 (October 1949).

9. Epperson, J. B. "TV Field Intensity Measurements," *Electronics,* Vol. 22, No. 3 (March 1949).

10. Evans, H. D. "Measurement Technique," *Electronic Industries,* Vol. 4, No. 7 (July 1945).

11. Frick, C. W. "A Study of Wave Shapes For Radio Noise Meter Calibrations," *Transactions of the AIEE,* Vol. 64 (1945), p. 890.

12. Germer, L. M. and Smith, G. S. "Arcing At Electrical Contacts On Closure," Part III — Development of An Arc," *Journal of Applied Physics,* Vol. 23, No. 5 (May 1952).

13. Haber, Fred. "Derivation of Some Formulas Applicable To Interference Prediction in Radar to Communication Receiver Interference," Moore School of Electrical Engineering, University of Pennsylvania, Technical Memorandum No. 5410-10, ASTIA No. AD-109891.

14. Hamburger, G. L. "Interference Measurements," *Wireless Engineer,* Vol. 25, Nos. 293, 294 (February, March 1948).

15. ————. "Investigation of the Measurement of Radio Interference," Moore School of Electrical Engineering, University of Pennsylvania, April 1957 to July 1958.

16. Jarva, W. "Electromagnetic Field Theory As Applied To Radio Interference Measurements," Filtron Company, Engineering Division Report.

17. ————. "Tech Note: Problems of Radio Interference Measurements," Naval Air Development Center, Report No. EL54149, February 1955.

18. ————. "Tech Note: Techniques For The Measurement of Spurious Radiations and Harmonics from Transmitters," *ibid,* Report No. EL-N5506, May 1955.

19. King, R. W. "Army Signal Corps Perfects New Type Noise Meter," *Electrical Engineering,* Vol. 64, No. 12 (December 1950).

20. ————. "IRE Standards On Receivers: Methods of Measurement of Interference Output of Television Receivers In the Range 300-10,000 KC," *Proceedings of the IRE,* Supplement 54 IRE 17 SI, Vol. 42, No. 9 (September 1954).

21. ————. "Standards On Radio Receivers: Open Field Method of Measurement of Spurious Radiation From FM and TV Broadcast Receivers," *Proceedings of the IRE,* Supplement 51 IRE 17 SI, Vol. 39, No. 7 (July 1951).

22. ————. *Proceedings of the IRE,* Supplement 56 IRE 27 SI, Vol. 44, No. 8 (August 1956).

23. ————. "Two Standard Field-Strength Meters For VHF," *Proceedings of the IRE,* Vol. 38, No. 9. (September 1950).

24. McNeely, J. K., and Konkle, P. J. "Locating Radio Interference With The Oscillograph," *Proceedings of the IRE,* Vol. 18, No. 7. (July 1930).

25. Newman, M. M., Schwantes, R. C., and Stahmann, J. R. "Aircraft Radio Interference Measurements," *Transactions of the AIEE,* Vol. 71 (1952).

26. ————. *Ibid,* Vol. 71, Part 2, No. 2 (September 1952), p. 211-215.

27. ————. Aircraft Radio Interference Measurements," *Electrical Engineering,* Vol. 72, No. 1 (January 1953).

28. ————. "Methods of Measuring Radio Noise," Edison Electric Institute, Publication No. G-9, 1940.

29. Perry, R. E. "Field Power Conversion," *Electronics,* Vol. 24, No. 8 (August 1951).

30. ————. "Measurement of Field Intensity Above 300 MC From R-F Industrial, Scientific and Medical Equipments," AIEE, No. 950.

31. Smith-Rose, R. "Radio Field — Strength Measurement," *Proceedings of the IEE,* Vol. 96, Part III (January 1949).

32. Thomas. "Radio Interference Measurements Techniques," *BuShips Journal,* NavShips 250-200, Vol. 4, No. 2 (June 1955), p. 33-36.

33. Vasaka, C. S. "Tech Note: Impedance Measurement of Stabilization Network AN/USA-2," Naval Air Development Center, Report No. EL-N5546 (May 1955).

ATTENUATION

1. Frick, C. "How To Minimize the Radio Influence of Electric Devices," *Electric Manufacturing,* Vol. 23 (March 1939).

2. Linder, E. G. "Attenuation of Electromagnetic Field In Pipes Smaller Than The Critical Size," *Proceedings of the IRE,* Vol. 30 (1942).

3. *Radio Interference Suppressors.* Sprague Electric Company, ASTIA No. AD-50997 (October 1954).

4. Sachs, H. M., and Albin, A. L. "Suppressing Radiation From Medical Electronic Equipment," *Electronics Industries and Tele-Tech,* Vol. 15, Nos. 68-70, November 1956 .

CONTROLLING

1. Aggers, C. V. "Methods of Controlling Radio Interference," *Transactions of the AIEE,* Vol. 59 (1940).

2. Albin, A. L., and McManus, J. E. "Radio Interference Control in Aircraft," *IRE Aeronautics Electronics Digest* (1955), p. 268-271.

3. Brueckmann, H. "Suppression of Undesired Radiation of Directional HF Antennas and Associated Feed Lines," *Proceedings of the IRE,* Vol. 46, No. 8 (1958).

4. Ingram, C. W. *Radio Interference Suppression.* London: Dorset House, 1939.

5. Knudson, L. I. "The Design of Reactors For Radio Interference Filters," *Transactions of the AIEE,* Vol. 69, AIEE 50-204 (1950).

6. Maylott, C. F. "Radio Interference Control," *Transactions of the AIEE,* Vol. 71, AIEE 52-300 (1952).

7. Pecota, W. "Design Techniques for Interference: Free Operation of Airborne Electronic Equipment," Frederick Research Corporation (1958).

8. ————. "Small Light Weight R-F Interference Suppressors Using Transistors," *IRE Convention Record,* Part 8 (1958).

9. Sanford, F. E., and Weise, W. "A Review of Radio Interference Investigation," *Transactions of the AIEE,* Vol. 56 (1937).

10. Short, B. H. "Physics of Automotive Radio Interference Elimination," *General Motors Engineering Journal,* Vol. 1, No. 5 (April 1954), p. 36-20.

ELECTRONIC AND ELECTRICAL EQUIPMENT

1. Albin, A. L., and Sachs, H. M. "Design of Electronic Equipment For Radio Interference Reduction," *Transactions of the AIEE,* Vol. 59 (1940).

2. ————. "Design of Electronic Equipment For Radio Interference Reduction," *Machine Design,* Vol. 28, No. 18 (September 1956).

3. Boesmiller, J. "Bad Commutation: Causes and Cure," *Power Engineering,* Vol. 58 (August 1954).

4. Campbell, R. D. "Radar Interference To Microwave Communication Services," *Transactions of the AIEE,* AIEE 58-817 (November 1958).

5. Chipman, R. A. "Effect of Radiation On Resonant Lines," *Electronics,* Vol. 26, No. 1 (January 1953).

6. Davidson, R. "Interference Suppression," *Wireless World,* Vol. 61 (April 1955).

7. "Design Techniques For Interference-Free Operation of Airborne Electronic Equipment," Wright Air Development Center, 1952.

8. Elimination of Radio Interference in Aircraft," Bureau of Aeronautics, U. S. Navy Publication NavAer 16-5Q-517.

9. Granger, J. V. N., and McRita, T. "Radio-Frequency Current Distribution on Aircraft Structures," *Proceedings of the IRE,* Vol. 39, No. 8, IRE 3975 (1951).

10. "Interference From Fluorescent Tubes," *Wireless World,* Vol. 56, No. 3 (March 1950).

11. *Manual of Installation and Maintenance Practices For The Reduction*

of Radio Interference in Aircraft. Bureau of Aeronautics, U. S. Navy Department.

12. Miedzinski, J., and Pearce, S. F. "Interference From Industrial R-F Equipment Performance of Screening Rooms," British Electrical and Allied Industrial Research Association, Technical Report M/T104, March 1949.

13. Milnor. "Control of Inductive Interference To Telegraph Systems," *Transactions of the AIEE,* Vol. 59 (1940).

14. Murray, J. G. "Current Rectification and High Frequency Interference In Inert Gas Welding," *Welding Journal,* Vol. 33, No. 6 (June 1954).

15. *Proceedings of the Unclassified Sessions of the Symposium on Electromagnetic Interference,* U. S. Army Signal Research and Development Laboratory, June 1958.

16. "Radio Interference Suppression of High Frequency Arc Welder," Coles Signal Laboratory, T-1219, PB 97469 (May 1949).

17. "Recommended Practice For Minimization Of Interference From Radio-Frequency Heating Equipment," AIEE Publication No. 951, May 1950.

18. Sarley, J. M., and Hendry, R. J. "Radio Interference Control As Applied To Business Machines," *IBM Journal of Research and Development* (October 1957).

19. Swan, A. G. "Radiation From R-F Heating Generators," *Electronics,* Vol. 19, No. 5 (May 1946).

20. "Tech Note: The Effect of Radio Interference in Airborne Electronics," Naval Air Development Center, Report No. EL-N55144, February 1955.

21. "Tests Indicate Interference Levels Generated By Fluorescent Lamps," *BuShips Journal,* NavShips 250-200, Vol. 3, No. 6 (October 1954), p. 33-35.

22. Thomas, L. "Radio Interference From Machine Tools," *BuShips Journal,* NavShips 250-200, Vol. 3, No. 7 (November 1954), p. 35-28.

23. Walters, G. "Suppression of Radio Interference in Fluorescent Lighting Installations," *Illuminating Engineering,* Vol. 49, No. 6 (June 1954).

24. Wright, F. H., and Zimmerman, S. A. "Evaluation of Radio Interference Voltages in Fluorescent Lighting Systems," *Transactions of the AIEE,* Vol. 75, AIEE 56-75 (1956).

Effect of Power Systems

1. "A Review of Past and Current Work on Electromagnetic Interference Voltage from Electric Power Transmission Lines," Hinchman

Corp., ASTIA No. AD-108685, November 1955.

2. Aggers, C. V., Pakala, W. E., and Stickel, W. A. "Effect of Radio Frequencies of a Power System on Radio Receiving Systems," *Transactions of the AIEE,* Vol. 62 (1943).

3. Davis, A. B. "How to Apply Telephone Noise Calculations to Power and Telephone Line Coordination," *Elec. News & Eng.,* Vol. 63, Nos. 10, 12 (May, June 1954).

4. Frost, P. B. and Gould, E. F. H. "Practical Aspects of Telephone Interference Arising from Power Systems," *Journal of the IEE,* Vol. 93, Part I (June 1946).

5. Greenblatt, S. "Leakage Parameters of Radio Frequency Cables," Rome Air Development Center, Research Report R-289-52, PIB-288.

6. Hunt, J. H., Johnson, A. A., and Lawrence, R. F. "Communication Interference from Power Lines Reduced by Transpositions" *Electric Light and Power,* Vol. 28, No. 2 (February 1950).

7. "Inductive Interference between Electric Power and Communications Circuits", Railroad Commission of the State of California, April 1919.

8. Jensen, M. "On Radiation From Overhead Transmission Lines," *Proceedings of the IEE,* Vol. 97 (1950).

9. Klewe, H. R. J. "Electrostatic Induction by Power Lines in Parallel Telephone Lines and at Crossings," *Proceedings of the IEE,* Vol. 98, Part I (March 1951).

10. ————. *Interference Between Power Systems and Telecommunication Lines.* London: Edward Arnold, Ltd., 1958.

11. Marshall, C. W. "Telephonic and Radio Interference from High Voltage Systems," *Engineering,* Vol. 170, No. 4410 (August 1950).

12. Moore, L. M., and Huntley, H. R. "Inductive Coordination of REA and Bell System Line," *Electrical World,* Vol. 124, No. 15 (October 1945).

13. Puroes, T. F. "Protection of Telephone Lines Against Power Interference," *Journal of the IEE,* Vol. 68, (1930), p. 495-498.

14. Rorden, H. L. "Radio Noise Influence of 230-KV Lines," *Proceedings of the AIEE,* Vol. 66 (1947).

15. Senn, J. C., and Wright, D. C. "A Practical Handbook for Location and Prevention of Radio Interference from Overhead Power Lines," Naval Civil Engineering Research and Evaluation Laboratory, Technical Memorandum, No. M-116, ASTIA No. AD-125060 (November 1956).

16. Senn, J. C., Gosley, A. W. "Reduction of Power Line Radio Interference," U. S. N. Civil Engineering Research and Evaulation Laboratory, PB 111666, 1955.

17. ————. *Ibid.* Technical Memorandum, M-095, ASTIA No. AD-81139, February 1955.

18. Smith, J. J. "Telephone Interference from A-C Generator Feeding Directly on Line with Neutral Grounded," *Transactions of the AIEE,* Vol. 49 (1930), p. 798-805.

19. Stigant, S. A., Lacey, H. M. "Interference Between Power Lines," *The Electrician,* Vol. 104 (1930), p. 696-698.

20. Whitehead, S., Morgan, P. D., Radley W. G., and Pidgeon, I. E. "The Inductive Effects and Earth Impedance of Earthed Power Systems," Electrical Research Association, United Kingdom, Report M/T6 (1930).

21. Wirkler, W. H., "Effect of Ground System and Power Cables on Direction Finder Site," Collins Radio Company (December 1940).

CROSSTALK

1. Aikens, A. J., and Taheler, C. S. "Noise and Crosstalk Control on N1 Carrier System." *Electrical Engineering,* Vol. 72, No. 12 (1953).

2. Albert, A. L. "Electrical Communications" New York: John Wiley and Sons, Inc. (1950).

3. Alford, R. S. "Crosstalk Measurements," *Bell Lab Record,* Vol. 15, No. 12 (August 1937).

4. Babcock, W. C., Rentrop, E., and Taheler, C. S. "Crosstalk on Open Wire Lines," Bell System Technical Publications, Monograph 2520, (1955), also *Bell System Technical Journal* (March 1956).

5. Booth, R. P., and Odarenko, T. M. "Crosstalk Between Coaxial Conductors in Cables," *Bell System Technical Journal,* Vol. 19 (1940).

6. Chapman, A. G. "Open Wire Crosstalk," *Bell System Technical Journal,* Vol. 13 (January, April 1934).

7. Harrison, C. W. "On Pickup of Balanced Four-Wire Lines," *Proceedings of the IRE,* Vol. 30, No. 11 (November 1942).

8. Hunter A., and Booth, R. P. "Cable Crosstalk: Effects of Non-Uniform Current Distribution in the Wires," *Bell System Technical Journal,* Vol. 14 (April 1935).

9. Little, J. G. "Low Frequency Crosstalk In Pulse Phase Modulation," *Wireless Engineering,* Vol. 32 (August 1955).

10. Schelkunoff, S. A., and Odarenko, T. M. "Crosstalk Between Coaxial Transmission Lines," *Bell Lab Journal,* Vol. 16 (1937).

11. Shetzline, R. A. "The Longitudinal Circuit," *Bell Lab Record,* Vol. 18, No. 1 (September 1939).

12. Stephenson, J. G. "Cross Pulse Puckup in Twisted Pair Cable," *Electronics,* Vol. 29, No. 2 (1956).

13. Weaver, M. A., Tucker, R. S., and Darnell, P. S. "Crosstalk and Noise Features of Cable Carrier Telephone System," *Bell System*

Technical Journal, Vol. 17, No. 1, (January, 1938), also *Transactions of the AIEE,* Vol. 57, No. 5 (May 1938).

14. Wendt, R. L. "Minimizing Noise in Electronics System," *Electronic Industries and Tele-Tech,* Vol. 15, No. 8 (August 1956).

Sources — Noise

1. "An Investigation of Electromagnetic Coupling Devices for Measurement of Noise Field," Signal Corps Engineering Lab, ASTIA No. AD-7288, August 1952.

2. Bennett, W. R. "Electrical Noise: Part I," *Electronics,* Vol. 29, No. 3 (March 1956).

3. ————. *Op. Cit.,* Part II, No. 4 (April 1956).

4. ————. *Op Cit.,* Part III, No. 5 (May 1956).

5. ————. *Op. Cit.,* Part IV, No. 6 (June 1956).

6. ————. *Op Cit.,* Part V, No. 7 (July 1956).

7. ————. "Sources and Properties of Electrical Noise," Bell System Technical Publications, Monograph 2324.

8. Dinger, H. and Raudenbush, J. E. "Antifriction Bearings as a Radio Noise Source," Naval Research Laboratory (July 18, 1952).

9. Landon, V. D. "A Study of the Characteristics of Noise", Institute of Radio Engineering (1936).

10. Lawson, A. B. and Uhlenbeck, G. E. *Threshold Signals.* MIT Radiation Lab Series No. 24, New York: McGraw-Hill Book Company, 1950.

11. Pierce, J. R. "Physical Sources of Noise," *Proceedings of the IRE,* Vol. 44, No. 5, IRE-5699 (May 1956).

12. Steele, H. L., Jr. "Physical Processes in the Fluorescent Lamp Which Cause Radio Noise," *Illuminating Engineering,* Vol. 49, No. 7 (July 1954).

13. VANderZiel, A. *Noise.* New York: Prentice Hall, Inc., 1954.

14. Wax, N. *Selected Papers on Noise and Stochastic Processes.* New York: Dover, Inc., 1954.

15. Weber, L. A. "Influence of Noise on Telephone Signalling Circuit Performance," Bell System Technical Papers, Monograph 2812.

Reduction

1. Burgess, R., Wendt, S. Cap. R. "Report on Electrical Noise Reduction," *Sperry Engineering Review* (April 1954).

2. Ewait, M. B. "Electrical Noise Suppression," *Machine Design* (September 1954).

3. Franke, H. C. "Noise Measurements of Telephone Circuits," *Elect. Ind. & Tele-Tech.* Vol. 14, No. 3 (March 1955).

4. Phillips, M. L. "Estimating the Ratio of Steady Sinusoidual Signal to Random Noise from Experimental Data," *Proceedings of the IRE,* Vol. 44, No. 5, IRE-5706 (May 1956).

5. Rodgers, D. C. "Suppressing Impulse Noise," *Wireless World,* Vol. 55, No. 12 (December 1949).

6. Schwartz, L. S. "Principles of Noise Reduction in Communication Channels, *Transactions of the AIEE,* Vol. 75, EE 56-74 (1956).

ELIMINATION

1. Bennett, W. R. "Methods of Solving Noise Problems," *Proceedings of the IRE,* Vol. 44, No. 5, IRE 5700 (May 1956).

2. Helstrom, C. W. "The Resolution of Signals in White Gausian Noise." *Proceedings of the IRE,* Vol. 43, No. 9, IRE-5481 (September 1955).

3. "Noise Free Instrument Cable." *Communications Engineering* (March 1953).

4. Owen, T. B. "Very High Frequency Radio Noise Elimination," *Transacations of the AIEE,* Vol. 63 (1944).

5. Rorden H. L. and Gens, R. S. "Investigation of Radio Noise As It Pertains to Design of High-Voltage Transmission Lines," *Transactions of the AIEE,* Vol. 71, AIEE 52-106 (1952).

6. Weinstein, G., Howell, H. H., Lowe, G. P., and Winter, B. J. "Radio-Noise Elimination in Military Aircraft," *Transactions of the AIEE,* Vol. 63 (November 1944).

SHIELDING

ELECTRONIC AND ELECTRICAL EQUIPMENT

1. Bethe, H. A. "Attenuation Through Holes," *Physical Review,* Vol. 66 (1944), p. 163-182.

2. Burruano, S. J. and Bailey, E. F. "Shielding and Potting," *Electronics,* Vol. 27, No. 10 (October 1954).

3. "Electromagnetic Shielding Metal," *Electronics,* Vol. 24 (April 1951).

4. Ellwood, W. D. "Magnetic Shields," *Bell Lab Record* (November 1938).

5. Gustafson, W. G. "Magnetic Shielding of Transformers at Audio Frequencies," *Bell System Technical Journal,* Vol. 17 (1938).

6. ————. "Magnetic Shields for Transformers," *Bell Lab Record,* Vol. 17, No. 3 (October 1938).

7. Hill, E. L. "The Shielding of Radio Waves by Conductive Coating," *Transactions of the IRE,* Vol. AP-3, No. 2 (April 1955).

8. Jorgensen, C. M. "Shielding in Modern Computer Design," *Automatic Control,* Vol. 8, No. 6 (December 1958).

9. Klingaman, G. W. "Shielding of Electronic Generators," *AIEE Conference Paper* (January 1948).

10. Klingaman, G. W., and Williams, G. H. "Shielding of Dielectric Heating Installation," *Electronics,* Vol. 18 (May 1945).

11. Manzi, M., Marsman, J. M., and Brenner, M. "Grounding Shielded Cable," *Electrical Manufacturing,* Vol. 50, No. 6 (December 1952).

12. "Radio in Aircraft: Shielding and Bonding Data," *Radio News* (January 1935).

13. "Shielding and Grounding of Microwaves (Microwaves Receivers)," MIT Radiation Laboratory Series No. 23 (1948).

14. "Shielding HF Circuits Can Be Effectively Engineered," *Electrical Manufacturing,* Vol. 38, No. 3 (September 1946).

15. Shives, S. L. "Effectiveness of Conduit as R-F Shielding," *Electronics,* Vol. 19, No. 2 (February 1946).

16. Sodaro, "Shielding Nomograph", *Electronics,* Vol. 27, No. 5 (May 1954).

17. "Suppression of Radiation Interference," *Electronic Engineering,* Vol. 22, No. 271 (September 1950).

18. Terman, F. "Shielding of Magnetic and Electrostatic Field." *Section 2, Radio Engineers Handbook.* New York: McGraw-Hill Book Company, 1st Ed., 1943, C.F. Item 626.

19. Vasaka, C. S. "Problems in Shielding Electrical and Electronic Equipments," Aeronautical Electronic and Electrical Laboratory, Naval Air Development Center, Report No. NADC-EL-N5507, ASTIA No. AD-68874, June 1955.

20. Wagner, G. F., McCann, G. D., and Lear, W. P. "Shielding of Sub Stations," *Transactions of the AIEE,* Vol. 61 (1942).

21. Wheeler, H. "Universal Skin Effect Chart for Conducting Material," *Electronics,* Vol. 25, No. 11 (November 1952).

22. Whiteman, R. A. "Shielding Industrial Electronic Generators," *Radio News Engineering Edition,* Vol. 38 (September 1947).

ELECTROMAGNETIC EFFECTS

1. Blackband, W. T. "Wire Braid Screens for R-F Cables," *Journal of the IEE,* Vol 1 - New Series (June 1955).

2. Costello, R. J., and McMichael, B. D. "Differences in Attenuation Between Large and Small Shielded Enclosures," *Electronics,* Vol. 30, No. 8 (August 1957).

3. Davidson, C. F., and others, "Power Loss In Electromagnetic Screens," *Wireless Engineers,* Vol. 23 (January 1946).

4. DeVore, C., "Measuring Effectiveness of Shielding Materials," *Electrical Manufacturing,* Vol. 52, No. 2 (August 1953).

5. Dinger, H. E., Raudenbush, J. E. "Measuring Shielded Efficiency of Screened Enclosures," Naval Research Laboratory, Report No. 3908, ASTIA No. AT1-122259, November 1961.

6. ————. "A Technique for Measuring the Effectiveness of Various Shielding Materials," Naval Research Laboratory, Report No. 4103 (January 1953).

7. "Electromagnetic Shielding Principles," *Rome ADC,* ASTIA No. AD-91297, Vol. I (March 1956).

8. "Electromagnetic Shielding Principles," *Rome ADC,* ASTIA No. AD-91292, Vol. II (March 1956).

9. Fluharty, R. G. "Shielding Characteristics of R-R Cable," *Transactions of the AIEE,* Vol. 64 (1945), AIEE 45-145; Part of Report of Conference on Radio Frequency Cables.

10. Gooding, F. H., and Slade, H. B. "Shielding of Communication Cables," *Transactions of the AIEE,* Vol. 74, AIEE 55-198 (1955).

11. Harber, F. "Generation of Standard Fields in Shielded Enclosure," *Proceedings of the IRE,* Vol. 43, No. 11 (November 1954).

12. Kesney, E. S. "A Basic Discussion of Shielded Enclosures," Ace Engineering & Machine Company, Bulletin No. 7.

13. Lawson, A. W., Fano, R. "Note on the Efficiency of Radiating Shields," *Review of Scientific Instruments,* Vol. 18, No. 727 (October 1947).

14. Levy, S. "Electromagnetic Shielding Effect," *Proceedings of the IRE,* Vol. 24, No. 6 (1936).

15. Lyons, W. "Electromagnetic Shielding," *Proceedings of the IRE.*

16. ————. "Experiments of Electromagnetic Shielding at Frequencies Between One and Thirty Kilocycles," *Proceedings of the IRE,* Vol. 21, No. 4 (1933).

17. Merrell, E. J. "Semi-Conducting of A-C Power Cable, *Transactions of the AIEE,* Vol. 65 (1946).

18. Murray, A. F. "Shielding High-Frequency Interference," *Elect. Ind. & Tele-Tech.* (August 1945).

19. Spring, W. S. "Magnetic Shielding," *Electrical Manufacturing,* Vol. 61, No. 2 (February 1958).

20. Teachman, E. A. "Shielding Effectiveness of Flexible Shielding Conduit," Aircraft Radio Laboratory, U. S. Army Signal Corps, Memo. Report ENG-92-854.

21. Tomiyasu, K. "Unbalanced Terminations On Shielded-Pair Lines," *Journal of Applied Physics,* Vol. 21, No. 6 (June 1950).

22. Wagner, C. F., McCann, E. D., and MacLane, J. G. "Shielding of Transmission Line," *Transactions of the AIEE,* Vol. 60 (1941).

23. Weinberger, E. F., and Auerbach, L. "Development of a Technique for Measuring Cable Shielding Effectiveness," Material Laboratory, N. Y. Naval Shipyard, NE-120816, ASTIA No. AD-119120, June 1956.

24. Wey, G. J. "Shielding of Permanent Magnets from Transient Magnetic Fields," *Transactions of the AIEE,* Vol. 60 (1941).

25. Whinnery, J. R. "Skin Effect Formulas," *Electronics,* Vol. 15 (February 1942).

26. Wigington, R. L., and Natham, N. S. "Transient Analysis of Coaxial Cables Considering Skin Effect," *Proceedings of the IRE,* Vol. 45, No. 2, IRE-5987 (February 1957).

DESIGN

1. Albin, A. L. "Designing Noise Free Enclosure Openings," *Electronics,* Engineer Issue, Vol. 31 (August 1958).

2. Anderson, A. R. "Cylindrical Shielding and Its Measurement at Radio Frequencies," *Proceedings of the IRE,* Vol. 34, No. 5, IRE 2623 (May 1946).

3. Castric, L. J., and Vasques, H. "The Evaluation of a Sectionalized Shielded Enclosure," Rome Air Development Center, ASTIA No. AT1170716.

4. Davidson, R. "Filter Element Nomographs," *Electronic Industries and Tele-Tech.,* Vol. 13, No. 2 (February 1954).

5. Eaglesfield, C. C. "Design of a Screened Room," *Electronics Engineering* (April 1956).

6. "Electromagnetic Shielding Principles," Vol. I, Rennselaer Polytechnic Institute, Troy, N. Y., Report RADC TR-56-43a, ASTIA No. AD-91297, March 1956.

7. ————. *Op. Cit.,* Vol. II, Report RADC TR-56-43b, ASTIA No. AD-91298.

8. Ferguson, J. G. "Shielding," *Bell System Journal* (August 1929).

9. "Final Report, Evaluation of Seams & Gaskets Used in Shielding Enclosures and Development of Correctives for Improvement," Naval Air Development Center, Report EL-52139.

10. "Grounding of the Shielded Enclosures," Shielding Inc., Bulletin No. 6576.

11. Hawthorne, E. I. "Electromagnetic Shielding with Transparent Coated Glass," *Proceedings of the IRE,* Vol. 42, No. 3, IRE-4883 (1954).

12. "Installation of Lighting and Accessories in the Universal Type Shielded Enclosure," Shielding Inc., Bulletin No. 81756.

13. "Interim Report Shielding Efficiency of Shielded Enclosures," Naval Research Laboratory., ASTIA No. AT1-152618, January 1951.

14. Intrator, A. M., and Freberg, C. R. "An Investigation Into the Use of Aluminum and Other Metals for Shielded Rooms," Naval Civil Engineering Laboratory, Technical Report No. 007, November 1949.

15. Intrator, A. M. "The Use of Steel Sheet for the Construction of Shielded Rooms," *Transactions of the AIEE,* Vol. 72, AIEE 53-197, (1953).

16. Jones, A. "Shielding Factor of Underground Cable Sheaths," *Proceedings of the IEE,* Vol. 100, Part 4, No. 5 (October 1953).

17. Lafferty, R. E. "High Frequency Shields," *IRE Convention Record,* Part 6, (1956).

18. Lessner, R. G., and Markham, A. S. "Simplification of Field Strength Computations for Shielded Enclosures," *Proceedings of the IRE,* Vol. 45, No. 3 (March 1957).

19. Lindgren, E. A. "How to Evaluate Shielded Rooms," *Electronic Design* (January 1956).

20. "Locates Grounds in Shielded Rooms," *Electronics,* Vol. 20, No. 134 (October 1947).

21. Longo, C. V., and Wolf, E. "R-F Filter Design," *Electronics,* Vol. 28, No. 2 (February 1955).

22. Masuch, J. J. "Ignition Shielding Design," *Aero Digest,* Vol. 41, No. 227 (November 1942).

23. McCullough, F. S. "Shielded Room Design," *Electronic Industries,* No. 1943.

24. Morgan, G. A., Jr. "Notes on Design, Construction and Evaluation of Shielded Rooms," Naval Research Laboratory, NRL Report No. 3576.

25. Newman, D. J. "Radiation Absorbers—Their Selection and Use," *Electronic Design* (February 1957).

26. Pine, C. R. "Construction of a Shielded Room in VHF Field," *Electronics,* Vol. 21, No. 4 (April 1948).

27. Pulsifir, V. "Bonding Materials, Metallic Mating Surfaces, and Low R-F Impedance," Armour Research Foundation.

28. Schelkunoff, S. A. "Theory of Shielding," *Bell Laboratory Record,* Vol. 14 (March 1936).

29. Schreiber, O. P. "R-F Tightness Using Resilient Metallic Gaskets," Armour Research Foundation, March 1956.

30. Schulz, R. B. "Evaluating Shielded Enclosures," *Elect. Ind. & Tele-Tech.,* Vol. 13, No. 2 (February 1954).

31. "Shielding Efficiency of Shielded Enclosures," Naval Research Laboratory, January 1951.

32. Stringer, W. E. "Evaluation of Radio Interference Characteristic of Stainless Steel Shielding Conduit", Naval Air Material Center, June 1947.

33. ————. "Evaluation of Seams and Gaskets Used in Shielding Enclosures, and Development of Correctives for Improvement," Aeronautical Electronics and Electrical Laboratory, Naval Air Development Center, Report NADC-EL-52139, ASTIA No. AD-9494, February 1953.

34. Terman, F., and Pettit, E. "Shielding of Signal Generators," *Electronic Measurements.* New York: McGraw-Hill Book Company, Chap. 15, 1952.

35. Tilley, R. H. "Shielded Room for High Voltage Tests," *Electric World,* Vol. 120 (December 1943).

36. "Type PS Semi-Conducting Shielding," American Steel and Wire Company.

37. Vasaka, C. S. "Theory, Design & Engineering Evaluation of Radio-Frequency Shielded Rooms," Naval Air Development Center, Report No. EL-54129, ASTIA No. AD117664, August, 1956.

38. ————. *Op. Cit.,* Report No. NADC EL-54129, ASTIA No. AD117564.

39. ————. "Short Cuts to R-F Shield Design," *Elect. Ind. & Tele-Tech.* (March 1957).

40. "Ventilation and Air Conditioning of Shielding Enclosures," Shielding, Inc., Bulletin No. 8365.

41. Wadex, W. G. "Magnetic Shielding with Multiple Cylindrical Shells," *Review of Scientific Instruments,* Vol. 27, No. 11 (November 1956).

42. Wright, D. S., and Freber, C. R. "A Theoretical Investigation of Electromagnetic Shielding," Naval Civil Engineering Laboratory, Technical Report No. 006, ASTIA No. AT1-202137, November 1949.

FILTERS

1. Bingley, P. "Filters for Rectifier Equipment," *Electrical Times,* Vol. 127, p. 779-781 (1955).

2. "Development of High Efficiency Low Pressure Radio Filters," Rollin Company, Department 1947.

3. Frich, C. W., and Zimmerman, S. W. "Aircraft Radio Noise Filters," *Aircraft Communications,* Vol. 23 (July 1943).

4. Geffe, Philip R. *Simplified Modern Filter Design.* New York: John. F. Rider Publisher, Inc., 1963.

5. "Power Line Filters," Sprague Electric Company, ASTIA No. AD-14908, April 1953.

6. "Practical Filters for Minimizing TV Interference," *Electronic Industries and Tele-Tech.,* Vol 9, No. 28 (January 1950).

7. Saxe, R. E., and McManus, J. E. "Investigation of Lossy Materials for Lowpass Dissipative Type Filters," Armour Research Foundation, ASTIA No. AD-131795, December 1956, and March, April 1957.

8. "Small Size Feedthrough Capacitors," Sprague Electric Company, October 1946.

GROUNDING
THEORY

1. Abbott, F. R. "Correction To Design of Optimum Buried Conductor R-F Ground System," *Proceedings of the IRE,* Vol. 40, No. 10, IRE-4338 (October 1952).

2. "Application Guide for the Grounding of Synchronous Generator Systems," *Transactions of the AIEE,* Committee Report, Vol. 72, AIEE 53-201 (1953).

3. "Application Guide on Methods of Grounding of Transmission Systems," *Transactions of the AIEE,* Committee Report, Vol. 72, AIEE 53-201 (1953).

4. Bewley, L. V. "Critique Ground Wire Theory," *Transactions of the AIEE,* Vol. 50 (1931).

5. Boise, W. K., and Hunter, E. M. "System Electrical Grounding," *Electric L. & P.,* Vol. 21 (November 1943).

6. "Bonding and Grounding Manual," Pacific Automation Products, PAP-EM-101.

7. Brenner, M., Mazi, M. and Marsman, J. H. "Grounding Coax and Shielded Cable," *Elect. News & Engineering,* Vol. 62, No. 8 (April 1953).

8. Brown, H. H., and Gross, E. T. B. "Practical Experience With Resonant Grounding In A Large 34.5 KV System," *Transactions of the AIEE,* Vol. 69. (1950).

9. Burruano, S. J. "Missile System Grounding, Bending and Shielding," Filtron Company, Inc., Report No. EM-26-1, Project FL-112A.
————. "Missile System Grounding, Bending & Shielding Considerations," *ibid.*

11. Butterworth, A., Gosland, L., and Shotter, R. "Impedance of Steel Conduit Used As Earth-Continuity Conductor," B.E. & A.I.R. Association, Technical Report V/T 111, 1951.

12. Clem, J. E. "Development of the Standard for Neutral Grounding Devices," *Transactions of the AIEE,* Vol. 69 (1950).

13. "Correlation of System Overvoltages and System Grounding Impedance," *Transactions of the AIEE, Committee Report.* Vol. 62 (1943).

14. Curdts, E. B. "Grounding Principles and Practices As Applied to Industrial Plants," James G. Biddle Company, Bulletin No. 25T4.

15. Dwight, H. B. "Calculation of Resistance to Ground," *Transactions of the AIEE,* Vol. 55 (1936).

16. ————. "Calculation of Resistances to Ground and of Capacitances," *Journal of Math & Physics,* MIT, Vol. 10 (1931).

17. Eaton, J. R. "Grounding Electric Circuits Effectively," *G. E. Review,* Vol. 44 (1941).

18. Engineering Reports, Vol. IV, Edison Electric Institute (1937).

19. ————. Vol. V, Edison Electric Institute (January 1943).

20. Gilbert, T. C. "Earth Leakage Protection," *Electrical Review* (June 1955).

21. Gross, E. T. B. "Trends in Earthing Practices in Transmission Systems," *Water Power,* Vol. 3, No. 12 (December 1951).

22. Gross, E. T. B., and Atherton, E. W. "Application of Resonant Grounding in a Power System in the U.S.," *Transactions of the AIEE,* Vol. 70, AIEE 51-64.

23. Gross, E. T. B., and Rao, K. J. "Analysis of the Delta Grounded Transformer," *Transactions of the AIEE,* Vol. 72, AIEE 53-270 (1953).

24. "Grounding of Instrument Transformer Secondary Circuits," *Transactions of the AIEE,* Committee Report, Vol. 66 (1947).

25. "Grounding of Industrial Power Systems," *Transactions of the AIEE,* Publication No. 853 (October 1956).

26. "Grounding Principles & Practice," *Electrical Engineering,* Part I, Vol. 64 (1945).

27. ————. *Op Cit.*, Part V.

28. "Grounding Procedures For Electronic Equipment," *U.S. Army Technical Manual*, TM-11-676.

29. "Grounding Shield Braid in Guided Missiles," *Electronics*, Vol. 28, No. 4 (April 1955).

30. Harrison, L. H. "Search For Better Frame Grounding Methods," *Coal Age* (February 1955).

31. Higgs, P. J. "An Investigation of Earthing Resistances," *Journal of the IEE*, Vol. 68 (February 1930).

32. Hoopes, J. E. "Modernize Substation Grounding Practice," *Electric World*, Vol. 150 (August 1958).

33. Johnson, A. A. "How To Apply Neutral Grounding Devices," *Westinghouse Engineer* (May 1943).

34. ————. "Generator Grounding," *Electric L. & P.* (March 1952).

35. Kaufmann, R. H. "Equipment Grounding: Is It Really Protecting Your Plant," *Power*, Vol. 99, No. 2 (February 1955).

36. Leitner, A., and Spence, R. D. "Effect of Circular Ground Plane On Antenna Radiation," *Journal of Applied Physics*, Vol. 21, No. 11, (October 1950).

37. Leland, J. S., and Goldsborough, S. L. "The Functions of Ground Preference in Carrier Current Relay Schemes," *Transactions of the AIEE*, Vol. 63 (1941).

38. Lewis, R. F., and Epstine, J. "Ground System as a Factor In Antenna Efficiency," *Proceedings of the IRE*, Vol. 25, No. 6 (June 1930).

39. Loucks, W. W., and Lemire, W. A. R. "Transmission and Distribution Grounding in the Hydro-Electric Power Commission of Ontario," *Transactions of the AIEE*, Vol. 70, AIEE 51-279 (1951).

40. "Manual on Ground Resistance Testing," James G. Biddle Company, Bulletin No. 25-J (1955).

41. McCann, G. D. "The Effect of Corona On Coupling Factors Between Ground Wires and Phase Conductors," *Transactions of the AIEE*, Vol. 62 (1943).

42. McCree, J. "Grounding of Power System 4,160 Volt Auxiliary System," *Transactions of the AIEE*, Vol. 76, AIEE 57-1099 (1957).

43. "Neutral Grounding of Low Voltage Systems," *Iron & Steel Engineering*, Vol. 29, No. 2 (February 1954).

44. "Principles & Practices in Grounding," Edison Electric Institute, Publication No. D-9 (October 1936).

45. Roberts, L. G. T. "Earthing of Low and Medium Voltage Distribution Systems in Regions of High Soil Conductivity," *Royal Engineers Journal*, Vol. 67 (March 1953).

46. Sall, G. W. "Frame Grounding Protection," Mining Congress Protection (March 1956).

47. Schelkunoff, S. "The Impedance and Its Application to the Problem of Reflection, Refraction, Shielding and Power Absorption," *Bell System Technical Journal,* Vol. 17 (1938), p. 17-48.

48. Schwarz, S. J. "Analytical Expressions For The Resistance of Grounding Systems," *Transactions of the AIEE,* Vol. 73, AIEE 54-201, (1954).

49. ————. "Let's Look At Station Grounding," *Electric World,* Vol. 143 (May 1955).

50. "Should We Ground Plant Neutrals," *Power,* Vol. 98, No. 6 (June 1954).

51. Soares, E. C. "Industrial Grounding," *Elect. Construction & Maintenance,* Vol. 51, No. 4 (April 1952).

RETURN CIRCUITS

1. Bowen, H. E., and Gilkeson, C. L. "Mutual Impedances of Ground-Return Circuits," *Transactions of the AIEE,* Vol. 49 (1930).

2. Clem, J. E. "Reactance of Transmission Lines With Ground Return," *Transactions of the AIEE,* Vol. 50 (1931).

3. Sunde, "Currents and potentials Along Leaky Ground-Return Conductors," *Transactions of the AIEE,* Vol. 55 (1936).

4. Towne, H. M. "Lightning Arrester Grounds Parts 1, 2 and 3," *G. E. Review,* Vol. 35 (March, May 1932).

ARCING

1. Fleis, J. D. "How Contact Arcing Can Be Minimized," *Electric Manufacturing,* Vol. 35 (January 1945).

2. Germer, L. M., and Daworth, F. E. "Erosion of Electrical Contacts on Make," *Journal of Applied Physics,* Vol. 20 (November 1949).

3. Peters, J. F. and Slepian, J. "Voltages Induced by Arcing Grounds," *Transactions of the AIEE,* Vol. 42 (1930).

RESISTANCE

1. Lantz, M. J. "Effect of Fault Resistance on Ground Fault Currents," *Transactions of the AIEE,* Vol. 72 (1953).

2. McCrocklin, A. J., and Wendland, C. W. "Determination of Resistance to Ground of Grounding Grids," *Transactions of the AIEE,* Vol. 71, (1952).

FAULTS

1. Clarke, E., Crary, S. B., and Peterson, H. A. "Overvoltages During Power System Faults," *Transactions of the AIEE,* Vol. 58 (August 1939).
2. Holbeck, J. I., and Lantz, M. J. "The Effects of Mutual Induction Between Parallel Transmission Lines On Current Flow to Ground Faults," *Transactions of the AIEE,* Vol. 62 (1943).
3. Hunter, E. M., Praget, E., and Light, P. H. "Determination of Ground-Fault Current and Voltages On Transmission Systems," *G. E. Review,* Vol. 42 (1939).

PROTECTION

1. "AIEE Lightning Reference Book," *Transactions of the AIEE.*
2. "Application Guide on Methods of Substation Grounding," *Transactions of the AIEE,* Committee Report, Vol. 73, AIEE 54-81 (1954).
3. Beach, R. "Static Electricity In Industry," *Electrical Engineering,* Vol. 65, No. 5 (May 1946).
4. Bullard, W. R., Hayes, J. B., and Saunders, H. O. "Electrical Protection of Telephone Systems," *Transactions of the AIEE,* Vol. 73 (September 1954).
5. Carpenter, L. J. "Equipment Grounding For Industrial Plants," *Electrical Engineering,* Vol. 73, No. 3 (March 1954).
6. Coleman, O. K. "Why Ground," *Electrical Engineering,* Vol. 75, No. 5 (May 1956).
7. Dorey, F. M. "System Ground In Industrial Plants," *Electrical Engineering,* Vol. 72, No. 12 (December 1953).
8. "Engineering Practice: Grounding Systems For Generating Stations and Substations," G. E. Publications, GEU-24D (1945).
9. Gross, E. T. B., Chitnis, B. V., and Stratton, L. J. "Grounding Grids for High Voltage Stations," *Transactions of the AIEE,* Vol. 72, AIEE 53-239 (1953).
10. Gross, E. T. B. "Sensitive Ground Protection For Transmission Lines and Distribution Feeders," *Transactions of the AIEE,* Vol. 60 (1941).
11. "Grounding of Industrial Power Systems," *Power,* Vol. 100, No. 10 (October 1956).
12. Heddeshimer, H. E. "A Compendium of Grounding Techniques for Personnel and Equipment Protection," *Transactions of the AIEE,* Vol. 76, AIEE 57-920 (1957).
13. "How Good Are Your System Grounds," *Power,* Vol. 100, No. 10 (October 1956).

14. Hughes, T. "Grounding—Center of Confusion," Parts I, II, III, IV, V, and VI, *Electric West,* Vol. 115 and 116 (November 1955, May 1956).

15. Inskip, L. S. and Watson, H. W. "Grounding of Portable Electrical Equipment," Bell System Technical Publications, Monograph 2396.

16. Kaufmann, R. H. "Hazards In Industrial Electrical Systems: Protective Grounding Systems," *Safety Maintenance & Production* (August 1954).

17. ————. "Some Fundamentals of Equipment Grounding Circuit Design," *Transactions of the AIEE,* Vol. 73, AIEE 54-244 (1954); (General Electric Publication GER-957A, IE-1058.33).

18. ————. "Now Its Equipment Grounding," *Factory Management & Maintenance,* Vol. 115, No. 12 (December 1957).

19. "Neutral Grounding of Industrial Power Systems," G. E. Publication, GET-1181E (IE-1058.30), November 1956.

20. Phelps, J. W. "Protection Problems on Telephone Distribution System," Bell System Technical Papers, Monograph 2631.

21. "Present Day Grounding Practices on Power Systems," *Transactions of the AIEE,* Committee Report, Vol. 66 (1947).

22. Schahfer, R. M., and Kintz, W. H. "Charts Show Ground Rod Depths For Any Resistance—In Advance," *Electric World,* Vol. 114 (1940).

23. "Sensitive Ground Protection," *Transactions of the AIEE,* Vol. 62, AIEE 50-70.

24. Stewart, W. H. "Let's Look At Electrical Grounds," *Pipe Line Industry,* Vol. 6, No. 3 (March 1957).

25. Strong, W. F. "Neutral Grounding Methods For Industrial Power Systems," *Industry & Power,* Vol. 58, Nos. 2 and 3, Parts I and II (February, March 1950).

26. ————. *Op Cit.,* Part III, No. 4 (April 1950).

27. Thacker, H. B. "Coming: More Grounded Systems," *Factory Management & Maintenance* (October 1955).

Earth Properties

1. AIEE Working Group 56.1. "Voltage Gradients Through Ground Under Fault Conditions," *Transactions of the AIEE,* Vol. 77, AIEE 58-98 (1958).

2. Bellaschi, P. L. "Impulse and 60-Cycle Characteristics of Driven Grounds," *Transactions of the AIEE,* Vol. 60, Part I (1941).

3. Bellaschi, P. L., and Armington, F. D. "Impulse and 60-Cycle Characteristics of Driven Grounds," *Transactions of the AIEE,* Vol. 62, Part III (1943).

4. Bellaschi P. L., Armington, F. D., and Snowden, W. D. "Impulse and 60-Cycle Characteristics of Driven Grounds," *Transactions of the AIEE,* Vol. 61, Part II (1942).

5. Card, R. H., "Earth Resistivity and Geological Structure," *Electrical Engineer,* Vol. 54 (1935), p. 1153-1161.

6. Fine, Harry. "An Effective Ground Conductivity Map," ASTIA No. AD 14117.

7. ————. "An Effective Ground Conducivity Map For Continental United States," *Proceedings of the IRE,* Vol. 42, No. 9, IRE-5044 (September 1954).

8. Hadley, W. A., and Eisenstadt, R. "Critical Soil Moisture Conditions Affecting Buried Transmission Cables," *Electrical Engineering,* Vol. 72, No. 11 (November 1953).

9. Jensen, C. H. "Deep Driven Grounds," Edison Electric Institute.

10. Morgan, P. D., and Taylor, H. G. "Resistance of Earth Electrodes," *Proceedings of the IEE,* Vol. 72 (1932).

11. Peters, O. S., "Ground Connections For Electrical Systems," Bureau of Standards, Technologic Paper 108, June 1918.

12. Rudenberg, R. "Comparative Properties of Grounding Electrodes," *Electric World,* Vol. 129 (January 1948).

13. Towne, H. M. "Impulse Characteristics of Driven Grounds," *G. E. Review,* Vol. 31, No. 1938.

14. Wait, J. R. "The Effective Electrical Constants of Soil At Low Frequencies," *Proceedings of the IRE,* Vol. 45, No. 10 (October 1957).

15. ————. "The Electric Fields of a Long Current Carrying Wire on a Stratified Earth," *Journal of Geophysical Research,* Vol. 57 (1952), p. 481-485.

16. Wait, J. R., and Wahler, A. M. "On the Measurement of Ground Conductivity at V.L.F.," Bureau of Standards, Report No. 5037, ASTIA No. AD 123137.

17. Zaborsky, "Efficiency of Grounding Grids with Non-Uniform Soil," *Transactions of the AIEE,* Vol. 74, AIEE 55-713 (1955).

18. Zaborsky, and Rittenhouse "Design Charts for Determining Optimum Ground Rod Dimensions," *Transactions of the AIEE,* Vol. 62, Part III (1943).

LIGHTNING PROTECTION

1. "Code For Protection Against Lightning," Bureau of Standards, Handbook No. 16.

2. "Lightning Protection For Electrical Equipment," Associated Factory Mutual Life Insurance Company, Bulletin 15.60.

3. McCann, G. D., Beck, E. C., and Finzi, L. A. "Lightning Protection for Rotating Machines," *Transactions of the AIEE,* Vol. 63 (1944).

4. Peterson, H. A., and Hunter, E. M. "System Overvoltages and Lightning Arrester Application," *Electric Light & Power,* Vol. 19 (1941).

5. "Testing Lightning Rod and Arrester Grounds," Associated Factory Mutual Life Insurance Company, Bulletin 15.66.

6. Towne, H. M. "Lightning Arrester Grounds," *G. E. Review,* Vol. 35, Parts 1, 2 and 3 (March, May 1932).

7. "Static Electricity," Associated Factory Mutual Life Insurance Company, Bulletin No. 12.21.

CATHODIC PROTECTION

1. Brown, G. H. "A Radial Ground System Chart," *Electronics,* Vol 11 (January 1938).

2. Coleman, W. E., and Frostick, H. G. "Electrical Grounding and Cathodic Protection at the Fairless Works," *Transactions of the AIEE,* Vol. 74, AIEE 55-110 (March 1955).

3. Compton, K. G. "Electrical Measurements and Their Interpretation In Underground Cable Corrosion Problems," *Corrosion,* Vol. 14, No. 5 (May 1958).

4. "Design of Grounding Systems to Mitigate Corrosion," National Association of Corrosion Engineers, TP-12, March 1952.

5. Headlece, J. F. "Cathodic Protection For Steel Mill Grounding System," *Iron & Steel Engineering,* Vol. 31, No. 3.

6. Kuhn, R. J. "Grounding and Corrosion Protecting on Underground Electric Power Cable Sheaths and Gas or Oil Filled Pipeline," *Transactions of the AIEE,* Vol. 71, AIEE 52-281 (1952).

7. Schaefer, L. P. "Electrical Grounding System and Corrosion," *Transactions of the AIEE,* Vol. 74, AIEE 55-111 (1955).

8. ————, "Corrosion Can Conquer Your Grounding System," *Industry & Powers,* Vol. 71, No. 1 (June 1956).

9. Schwarz, E. W., and Wainwright, R. M. "Cathodic Protection Circuits," *Transactions of the AIEE,* Vol. 74, AIEE 55-265 (1955).

10. Sudrabin, L. P. "Importance of Corrosion and Cathodic Protection in Modern Engineering," *Transactions of the AIEE,* Conference Paper, (January 1953).

MISCELLANEOUS
Circuit Analysis

1. Carson, J. R. "Wave Propagation in Overhead Wires with Ground Return," *Bell System Technical Journal,* Vol. 5 (1926) p. 539-554.

2. Fortescue, C. L. "Method of Symmetrical Coordinates Applied to the Solution of Polyphase Networks," *Transactions of the AIEE,* Vol. 37, (1918), p. 1027-1140.

3. Gardner, M. F., and Barnes, J. L. "Transients in Linear Systems." New York: John Wiley and Sons, 1942.

4. Goldman, S. *Frequency Analysis, Modulation and Noise.* New York: McGraw-Hill Book Company, 1948.

5. Johnson, W. C. *Transmission Lines and Networks.* New York: McGraw-Hill Book Company, 1950.

6. King, R. W. P. *Electromagnetic Engineering.* New York: McGraw-Hill Book Company, 1945.

7. Lawson, J. L., and Uhlenbeck, G. E. *Threshold Signals.* MIT Radiation Lab. Series, New York: McGraw-Hill Book Company, Vol. 24, 1950.

8. Mason, W. P. *Electromechanical Transducers and Wave Filters,* New York: D. Van Nostrand Company, 1946.

9. Ramo, S., and Whinnery, J. R. *Fields & Waves in Radio.* New York: John Wiley and Son, 1944.

10. Schelkunoff, S. A. *Electromagnetic Waves.* New York: D. Van Nostrand Company, 1948.

11. Slater, J. C. *Micro Wave Transmission.* New York: McGraw-Hill Book Company, 1942.

12. Terman, F. E. *Radio Engineers Handbook.* New York: McGraw-Hill Book Company, 1943.

13. Wilheim, R., and Waters, M. *Neutral Grounding in High Voltage Transmission.* Amsterdam: Elsevier Publishing Company, 1956.

Standards and Regulations

1. AN-I-24a: Army-Navy Aeronautical Specification Interference Limits: Air Craft Installations, Radio, July 1947.

2. AN-I-40: Army-Navy Aeronautical Specification Interference Limits: Propeller System: Radio, August 1947.

3. AN-I-42: Air Force-Navy Aeronautical Specification Interference Limits and Tests: General Electronic Equipment, May 1948.

4. Bailey, G. Measurements and Standards for Control of Spurious Radiation, *Transactions of the IRE,* Vol. PGBTR-6.

5. Bibliography on High Voltage Transmission Line Corona and Radio Interference and Fundamental Corona Processes-1958-ERB-491 Radio & Eng. Elec. Div. National Research Council, Ottawa, Ontario, Canada.

6. Chessin, P. L. "A Bibliography on Noise" *Transactions of the IRE,* Vol. IT-1, No. 2 (September 1955).

7. International Electrotechnical Commission International Special Committee on Radio Interference. Report of Plenary Session. Report No. R. I. 12, Published by Central Office of the IEC, Geneva, October 1953.

8. JAN-I-225: Interference Measurements, Radio — Methods of, June 1945.

9. Lunden, C. D. *Bibliography of Radio Noise and Interference.* Washington: International Electronics Engineering, Inc., 1958.

10. Measurements of Field Intensity above 300 MC from R-F Industrial, Scientific and Medical Equipments, AIEE Standard 950.

11. MIL-B-5087: Bonding, Electrical for Aircraft, November 1949.

12. MIL-C-11693 (Signal Corps): Capacitors (Feedthrough Suppression), AC & DC .

13. MIL-C-12889 (Signal Corps : Capacitors, Fixed Paper Dielectric (Bypass Suppression).

14. MIL-E-4957A (ASG): Enclosure, Electromagnetic Shielding, Demountable, Prefabricated for Electronics Test Purposes, November 1954. Amendment, 1 February 1956.

15. MIL-F-15733C: Filters, Radio Interference, September 1955.

16. MIL-I-6051 (BuAer): Interference Limits and Methods of Measurements; Aircraft Radio and Electronics Installation, March 1950 (supersedes AN-I-24a).

17. MIL-I-6051A (USAF): Interference Limits and Method of Measurement, Electrical and Electronic Installation in Airborne Weapons Systems and Associated Equipment. January 1953 (used in lieu of MIL-I-6181).

18. MIL-I-6181 (BuAer): Interference Limits and Tests: Aircraft Electrical and Electronic Equipment, June 1950 (supersedes AN-I-42).

19. MIL-I-6181B: Interference Limits and Tests and Design Requirements. Aircraft Electrical and Electronic Equipment, May 1953 (supersedes MIL-I-6181 and MIL-I-6181A).

20. MIL-I-6722 (BuAer): Interference Limits, Propeller Systems, Radio, June 1950.

21. MIL-I-11683A: Interference, Suppression, Radio, Requirements for Engine Generators and Miscellaneous Engines.

22. MIL-I-16910A (Ships): August 1954.

23. MIL-I-25171 (USAF): Interference Limits and Tests for Modified Reconditional Aircraft, March 1955.

24. MIL-I-26600 (USAF): Interference Control Requirements, Aeronautical Equipment.

25. MIL-P-25053 (USAF): Precipitation Static Limits and Method of Measurement, Aircraft Electronic Installations, November 1954.

26. MIL-S-10379A: Suppression, Radio Interferences, General Requirements for Vehicles.

27. MIL-S-11748A (Signal Corps): Suppression Requirements for Electrical and Electronics Equipment, May 1956.

28. MIL-STD-220: Method of Insertion Loss Measurement for Radio-Frequency Filters, June 1952 (supersedes MIL-I-1657).

29. MIL-STD-285: Method of Attenuation, Measurement for Enclosures, Electromagnetic Shielding for Electronic Test Purposes.

30. Nexon Industry Coordination of Microwave Communication System. *Electrical Engineering,* Vol. 73, No. 6, June 1954.

31. *Radio Spectrum Conservation,* New York: McGraw-Hill Book Company, 1952.

32. "Spectrum Conservation," *Electronics,* Vol. 26, No. 1, January 1953.

33. Standards on Radio Receivers: Open Field Method of Measurement of Spurious Radiation from FM and TV Broadcast Receivers 1951 — 511Re 17:S1 (also *Proceedings of the IRE,* Vol. 39, No. 7, July 1951).

34. Standards on Receivers: Methods of Measurement of Interference Output of Television Receivers in the Range of 300-10,000 KC, 1954 54 IRE 17:51 (also *Procedeings of the IRE,* Vol. 42, No 9., September 1954).

35. White, M. "Frequency Allocation for Aviation Electronics" *Aeronautical Engineering Review,* Vol. 10, No. 5, (May 1954).

36. 16E4 (Ships): Electronic Equipment, Naval Shipyard Shore; General Specification, August 1949 (Amendment, 2 September 1952).

INDEX

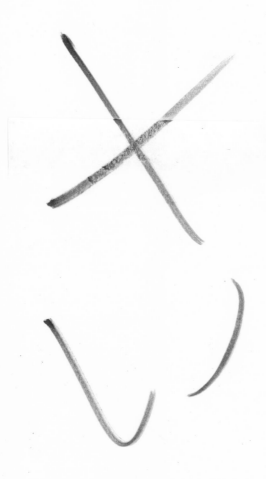